Benchmark Papers
in Genetics

Series Editor: David L. Jameson
University of Houston

PUBLISHED VOLUMES

GENETICS AND SOCIAL STRUCTURE / *Paul Ballonoff*
GENES AND PROTEINS / *Robert P. Wagner*
DEMOGRAPHIC GENETICS / *Kenneth M. Weiss and Paul Ballonoff*
MUTAGENESIS / *John W. Drake and Robert E. Koch*
EUGENICS: Then and Now / *Carl Jay Bajema*
CYTOGENETICS / *Ronald L. Phillips and Charles H. Burnham*
STOCHASTIC MODELS IN POPULATION GENETICS / *Wen-Hsiung Li*
EVOLUTIONARY GENETICS / *D. L. Jameson*
GENETICS OF SPECIATION / *D. L. Jameson*

RELATED TITLES IN OTHER BENCHMARK SERIES

MICROBIAL GENETICS / *Morad Abou-Sabé*
CONCEPTS OF SPECIES / *C. N. Slobodchikoff*
MULTIVARIATE STATISTICAL METHODS: Among-Groups Covariation /
   William R. Atchley and Edwin H. Bryant
MULTIVARIATE STATISTICAL METHODS: Within-Groups Covariation /
   Edwin H. Bryant and William R. Atchley

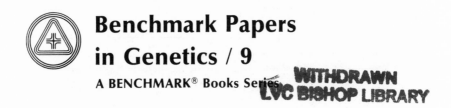

**Benchmark Papers
in Genetics / 9**
A BENCHMARK® Books Series

GENETICS OF SPECIATION

Edited by

D. L. JAMESON
University of Houston

Dowden, Hutchinson & Ross, Inc.
Stroudsburg, Pennsylvania

Copyright © 1977 by **Dowden, Hutchinson & Ross, Inc.**
Benchmark Papers in Genetics, Volume 9
Library of Congress Catalog Card Number: 77–7278
ISBN: 0–87933–302–2

79   78   77   1   2   3   4   5
Manufactured in the United States of America.

LIBRARY OF CONGRESS CATALOGING IN PUBLICATION DATA

Main entry under title:
Genetics of speciation.
   (Benchmark papers in genetics; 9)
   Bibliography: p.
   Includes indexes.
   1. Origin of species—Addresses, essays, lectures. 2. Genetics—Addresses,
essays, lectures. I. Jameson, David L.
QH380.G46   575.01'62   77–7278
ISBN 0–87933–302–3

Exclusive Distributor: **Halsted Press**
A Division of John Wiley & Sons, Inc.
ISBN: 0–470–99285–9

SERIES EDITOR'S FOREWORD

The study of any discipline assumes the mastery of the literature of the subject. In many branches of science, even one as new as genetics, the expansion of knowledge has been so rapid that there is little hope of learning of the development of all phases of the subject. The student has difficulty mastering the textbook, the young scholar must tend to the literature near his own research, the young instructor barely finds time to expand his horizons to meet his class-preparation requirements, the monographer copes with a wider literature but usually from a specialized viewpoint, and the textbook author is forced to cover much the same material as previous and competing texts to respond to the user's needs and abilities.

Few publishers have the dedication to scholarship to serve primarily the limited market of advanced studies. The opportunity to assist professionals at all stages of their careers has been recognized by the publishers of the Benchmark series and by a distinguished group of Benchmark volume editors knowledgeable in specific portions of the genetic literature. These editors have selected papers and portions of papers that demonstrate both the development of knowledge and the atmosphere in which that knowledge was developed. There is no substitute for reading great papers. Here you can learn how questions are asked, how they are approached, and how difficult and essential it is to obtain definitive answers and clear writing.

This book includes selected papers on the genetic nature of species, the origin and development of isolating mechanisms, the structure of natural populations, and the modes of the origin of species. The discussion emphasizes the development of the understanding of the genetics of the process of speciation.

The volume is an integral part of the Benchmark Papers in Genetics series. The emphasis on the genetic basis of species, isolating mechanisms, and speciation processes provides a unique approach not found in other treatments of speciation.

DAVID L. JAMESON

PREFACE

This volume summarizes the development of an understanding of the genetic basis of the origin of species. The papers have been selected to emphasize some of the divergent opinions concerning the nature of species, the origin of new species, and the basis and origin of isolating mechanisms. I have selected papers which emphasize the origin and development of species differences and of saltational events.

Benchmark volumes do not attempt to review the literature. That is the job of the *Annual Review of Genetics* and other existing publications. Benchmark volumes present a selection of papers and provide a discussion which illustrates their importance to the development of the field. Many definitions of Benchmark papers are possible. They are papers which provide understanding to colleagues and to students. They stimulate research, change the way others think about their own research, and contribute significantly more than the average paper to the general advance of the field. They are not just papers which are widely quoted nor are they representative of priority. Indeed, if Mendel's paper had not been rediscovered until 1930 it would have been an intellectual curiosity—instead it served as the focus of a great expansion in knowledge.

Consideration of major authors, significant studies, species and groups of species, and a survey of the journals produced a list that included more than twice as many papers as could possibly be included in an oversized volume. I asked several colleagues to compile comparable lists. The similarity in these expanded lists was considerable, as would be expected. I then reduced the lists by discarding my own work and reducing the contributions of each author to a single paper. This was extremely difficult with major contributors such as E. Mayr and S. Wright and in the case of Lewis, Dobzhansky, and Haldane it proved impossible. I then considered reducing the list by a reduction of papers to one for each organism, but quickly abandoned this as impractical. I essentially eliminated the subject of hybridization, leaving this topic to other workers and volumes. Polyploidy went the same way and G. L. Stebbins quickly rescued me. I then eliminated most papers which did not emphasize the genetic mechanism.

Final reductions were accomplished by focusing my objectives and building linkages between the papers. The list that existed at this point is discussed in the book. The last reduction in the list and indeed the most painful came with the necessity to meet the publisher-imposed limit on the number of pages. This required letters to some colleagues to explain why I had to omit their cherished words when I had previously requested permission to use them. I am solely responsible for the final selection. Many colleagues offered suggestions and they were appreciated. James Crow, Sewall Wright, and W. Atchley kindly read the manuscript.

This book is dedicated to W. F. Blair, a leader in the development of an understanding of the gene in natural populations of vertebrates. The volume is contribution number 2119 of the Laboratory of Genetics of the University of Wisconsin.

DAVID L. JAMESON

CONTENTS

Contents

PART V: THE NATURE OF THE SPECIATION PROCESS

CONTENTS BY AUTHOR

INTRODUCTION

Speciation, the process by which the origin of species occurs, is the fundamental problem for a large portion of genetics and biology, a fact clearly recognized by Darwin. In its simplest form speciation may be described as the process by which a population, or a group of interbreeding populations, becomes reproductively isolated from another population, or group of interbreeding populations. Thus, one definition of a species is "a population, or group of interbreeding populations, reproductively isolated from other populations." We need to emphasize that the reproductive isolation that is important is that found in nature. Organisms may interbreed in the confines of the laboratory, but we are concerned with what actually happens in nature. This definition had its beginnings in the nineteenth century and culminated with the synthetic theory of evolution developed in the 1930s, 1940s, and 1950s by many workers including especially Dobzhansky (1951), Mayr (1942), Simpson (1944, 1953), Stebbins (1950), and Huxley (1942).

There are a number of classifications of speciation (Bush, 1975; Ayala, 1975; Wright, in press) and a variety of speciation processes have been described. For the first part of this discussion we can reduce the classification to two processes. First, the gradual change which a population makes through time, called *anagenesis*. Second, the splitting of two or more populations or groups of populations into reproductively isolated lineages, called *cladogenesis*. The two were discussed as distinct processes requiring separate treatment by Dobzhansky (1937).

ANAGENESIS

The change which accompanies the evolution of a population or group of populations, i.e., a species, as it responds to changing environmental conditions will result in genetic changes in the species. Thus, the paleontologist can trace the evolution of a group of populations through successive beds of geologic strata. When he notes that the morphological differences are similar to those recognized between contemporary living species he identifies and describes the new species. If a contemporary population is very widespread the evolutionary forces at one end of the distribution may be very different from those at another end. If the individuals in the species are rare the systematist may encounter specimens only from the ends of the range, and since the morphological differences are similar to those recognized between other contemporary living species he may describe the two forms as different species. Obviously he has inadequate information about a widespread group of interbreeding populations. Unlike the paleontologist, the contemporary biologist can sometimes bring the two forms into the laboratory and test for the presence of reproductive isolation. If the paleontologist were equipped with a time machine and could test for reproductive isolation between samples from all time intervals he could identify gene exchange (interbreeding) from the earliest to the latest population. Similarly, the biologist may be able to identify that various subunit lineages of the groups of populations are partially reproductively isolated from each other. Thus temporal and geographic variability occurs in those characteristics which assure that gametes are not wasted but are contributed to the next generation of zygotes.

One of the persistent issues in the development of the genetics of speciation has centered on the diverse opinions concerning whether anagenesis is a slow gradual process or is subject to jumps or saltations. Darwin championed the position that slow gradual continuous change would result in evolutionary processes. Perhaps the most outspoken proponents of saltations were Hugo de Vries and Richard Goldschmidt. The latter felt that higher categories could be best explained by massive genetic reorganization producing opportunistically favorable individuals (1940). These individuals were termed "hopeful monsters" by some, and his position was not extensively supported at the time. On the other hand, Galton (1894) contended that both processes were supportable and T. H. Huxley, W. Bateson, G. G. Simpson, and many others supported saltation in one form or another. As we shall see polyploidy is one mechanism of saltation.

An additional persistent issue in the development of an understanding of anagenesis has been the diverse opinions concerning the role of deterministic and stochastic events. These discussions have an earlier history but positions prior to the 1920s need not concern us. Fisher (1930), Haldane (1932), and Wright (1931, 1932) had divergent opinions on the relative significance of deterministic and stochastic factors in evolution and their positions will be discussed later. More recently Kimura (1968) has championed the development of stochastic phenomena as a major component of natural selection. The Benchmark papers on stochastic models have been presented by Li (1977). Most students of evolutionary processes are more comfortable with deterministic models because they provide a more direct method of measuring natural events. Since both deterministic and stochastic processes occur, future studies will emphasize the understanding of the interaction of both in theoretical analysis and in natural populations.

CLADOGENESIS

The splitting of groups of populations into two or more lineages provides the opportunity for the differential accumulation of variability in the reproductive characteristics in the separate lineages. During the process of converting one species into two, considerable gene change is assumed to occur, presumably changes in gene frequencies, changes in interacting systems of genes, and changes in numbers and arrangements of the chromosome complement. A number of characteristics have been identified which provide for the isolation between two species. Several questions of interest to students of cladogenesis are identifiable:

1. How much and what kinds of genetic differences occur between populations, lineages, races, and species and groups of species?
2. What is the genetic basis of the isolation between two populations? species?
3. What are the origins of the isolation mechanisms?

We can examine the process of cladogenesis by examining the successive steps as one species splits into two. This is the approach of the paleontologist, but has severe sampling, observational, and experimental limitations. On the other hand, the contemporary biologist is required to compare various situations and attempt to order or serialize the processes. At first this appears straightforward, but the situation is complex because of the difficulties inherent in determining either direction or rate in a process observed at a single time. For example, we can ask the following questions: Are the differences between two populations a function of time, independent of whether or not reproductive isolation has occurred? Is rate of change of two populations in different environments different because the forces of change are different or is the rate of change constant? Do different parts of the genome evolve at different rates? Are the lineages converging or diverging?

The environmental changes in North America over the past 25,000 years are clearly recorded in the sedimentary deposits of ponds and

3

lakes. The distributions of many species have shifted in response to the expansion and retreat of the glaciers and the presence or reduction of thermal maxima. Populations separated by these events evolved isolated from one another for many generations. Continual environmental change provided the opportunity for divergent populations to again come in contact. For example, in the southern United States populations which retreated into Florida and northern Mexico during glacial advances have expanded to meet or overlap. This has produced a great outdoor laboratory for considerable exploration and investigation. Similar changes in the environment and the distribution of organisms have occurred in the western United States.

Another great outdoor natural laboratory is provided by islands where populations can become isolated from the parent populations. Clusters of islands some distance from the mainland have provided the opportunity for considerable cladogenesis, but mountains in a desert or lakes in a plain might also serve if isolation was complete and long enough for the required genetic reorganization. One characteristic of such islands is that they will be invaded by only a small number of founders. If this invasion is by a single gravid female, the genetic diversity may be constrained, but more important the variability imposed by the continual immigration from elsewhere in an unisolated population will be absent. Additionally, on an island the variety of occupied niches will probably be less, thus providing a different set of interspecific competitors, predators, and prey species. The number of closely related species may be very high, but the island fauna and flora is generally depauperate when compared to the mainland. Thus the background on which the genotype of the founder can capitalize is different than on the mainland and there are considerable opportunities for the rapid reorganization of the genotype in isolation. This process can lead to very rapid speciation (Mayr, 1959). We conclude that there appears to be a significant difference between the isolation of large groups of populations on the mainland and the isolation of peripheral populations such as those on the islands. In anagenesis, the continuous process of change and the production of new species, genera, and families in linear sequences is more important and interesting than is the determination of the level of difference required to distinguish a parental from a daughter species. Similarly, in cladogenesis, the most interesting phenoma is that species do split and diverge and the definition of the degree of difference is not as interesting as is the study of the process and sequence of divergence.

HYBRIDIZATION

This subject has widespread implications for any discussion of evolution or speciation. The origins of evolutionary concepts lie with the plant hybridizers and the research has included crosses between lineages as close as siblings and as distantly related as families. When individuals from one lineage cross with individuals from a different lineage a variety of genetic phenomena are observed. Crosses between two inbred lines of crops can produce an increase in the viability or productivity of the hybrid; heterosis or hybrid vigor are terms used to describe this phenomena. Crosses between lineages in nature also sometimes produce heterotic hybrids. Other crosses may produce individuals with less viability representing partial isolation or the crosses may produce no offspring.

For example, consider these cases. First, when the two lineages are sufficiently separated in nature that only occasional hybrids occur (in the zoo or garden, for example) the biologist may take this opportunity to study the kinds and amounts of differences in genetic variability in the two populations. On the other hand, two populations may be partially isolated and these genes then have the opportunity to contribute to the variability of the population. This occasionally may be true even when the two lineages have well-established reproductive isolating mechanisms which prevent the free flow of genetic variability.

Third, we can consider the case described by Wright where a large population is variously subdivided into smaller partially isolated subpopulations. Local mass selection has produced a subpopulation with a high adaptive value which diffuses "throughout the species as a result of excess population growth and excess emigration, followed by the appearance of still more successful centers of diffusion at points of contact" (Wright, 1965:86).

If Wright's three-phase shifting balance theory of anagenesis is our best description of nature (and it currently seems to be) then hybridizations between differentiated local populations is the most common form of genetic exchange between populations in nature. This type of exchange is extremely difficult to measure because of the inability to identify those populations and individuals exhibiting higher selective values at particular points of contact. The presence of gene flow between morphologically distinct populations that are in contact following geographical or ecological isolation is much easier to measure. Many of the populations isolated during environmental extremes develop genetic modifications which adapt them to different ecological situations. When populations again occupy the same geographic localities they are ecologically isolated by habitat, time of mating, or preferences in mating. Additional environmental changes which break down the ecological differences provide the opportunity for points of contact between populations (see Anderson and Stebbins, Paper 22). The activities of man include environmental influences which have increased these contacts. Since what happens at the point of contact is independent of the source of environmental change, one thrust of man's activity has been to increase the numbers and frequencies of contacts between species. Unfortunately, another has been species extinction.

Two phenomena associated with hybridization in nature are of interest to us. Genes from one population may disperse from that population into another and increase the variation of the recipient population. This process is described as introgression (Anderson, 1949). Additionally, intermediate individuals resulting from a cross between two populations may be particularly suited for the intermediate habitat and be able to thrive where neither parent is successful. Attempts to perform laboratory crosses between different lineages have provided a variety of information about premating and postmating isolation. We have selected few papers using hybridization techniques for this volume because the literature is so vast that a separate volume will be required. For the interested, the historical aspects are given in Roberts (1929), and Olby (1966). Dobzhansky (1937, 1970), Stebbins (1950, 1971), Grant (1971), and White (1973) review vast literature.

ISOLATING MECHANISMS

Determination of the amount of variation within and between various lineages provides us with an estimate of the amount of genetic differences. However, even in the occasional situation where the siblings are extremely closely related we learn little about the process or about the key elements involved in establishing isolation. Additionally, nature is varied and while some sibling species have a large amount of identifiable difference other species appear to be only slightly different—a few genes, a single chromosome rearrangement, or a change in the number of chromosome sets.

ORIGIN OF ISOLATING MECHANISMS

The great controversies in the study of speciation appear to focus on the origin of isolation mechanisms. How much physical separation of the lineages is required and for how long? Can a species arise by a large change in the genetic structure (saltation) in a very short period of time? This is not a recent question, is not really solved, and will likely be with us for a while.

Ancient Greeks, Arabians, Romans, and medieval Europeans believed in the transmutability of the species, often instantaneously from one form to another. They also perceived the origin of new forms from hybrids. The theological position of the 1700s was based on the biblical versions of the original creation and allowed for no change.

6

Linnaeus developed a system of classification which provided some rigidity to and organization of the existing species. Zirkle (1959) has discussed these early concepts and points out that an understanding of the evolution of species requires first an understanding that species have certain stability.

After the appearance of the *Origin of Species by Natural Means of Selection* most naturalists followed the position of Darwin that species arose by slow and continuous change of continuous characters. Most naturalists (Wagner, 1868; Jordan, 1905; Gulick, 1873, 1904) also assumed that some geographical isolation was involved in the process. Many other prominent scholars, for example, Huxley (1887) and Galton (1894) felt that species arose by saltational changes rather than from slow continuous processes. The differences were a central issue in the arguments between the Mendelians and the statisticians following the rediscovery of Mendel's work. Hugo de Vries (1889) discovered varieties of *Oenothera* which bred true and grew among the wild type plants. He claimed to have discovered the means (mutations) by which new species arose in a single step. While his conclusions proved wrong, his discovery of what later proved to be a fundamental genetic process (chromosomal rearrangements) provided a basis for an understanding of the gene and its instability and later of the process of speciation.

In the first third of this century the study of evolutionary genetics emphasized anagenesis rather than cladogenesis and the origin of species received relatively little direct attention. R. A. Fisher was a supporter of the effect of gradual continuous change while J. B. S. Haldane and S. Wright leaned more on the possibile importance of large changes in interaction systems through, for example, chromosomal rearrangements, polyploidy, or hybridization.

In the 1940s and 1950s the results of an expanded scientific effort shed considerable light on the role of geographic isolation as a major source of the first steps of speciation in most situations. The role of isolation has been reviewed in many places, but Mayr, a major proponent of the thesis, has provided us with an expanded version (Mayr, 1963).

Data have also accumulated to support the origin of many species under sympatric conditions where the new individuals could be expected to come into contact with individuals of the parent species. Additionally, other models have been proposed; these include parapatric and stasipatric models. This has been reviewed recently by Bush (1975).

THE NATURE OF THE SPECIATION PROCESS

Recently workers have recognized that the great variety of species are not easily understood using a single process of speciation. The reorganization of the genome which accompanies the genetic process is variable and the amount of differentiation required to produce reproductive isolation cannot be stated in simple numerical terms. Additionally, there is a growing unrest with the constraints of the synthetic theory as a complete explanation of evolution and particularly speciation. This unrest provides stimulating new ideas, new approaches, and the use of new methods of analysis to an already exciting field of biology.

THE GENETICS OF SPECIATION: MOSTLY ANIMAL

Perhaps we should clarify which portion of the speciation process this volume proposes to cover. Both hybridization and polyploidy are to be covered in other volumes. Since speciation and evolution in plants requires emphasis on these two topics, this volume examines the literature on animal species and draws only a few papers from plant material. The volumes on hybridization and on polyploidy will probably include little animal material.

The papers are arranged in three broad categories emphasizing population structure, isolation, and processes. In the first section we selected papers which provided for the understanding of the genetic structure of populations and arranged these in historical order. The next three sections concern isolation, first the genetic basis of isolation, second some theoretical studies, and then some experimental studies. The final section presents papers which review the state of knowledge of all or a significant portion of the literature and papers which describe particular speciation processes.

Table I-1. Classification of speciation

This table identifies the various processes emphasized in the discussion in the volume. There are other classifications and other types which may or may not fit within the designated categories.

Cast of Characters	*Comments*
ANAGENESIS	Results from mutation, mass selection, selective diffusion and random drift.
STASIPATRIC	Speciation which results from the origin, within the range of the species, of chromosomal rearrangements which are superior as homozygotes to the inferior heterozygotes. Also called parapatric.
CLADOGENESIS	*Type A.* Changes in chromosomal structure by polyploidy, inversion, fusion, and internal chromosomal rearrangements. May occur sympatrically or allopatrically and may or may not be saltational. *Type B.* Changes which result from the slow accumulation of allelic and loci changes during isolation. Probably occurs only allopatrically.

Table I-2. Isolating mechanisms

    I. PREMATING —Mechanisms which prevent the exchange of genetic material.
        A. Geographical, seasonal, and habitat differences which separate the individuals.
        B. Ethological differences which prevent successful mating.

  II. POSTMATING —Mechanisms which prevent the successful development of the zygote, i.e., to sexual maturity and reproduction. Includes infertility, inviability, and reduced fertility of offspring.

Part I

THE NATURE OF POPULATIONS, RACES, SUBSPECIES, AND SPECIES

Editor's Comments
on Papers 1 Through 7

We have defined a species as a population, or a group of interbreeding populations, reproductively isolated from other populations. To
trace the historical development of these terms in the early literature is
a task filled with pitfalls. Botanists and zoologists perceive these concepts differently because plants and animals are different. Naturalists,
systematists, and geneticists base their understanding on entirely different backgrounds. Naturalists are concerned with what they see in
nature, systematists with what they can organize and arrange, and
geneticists with what they can hypothesize, analyze in the lab, measure,

and test. The diverse backgrounds and approaches, described here in broad strokes and greatly simplified, make it difficult to be sure that a term used by a writer fifty years ago has much relation to the use of that term today. To say that the problems of divergent approaches still exist is not an oversimplification.

Following the rediscovery of Mendel's work and the development of the "mutation" concept of de Vries the great controversy reached major proportions. Weldon and Pearson believed in the gradual continuous evolution of continuous characters as proposed by Darwin, while Bateson believed that evolution occurred by discontinuous steps. This story has been described in some detail by Provine (1971). The various studies which demonstrated the Mendelian basis of quantitative characters and develop an understanding of anagenesis have been reviewed and reprinted in the Evolutionary Genetics volume of this series.

Between 1900 and 1930 many workers contributed to an understanding of mendelism, particularly in domestic organisms. Genetic principles were used by naturalists and systematists to interpret their findings. A few workers were able to study the variability discovered in nature and make Mendelian analyses of this variability. J. Schmidt (Paper 1, 1917, 1919, 1920) made crosses between individuals which naturalists recognized as different races. By measuring the size and shape of fishes and counting the number of vertebrae and fin rays, fisheries biologists are able to determine statistically that large wide ranging species are divided into somewhat isolated local forms or races. Schmidt, seeking to determine the conditions responsible for the racial difference, was able to determine that environmental features could be measured which sometimes were related to differences in the characters and which sometimes were not. He showed that the number of rays was higher when the fish were raised in warm temperatures than when the fish were raised in cool temperatures, and that the temperature of the mother during pregnancy had a similar influence.

Schmidt maintained at the same temperature some parents with a high number of fin rays and others with a low number of fin rays. He found that the offspring had the same number of rays as the parents and that the primary source of this racial character was hereditary. Schmidt was able to confirm this conclusion in other species (1920). In still other species he made diallel crosses mating each female with each male and measuring a number of characteristics in both the parents and the offspring. He obtained estimates of the proportion of the variability which could be attributed to environmental factors and that which could be attributed to genetic factors. He felt that the racial characters in these fishes were primarily genetic.

In 1913 F. B. Sumner began a series of studies on the genetics, distribution and evolution of the deer mice, *Peromyscus.* He found that some populations differed from others in greater amounts than were the differences between other populations, but that the amount of identifiable genetic differences were not always proportional to morphological differences. He collected mice from climatically different localities and raised them in the same environment. Sumner (1917) concluded that subspecific differences are largely hereditary. Sumner (1924) also transplanted animals from one locality to another and found that they did not change over several generations. He maintained animals from various localities under desert conditions (high temperature and low humidity) and concluded: "On the whole, one can not fail to be impressed by the comparative stability of these various races of mice under very marked alterations in the physical environment" (1924:505). After twenty years of investigation he noted that multiple factors provided "a fairly adequate interpretation of the inheritance of subspecific characters." When Sumner began his studies he was sympathetic with a Lamarckian view of the origin of geographic variation. By 1933 he believed that most races began as an isolated unit which rapidly expanded until it came in contact with other populations (races), this was then followed by hybridization between the forms producing zones of integration. Subspecies did not arise from single acts of mutation because the differences between subspecies depended on many characteristics. Sumner (1929a, b, 1934) found frequent serial gradations of various characters which could sometimes be correlated with gradients in the physical environment. He believed selection and the direct effect of the environmental conditions contributed to the accumulation of the multiple factoral differences observed. Sumner made several benchmark contributions, but his papers are too long to be included in this volume.

By the end of the first third of the twentieth century Fisher, Haldane, and Wright had been able to synthesize the evolutionary processes in a form which provided a basis for future studies of population genetics and of the processes of speciation. Their work, which appeared in a series of papers and culminated in the early 1930s in small books and large papers, represented a major benchmark in modern biology. This work has been reviewed in the *Evolutionary Genetics* volume of Benchmark Papers in Genetics, but needs to be summarized here for continuity.

Haldane (1924–1932) held that species are in equilibrium for most genetic characteristics. The forces of selection, mutation, and migration are small and balance each other and therefore evolution is extremely slow; this allows chance to play a significant role. Speciation, according to Haldane (1927, 1929, 1930), results from hybridization, polyploidy, and shifts in the multigene metastability which accompanies isolation (presumably geographic).

14

Fisher (1930) believed that populations evolve mostly by slow continuous change in quantitative characteristics. He stated that natural selection is the driving force of evolution because mutation and other forces have such low measurable influence. He considered multiple factors with multiple alleles and the interaction between them and arrived at a general statement which he called the Fundamental Theorem of Natural Selection: "The rate of increase of any organism at any time is equal to its genetic variance in fitness at that time" (p. 37). Fisher suggested that geographic isolation was responsible for the splitting of species in most cases. In other cases speciation may result from variations in dispersal ability or preference, habitat preference, and sexual preferences which arise from different selective forces in the widespread geographic distribution of most species.

In 1931 and 1932 S. Wright presented what he later called the three-phase shifting balance theory of evolution. Wright believes that large populations are variously subdivided into smaller local units variously isolated with a continually shifting differentiation among the units. The differentiation results from more or less *random processes* which allow the local population to cross shallow saddles in the surface of selective values. In the second phase *local mass selection* leads to occupation of the higher peaks. This is followed by the *diffusion* of successful populations. Wright suggested "the splitting of species depends on the effects of more complete isolation, often made permanent by the accumulation of chromosome aberrations, usually of the balanced type" (1932:366).

The great plasticity of growth form in plants led plant scientists to regard geographic differences in a species as being the result of environmental effects. As early as 1922 Turesson demonstrated that seeds from different appearing individuals from various parts of the distribution of some species would retain their basic identities when grown in a common environment. The most intensive early work of this type was done by Clausen et al. (Paper 3) with their study of *Potentilla glandulosa* in California. Plants from the Sierra Nevada subalpine, the dry Sierra foothills, and the Pacific coast were exchanged reciprocally and grown in experimental plots to determine the genetic basis of the various characteristics. Low elevation forms were not successful in the alpine; the alpine forms remain dwarf and are not very successful on the coast but grow with considerable vigor in the foothills. Clausen et al. (Paper 3) suggest the populations are regulated through the interaction of many genes in a balanced system in harmony with their environment. Later Hiesey (1964) reviewed the results of studies on three complexes. *Potentilla glandulosa, Achillea millefolium,* and *Mimulus cardinalis-lewissi,* and concluded that multiple factor inheritance of the characters distinguishing the ecological races was the rule. He suggested the principle of *genetic coherence* was required to characterize the races

15

because F_2 progeny of corsses between races tend to segregate with a higher frequency of parental-like types than would be predicted on the basis of free random recombination.

Lewis and Raven (Paper 4) examined three species of *Clarkia* in the western coastal mountains. They concluded that *C. amoena* gave rise to *C. ribicunda*. A third species, *C. franciscana*, was proposed to have arisen from *C. ribicunda* by a rapid reorganization of the chromosomes during a reduction in population numbers by severe environmental stress. Gottlieb (1973) studied enzyme systems in these species and found that *C. franciscana* was fixed for alleles that are not present in either of the other species and that this species was much more monomorphic. Bartholomew et al. (1973) examined fifty-nine populations of *C. ribicunda* and one of *C. franciscana* for eleven morphometric characters. The absence of broadly based geographic trends, the high interfertility, periodic small population size, short life, and limited dispersal led them to conclude that *C. ribicunda* was uniquely qualified to serve as progenitor of other species by saltational speciation.

Clearly, by the 1950s enough work has been done with natural populations by people who understood Mendelian principles to have a fair idea of the genetic structure of some of those populations. Crosses between individuals from various parts of widespread species suggested a multitude of differentiation between populations, races, and species. While it is one thing to cross individuals from different parts of the distribution of a wide ranging species, it is an entirely different matter to estimate how many genes are different between two species. The effects of species specific gene differences are even more difficult to analyze.

The advent of the techniques of molecular biology began to shed some light on the number of allelic substitutions which were different in different species. The pioneer benchmarks are those of Hubby and Throckmorton (1965: Paper 5). The principle that nucleotide sequence implies amino acid sequence which implies polypeptide chains which implies a specific enzyme or protein allows the identification of allelic substitutions by determining the isozymes from electrophoretic analysis. For various reasons the estimates of the amount of genetic differences based on electrophoretic analysis are underestimates (see Lewontin, 1974). Hubby and Throckmorton compared the isozymes from ten species of the *Drosophila virilis* group. These species had also been subject to extensive analysis of chromosomal rearrangements (Stone et al., 1960) and a phylogenetic analysis was already available. Comparing the molecular and the chromosomal data provided estimates of the amount of single gene substitution which accompanied the speciation process. The common ancestor provided approximately 60 percent of the genetic material, and about 15 percent was unique to the individual species.

Next Hubby and Throckmorton turned their attention to a study of the amount of genetic difference between sibling species when compared to a more distant near relative. They found that the siblings shared proteins with identical mobility in 50 percent of the cases while they shared identical mobility only 18 percent of the time with the near relatives.

Irwin and Cole (1936) and others studied the magnitude of serological differences between individuals from different columbid (dove) lineages and their hybrids. These magnitudes were then used to estimate the relative relationships between various species. Recently Wilson et al. (Paper 6) examined a large number of pairs of species which were capable of making viable hybrids. The average difference between pairs was less for mammals than for frogs. They conclude that the ratio of regulatory evolution to protein evolution is higher for mammals than for frogs. They and others have suggested that isozyme differences may not represent the best measure of isolation because morphological and reproductive differences are not parallel to protein differences. They suggest differences in regulatory mechanisms are more important in determining the differences between species.

Ayala et al. (Paper 7) analyzed different taxa of the *Drosophila willistoni* groups comparing geographical populations, subspecies, semispecies, sibling species, and morphologically different species. The number of substitutions per locus at each level was determined and they noted that geographical populations differed by only 0.03 per locus while subspecies and semispecies differed by 0.23 and 0.22 respectively. Sibling species differed by 0.58 and species by more than 1.0. They concluded that geographic isolation provided the opportunity for subspecies to develop considerable genetic differences. The actual development of isolation mechanisms required little more genetic change.

As Dobzhansky (1941) and Mayr (1942) pointed out, the species, as a biological identifiable unit, "usually is subject to no dispute at all." This alone suggests its identification as a natural unit. The gaps between species are the result of discontinuities in the genetic arrays. The gaps are maintained by isolating mechanisms. Of interest to us now is the species itself. Just how integrated is the species population? Certainly large, widely distributed species generally exhibit more variability than populations with restrictive ecological or geographical ranges, as was recognized by Darwin and reaffirmed by many others since.

Are the populations which make up a species comparably integrated such that they evolve in parallel to secular changes in the environment even though gene exchange between them may be low for some significant portion of the time? How is it that a variety of measurable genotypes nevertheless will develop individuals that are adaptively comparable? The processes of canalization and homeostasis have been evoked, but these may describe rather than explain the end result. The unit of population genetics starts with the allele, while evolutionary theory emphasizes subpopulations and populations. Speciation has typically concerned itself with interbreeding populations, races, sub-species and species. Are subspecies and races incipient species as Darwin thought? Are they merely examples of variation and is speciation really an entirely different process, as Goldschmidt (1940) suggested?

Clearly there are more questions than there are answers. Certainly each of the above questions has different answers in diverse situations. But the fact is that our best understanding of the population and the species is inadequate; there is much to be learned.

The papers in this section were selected to provide an understanding of the nature of natural populations and to provide an estimate of the relative magnitude of the differences between closely related species. Ayala (1975) considers the determination of the amount of genetic differentiation which occurs during the process of speciation as the "cardinal problem of evolutionary genetics". To understand this process we will need to know more about the kinds of genetic isolation associated with various amounts and types of reproductive isolation. Following that we will turn to a consideration of the origins of genetic isolation.

1

RACIAL STUDIES IN FISHES

II. EXPERIMENTAL INVESTIGATIONS WITH *LEBISTES RETICULATUS* (PETERS) REGAN

By JOHS. SCHMIDT, D.Sc.

Director of the Carlsberg Physiological Laboratory,
Copenhagen, Denmark.

(With One Graph.)

I. *Introduction.*

The purpose of the experiments about to be discussed was to contribute information on the rather obscure question whether, or to what extent, quantitative racial characters are hereditary.

The tropical-American Cyprinodont *Lebistes reticulatus* (Peters) Regan[1] was employed in the experiments. I have previously used this little aquarium-fish in experimental investigations, namely for the purpose of demonstrating the importance of environment on the numbers of organs (dorsal rays).

Lebistes reticulatus is, like so many of its relatives, *viviparous*, and under favourable conditions the female brings into the world, at intervals of about 4 weeks, a considerable number of young. The young possess at birth the full number of vertebrae, dorsal rays, etc., which is therefore recognisable immediately after birth.

The experiments fall into two groups, of which the first helps to elucidate the importance of *external factors* (temperature) upon the number of dorsal rays. The second is concerned with the question whether hereditary differences, i.e. differences dependent upon *internal factors*, may be proved to exist in different individuals. Before I proceed to discuss the experiments, I may draw attention to the fact that the

---

[1] C. Tate Regan, "A revision of the Cyprinodont Fishes of the Subfamily Poeciliinae," *Proc. Zool. Soc. London* 1913, Vol. II. pp. 977—1018, 1913.

number of dorsal fin rays in *Lebistes reticulatus* varies from 5 to 8. By far the most usual number is 7.

A more detailed account appears in Vol. XIV, Nos. 1 and 5, of the *Comptes-Rendus des Travaux du Laboratoire de Carlsberg*, Copenhagen.

II. *Importance of External Factors.*

The principle was to vary the temperature for the same pair of parents from one period of pregnancy to the other, and then determine the number of dorsal rays in the various broods of offspring. In the beginning I had no means of maintaining a constant temperature in the aquaria, and was therefore compelled to limit myself to stating that the animals in the experiments were kept at a "low," "medium" and "high" temperature, in which "medium" temperature was ca. 6° above "low" and ca. 3° below "high." "Low" temperature was generally equivalent to ca. 19° Centigrade, varying between ca. 17° and ca. 23°.

In the experiments 5 different pairs of *Lebistes reticulatus* were used. The results of these investigations can be seen from Tables I—V, each of which shows the number of rays in several broods from the

TABLES I—V. *Number of dorsal rays in offspring of the same pairs of parents at different temperatures.*

TABLE I. ♂ 7 × ♀ 7.

No. of rays	High temperature Born 12 March	Medium temperature Born 13 April	Low temperature Born 1 June	Low temperature Born 25 July	High temperature Born 25 Sept.
8	9	—	—	1	4
7	6	20	25	33	16
6	—	—	13	4	—
n	15	20	38	38	20
a	**7·600**	**7·000**	**6·658**	**6·921**	**7·200**
σ	±0·532	—	±0·498	±0·390	±0·414
P. E. A.	±0·093	—	±0·054	±0·043	±0·062
Fl.	±0·465	—	±0·270	±0·215	±0·310

TABLE II. ♂ 8 × ♀ 8.

No. of rays	Medium temperature Born 12 April	Low temperature Born 29 May
8	15	—
7	29	27
6	—	5
n	44	32
a	**7·341**	**6·844**
σ	±0·483	±0·399
P. E. A.	±0·049	±0·048
Fl.	±0·245	±0·240

TABLE III. ♂ 8 × ♀ 7.

No. of rays	Medium temperature Born 23 May	Low temperature Born 14 July
8	8	—
7	49	31
6	—	6
n	57	37
a	**7·140**	**6·838**
σ	± 0·351	± 0·399
P. E. A.	± 0·031	± 0·044
Fl.	± 0·155	± 0·220

TABLE IV. ♂ 6 × ♀ 6

No. of rays	Medium temperature Born 1 April	Medium temperature Born 27 May	Low temperature Born 13 July
8	1	1	—
7	11	31	15
6	3	6	21
n	15	38	36
a	**6·867**	**6·868**	**6·417**
σ	± 0·565	± 0·439	± 0·505
P. E. A.	± 0·098	± 0·048	± 0·057
Fl.	± 0·490	± 0·240	± 0·285

TABLE V. ♂ 6 × ♀ 6.

No. of rays	Medium temperature Born 7 May	Low temperature Born 19 June	Low temperature Born 14—15 August
8	—	—	—
7	11	17	35
6	—	11	18
5	—	2	—
n	11	30	53
a	**7·000**	**6·500**	**6·660**
σ	—	± 0·636	± 0·487
P. E. A.	—	± 0·078	± 0·045
Fl.	—	± 0·390	± 0·255

same pair of parents. The date of birth of the young is noted in each case, as also whether developed at low, medium, or high temperature.

It is distinctly evident from the tables that the different broods do exhibit a difference in the number of dorsal fin rays, and it is further seen that the average *number of rays was greater where the young had been developed at a high temperature than where their development took place at a low temperature.*

In all my later experiments this result has been confirmed. I will content myself with discussing a single one of the later experiments, which, technically speaking, had the advantage over the preceding ones in that the temperature in the aquaria could be kept constant, there being a fluctuation of only one-tenth of a degree ($\pm$ 0·1). The two parents had respectively 7 and 5 rays in the dorsal fin. The experiment took place partly at 25°, partly at 18°. The three first broods were produced at 25°, following which the parents were maintained at 18°, from the day the third brood was born until the birth of the fourth brood. After this the temperature was raised again to 25°, at which degree the development of the last broods of young took place. The result of the experiment is given in Table VI.

TABLE VI.

Number of dorsal rays in offspring of the same pair of parents at different temperatures.

No. of rays in offspring	No. of Specimens					
	25° Brood 1 Born 15/5 1918	25° Brood 2 Born 10/6 1918	25° Brood 3 Born 6/7 1918	18° Brood 4 Born 21/9 1918	25° Brood 5, 6, 7 Born 25/10, 21/11, 24/12 1918	25° Brood 1, 2, 3, 5, 6, 7
7	8	13	29	6	51	101
6	1	2	3	13	4	10
5	—	—	—	1	—	—
n	9	15	32	20	55	111
a	**6·889**	**6·867**	**6·906**	**6·250**	**6·927**	**6·910**
σ	±0·333	±0·352	±0·296	±0·550	±0·262	±0·283
P.E.A.	±0·075	±0·061	±0·035	±0·083	±0·024	±0·018
Fl.	±0·375	±0·306	±0·177	±0·415	±0·129	±0·092

Thus we see, that whilst the broods developed at 25° had an average of 6·91 rays, the average number of rays fell to 6·25 at 18°. The difference between the averages was thus 0·660 and the probable error of this difference $\pm$ 0·085.

As all experiments in this connection have given a similar result, it may be taken as proved that the number of rays in the dorsal fin of the offspring *is affected to a considerable degree by the temperature* to which the mother is subjected whilst in a state of pregnancy. Remarkable besides is the great difference in the duration of pregnancy at the different temperatures; which at 25° lasted ca. 1 month, at 18° more than 3 months.

III. *Importance of Internal Factors.*

The object of the experiments about to be discussed was to investigate whether hereditary differences in the number of dorsal fin rays could be proved to exist. The principle of the experiments was to maintain *different* pairs of parents in the *same* environment, and see whether the offspring were different as regards the number of rays.

The specimens employed in the experiments were selected from two races with which since 1915 selection experiments had been undertaken, partly towards a high, partly towards a low number of dorsal rays. The parents had, respectively, both 8 and both 6 rays in the dorsal fin. In each case the specimens were kept at a constant temperature, viz. 25°. In addition, in order to secure uniform environment, the specimens whose offspring should be compared were placed in the same aquarium, separated only by a trelliswork of thin glass tubes. In other words they lived in quite the same body of water, maintained at a constant temperature. The aquarium contained no plants, but a continuous stream of atmospheric air bubbled through the water.

The experiment falls into two series, A and B. In series A there were employed partly ♂ 269 and ♀ 270 (each with 6 rays), partly ♂ 267 and ♀ 268 (each with 8 rays). For series B there were employed partly ♂ 274 and ♀ 273 (each with 6 rays), partly ♂ 276 and ♀ 275 (each with 8 rays). All the experimental fish in series A were kept in the same aquarium which stood at the side of the one in which all the fishes belonging to series B were placed.

From the appended Table VII and from the graph on p. 152 one remarks that there was in both series a very great difference in the

TABLE VII.

Number of dorsal rays in offspring of four different pairs of parents at a constant temperature of 25° C.

	Series A		Series B	
	♂ 269 × ♀ 270 both 6 rays	♂ 267 × ♀ 268 both 8 rays	♂ 274 × ♀ 273 both 6 rays	♂ 276 × ♀ 275 both 8 rays
No. of rays in offspring	Brood 1, 2, 3, 4 Born 23/9, 17/10, 9/11, 4/12 1918	Brood 1, 2, 3, 4 Born 27/9, 23/10, 19/11, 17/12 1918	Brood 1, 2, 3, 4 Born 29/9, 24/10, 21/11, 18/12 1918	Brood 1, 2, 3 Born 29/9, 26/10, 26/11 1918
8	—	54	—	40
7	62	10	51	3
6	25	—	23	—
n	87	64	74	43
a	**6·713**	**7·844**	**6·689**	**7·930**
σ	± 0·455	± 0·366	± 0·466	± 0·258
P. E. A.	± 0·033	± 0·031	± 0·037	± 0·027
Fl.	± 0·165	± 0·154	± 0·183	± 0·133

average number of rays in the offspring of fishes with 6 and with 8 rays, namely in the first series **1·131** (Probable error of difference = 0·045) and in the second **1·241** (P.E. Diff. = 0·045).

This difference cannot be due to difference in environment because the fishes swam in the same aquarium, indeed in the very same water

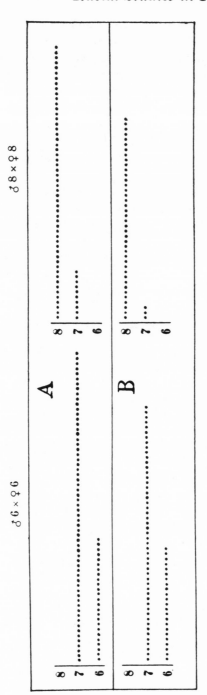

EXPLANATION OF THE GRAPH.

Number of rays in the dorsal fin in offspring of 4 pairs of parents all kept at 25°. Graphical representation of the experiment given in Table VII.

The figures give the number of rays; each dot represents one individual member of the offspring. The two upper graphs refer to Series A; the two lower ones to Series B of the experiment. The two graphs on the left represent offspring of parents having 6 rays in the dorsal fin, the two on the right represent parents with 8 rays.

It is to be seen that in each series the offspring is different in spite of the environment being identical.

at a constant temperature and with regular ventilation. The conditions with regard to uniformity were in my opinion the most favourable possible and I cannot but conclude from the present experiment, that the *difference proved to exist in the offspring of parents with respectively 6 and 8 rays is of hereditary (genotypical) nature.*

IV. *Concluding Remarks.*

The investigations here treated fall into two groups: (1) Experiments in which the *same mother* was exposed to *different environments* in different periods of pregnancy and (2) Experiments in which *different mothers* were exposed to the *same environment*, have thus succeeded in elucidating these rather complicated questions.

It has been shown that the number of organs may be very susceptible to environment, but that this fact cannot—under suitable experimental conditions—disguise the fact, which we specially wanted to demonstrate, viz. that there are or may be differences of hereditary nature between the various individuals.

This proof is of considerable interest for our view upon the nature of " races " in fishes, and supports in a high degree the opinion expressed by me at a previous occasion[1]: " My view then, with regard to the nature of ' races ' in fishes, as characterised by our population analyses, is briefly this.: A fish ' race ' is largely a statistical conception. It implies a mixing of different genotypes, and the average values characterising the ' race ' are primarily dependent upon the quantitative proportion between these ; only secondarily on the environment."

[1] Johs. Schmidt, "Racial Studies in Fishes. I. Statistical Investigations with *Zoarces viviparus*, L.," *Journal of Genetics*, Vol. VII. p. 117, 1918.

2

Reprinted from *Amer. Naturalist* **74**:232–248 (1940)

BREEDING STRUCTURE OF POPULATIONS IN RELATION TO SPECIATION[1]

PROFESSOR SEWALL WRIGHT

THE UNIVERSITY OF CHICAGO

INTRODUCTION

THE problem of speciation involves both the processes by which populations split into non-interbreeding groups and those by which single populations change their characteristics in time, thus leading to divergence of previously isolated groups.

The first step in applying genetics to the problem is undoubtedly the discovery of the actual nature of the genetic differences among allied subspecies, species and genera in a large number of representative cases. Differences which tend to prevent cross-breeding are obviously especially likely to throw light on the process of speciation, but all differences are important.

Our information here is still very fragmentary. We know enough, however, to be able to say that there is no one rule either with respect to cross-sterility or to other characters. In some cases the most significant differences seem to be in chromosome number and organization. At the other extreme are groups of species among which gross chromosome differences and even major Mendelian differences are lacking, both cross-sterility and character differentiation depending on a multiplicity of minor gene effects. In general, there are differences at all levels (*cf.* Dobzhansky, 1937).

But even if we had a complete account of the genetic differences within a group of allied species, we would not necessarily have much understanding of the process by which the situation had been arrived at. A single mutation is not a new species, except perhaps in the case of polyploidy. The symmetry of the Mendelian mechanism

---

[1] Read at a joint symposium on ''Speciation'' of the American Society of Zoologists and the Genetics Society of America, American Association for the Advancement of Science, Columbus, Ohio, December 28, 1939.

is such that any gene or chromosomal type tends to remain at the same frequency in a population except as this frequency is changed either by some steady evolutionary pressure (such as that due to *recurrent* mutation, to various kinds of selection, to immigration and to differential emigration) or by the accidents of sampling, if the number of individuals is small. The elementary evolutionary process, from this view-point, is change of gene frequency.

It is to be expected that the nature of the process will be found to be affected by what I have called the breeding structure of the species, and it is this aspect of the matter that I wish to discuss here. Such a discussion involves at least three steps. First, there is the observational problem of determining what the breeding structures of representative species actually are. Naturalists are only beginning to collect the detailed information which turns out to be necessary, but that which we have indicates situations of great complexity. The second step is that of constructing a mathematical model which represents adequately the essential features of the actual situation while disregarding all unimportant complications. The third step is the determination of the evolutionary implications of a given breeding structure in relation to mutation and selection. As difficult problems of description and mathematical formulation are also involved in the cases of mutation and selection pressures, the whole problem is exceedingly complex. I can only discuss the implications of certain very simple models of breeding structure, chosen partly because they appear to correspond to situations which one might expect to find in nature, but partly also because of mathematical convenience.

Evolution under Panmixia

The simplest situation, under biparental reproduction, is that of a large population, breeding wholly at random (panmixia). If sufficiently large, variability due to accidents of sampling is negligible. Each gene frequency shifts steadily under the pressures of selection and recurrent mutation. Mathematical formulations of these pressures have been given. Letting q be the frequency of a given gene, $(1-q)$ that of its alleles, u and v the mutation rates respectively from and to the gene in question and $\overline{W}$ the mean selective value of all possible genotypes, weighted by their frequencies, the change in gene frequency in a generation is given by the following formula (Wright, 1937):

$$\Delta q = v(1-q) - uq + \frac{q(1-q)\delta\overline{W}}{2\overline{W}\delta q}$$

For a gene which causes the same difference from its allele in all combinations and which lacks dominance, the term for selection pressure reduces approximately to $sq(1-q)$, where s is the selective advantage over the allele.

The numbers of generations necessary for any given shift in gene frequency, under various hypotheses, have been presented by Haldane (1932 and earlier). This sort of process has been taken as typical of evolutionary change by R. A. Fisher (1930), who has compared its unswerving regularity to that of increase in entropy in a physical system.

If, however, conditions are constant, this process comes to an end at an equilibrium point at which opposing pressures balance each other ($\Delta q = 0$). At this point there is stability of the species type in spite of continual occurrence of mutations, an extensive field of variability and continuous action of selection. On the other hand, conditions never are wholly constant. It is possible that evolution, in each series of alleles, may consist of an unswerving pursuit of an equilibrium point, which is itself continually on the move because of changing conditions.

The postulate that variations in gene frequency, due to accidents of sampling, are negligible calls for some comment. The variance in one generation is $\sigma^2_{\Delta q} = \dfrac{q(1-q)}{2N}$ in a diploid population of effective size N. This is cumu-

lative and may cause wide divergence from equilibrium
if the population is not too large. The systematic evolutionary pressures directed toward equilibrium and this
sampling variance determine between them a certain distribution of values of the gene frequency instead of a
single equilibrium point. The general formula can be
written as follows (Wright, 1937) :

$$\varphi(q) = (C/\sigma^2_{\Delta q}) e^2 \int (\Delta q/\sigma^2_{\Delta q}) dq$$

For the values of Δq and $\sigma^2_{\Delta q}$ given above this reduces to

$$\varphi(q) = C\overline{W}^{2N} q^{4Nv-1}(1-q)^{4Nu-1}$$

In the special case of no factor interaction and no dominance, the term $\overline{W}^{2N}$ becomes approximately e^{4Nsq}. There
is a marked tendency toward chance fixation of one allele
or another if $4Ns$, $4Nv$ and $4Nu$ are all less than 1 while
such variability is negligible if these quantities are large
(*e.g.*, as large as 100).

The possible evolutionary significance of these random
variations in gene frequency in a panmictic population
has been considered elsewhere (Wright, 1931, 1932) and
will not be discussed further here.

Mating never is wholly at random. It is important to
determine whether departures from panmixia have significant effects on the evolutionary process and if so
whether these consist merely in impeding the pursuit of
equilibrium or whether they may not bring about progress of a different sort.

One limitation on the effectiveness of selection in a
panmictic population is that it can apply only to the *net
effects* in each series of alleles. It is really the organism
as a whole that is well or ill adapted. A really effective
selection pressure should relate to genotypes not genes.
But in a panmictic population, combinations are formed
in one generation only to be broken up in the next.

If a selective value (W) is assigned to every one of the
practically infinite number of possible combinations of
genes of all loci, the array of such values forms a surface
in a space of at least as many dimensions as there are
loci, more if there are multiple alleles. Because of non-

additive factor interactions, this surface in general has innumerable distinct peaks (*i.e.,* harmonious combinations) each surrounded by numerous closely related but slightly less adaptive combinations and separated from the others by valleys. Selection according to net effect can only carry the species up the gradient to the nearest peak but will not permit it to find its way across a valley to a higher peak. Evolution would have a richer field of possibilities under a breeding system that permitted exploration of neighboring regions in the surface of adaptive values, even at some expense in momentary adaptation.

A somewhat similar situation holds within systems of *multiple alleles* (*cf.* Timoféëff-Ressovsky, 1932). There is presumably a limit to the number of alleles that can arise from a given type gene by a single act of mutation. But each of these mutations presumably can give rise to mutations at two steps removed from the original type gene and so on in an indefinitely extended network. If there is approximate fixation of one allele (to be expected in general under panmixia), only those mutations that are at one or two removes have any appreciable chance of occurrence. There will be continual recurrence of the same mutations without real novelty. A breeding system that tolerates a continually shifting array of multiple alleles in each series in portions of the population, gives the opportunity for a trying out of wholly novel mutations which occasionally may be of great value. The question then is whether there are breeding structures that permit trial and error both within each system of multiple alleles, and within the field of gene combinations, in such a way as to give a richer field of possibilities than under the univalent determinative process in a panmictic population.

EVOLUTION UNDER UNIPARENTAL REPRODUCTION

At the opposite extreme from the system of random mating is that in which there is uniparental reproduction.

Under vegetative multiplication, or under diploid parthenogenesis, each individual produces a clone in which all individuals are of exactly the same genotype, except for occasional mutations. Continued self fertilization also leads to the production of groups of essential identical individuals.

Suppose that a highly variable panmictic population suddenly shifts to uniparental reproduction. Selection then would be between genotypes. Those combinations that are most adaptive would increase, including perhaps rare types that would have been broken up and lost under panmixia. The less adaptive combinations would soon be displaced. Selection would be exceedingly effective until only one clone was left in each ecological niche. But at this point evolution would come to an end, except for the exceedingly rare occurrence of favorable mutations.

It is obvious that a certain combination of the preceding systems should be much more effective than either by itself (*cf.* Wright, 1931). Prevailing uniparental reproduction, with occasional crossing would permit an effective selection by genotypes to operate in a continually restored field of variability. This combination is of course one that has been used most effectively by plant breeders. It is found in many plants and animals in nature and has presumably been an important factor in their evolution.

The demonstration of the evolutionary advantages of an alternation of periods of uniparental reproduction with cross-breeding may seem to prove too much, since it is not usual in those groups that are usually considered to have evolved the most, the higher arthropods and vertebrates. Perhaps, however, there are other systems which also bring about differentiation of types and thus a basis for selection based on type rather than mere net gene effect, and which have more stability than arrays of clones.

EVOLUTION IN SUBDIVIDED POPULATIONS

A breeding structure that happens to be very convenient from the mathematical standpoint is one in which the species is subdivided into numerous small local populations which largely breed within themselves but receive a small proportion of their population in each generation from migrants which can be treated as random samples from the species as a whole. The basis for the partial isolation may be geographical, or ecological or temporal (breeding season). In the latter two cases an adaptive difference is postulated. We are not here considering the origin of this but rather its consequences on other characters.

Whatever the mechanism of isolation, its evolutionary significance can be evaluated in terms of the effective size of population (N) of the isolated group, the effective rate (m) of exchange of individuals between the group (gene frequency q) and the species as a whole (gene frequency q_t) and the local selection coefficient. It will be convenient here to write s for the net selection coefficient and to ignore mutation pressure (Wright, 1931).

$$\Delta q = sq(1-q) - m(q-q_t)$$

If s in a local population is much larger than m, we have approximately

$$\hat{q} = 1 - \frac{1}{s}\,[m(1-q_t)] \qquad \text{if } s \text{ is positive}$$

$$\hat{q} = \frac{mq_t}{(-s)} \qquad \text{if } s \text{ is negative}$$

If the values of s among local populations show differences greater than m, there will be marked adaptive differentiation of such populations. There is an approach toward fixation of the locally favored gene largely irrespective of the frequency in the species as a whole.

The importance of isolation in evolution seems to have been urged first by M. Wagner as permitting divergent evolution under the control of different environments. Wagner thought of environment as directly guiding the course of evolutionary change, when its effects were not swamped by those of cross-breeding. A similar view has been held by many others since his time who have considered such orderly clines among geographical races as those described by the laws of Bergmann, Gloger, and Allen. While direct control over mutation is not in line with present knowledge of genetics, indirect control through differential selection seems probable enough in these cases (*cf.* Dobzhansky, 1937; Huxley, 1939).

Davenport (1903) and Goldschmidt (1934) have stressed the likelihood of the spreading of the range of species by the diffusion of preadaptive mutations into territories in which they are isolated from the first by the inability of the typical members of the species to live. Goldschmidt has interpreted the major differences among races of *Lymantria dispar* in this way. He finds these differences primarily in such physiological characters as developmental rate, length of diapause, etc. Mathematically, this would be a special case of the foregoing scheme.

Differential selection has been considered so far as a factor making only for divergence of groups within the species and thus tending toward splitting of the latter. There is a possibility, however, that it may be a factor making for progressive evolution of the species as a unit. Particular local populations may, by a tortuous route, arrive at adaptations that turn out to have general, instead of merely local, value and which thus may tend to displace all other local strains by *intergroup* selection (excess emigration). In terms of our multidimensional surface of adaptive values, a particular substrain may be guided from one peak to another by a circuitous route around a valley which would probably not have been found except by such a trial and error mechanism. As different alleles may approach fixation in different populations, mutations at two or more removes from the original type have more opportunity for occurrence than if the population were homogeneous. Thus there may be trial and error within series of alleles as well as between gene combinations.

Let us now turn to the case in which the local selection coefficient is smaller instead of larger than m. The local equilibrium frequency ($\hat{q}$) is approximately as follows.

$$\hat{q} = q_t + \frac{sq_t}{m}(1 - q_t)$$

The values in different local populations in which s is smaller than m are clustered closely about the mean gene frequency, q_t. Selection causes no important differentiation. There may however be variability of each local population due to accidents of sampling if N is small and, consequently, much non-adaptive differentiation among such populations at any given moment.

$$\varphi(q) = Ce^{4Nsq} 4Nmq_t - 1 (1-q)^{4Nm(1-q_t)-1}$$

Figure 1 shows the form of the distribution for various values of Nm, taking $q_t = \frac{1}{2}$ and assuming no selection ($s = 0$). The variance in this case is as follows.

$$\sigma^2_q = \frac{q_t(1-q_t)}{4Nm+1}$$

The distribution of gene frequencies is U shaped, implying random drifting from fixation in one phase to another if m is less than $\dfrac{1}{4Nq_t}$ and $\dfrac{1}{4N(1-q_t)}$. This again would permit trial within each series of alleles, and also between gene combinations.

The latter at least would be important even with larger values of m relative to $\frac{1}{4}N$. With $Nm = 5$, the standard deviation of values of q is 22 per cent. of its limiting value $\sqrt{q(1-q)}$. Such variability tends to become unimportant however if Nm is much larger.

Gulick seems to have been the first to point out the possible significance of isolation in bringing about a nonadaptive differentiation of local races. He has been followed by others, notably recently by Kinsey in his studies of the gall wasps of the genus Cynips (1929, 1936). A study of eleven isolated mountain forests in the Death Valley region by Dobzhansky and Queal (1938) showed a close approach to random mating with no appreciable selection within localities. Between localities on the other hand, frequencies ranged from 51 per cent. to 88 per cent., 2 per cent. to 20 per cent., 8 per cent. to 39 per cent. with standard deviations which can be accounted for by an effective value of Nm of about 5.1. The much greater standard deviation for the range of *D. pseudoobscura* as a whole shows that this differentiation is cumulative with distance.

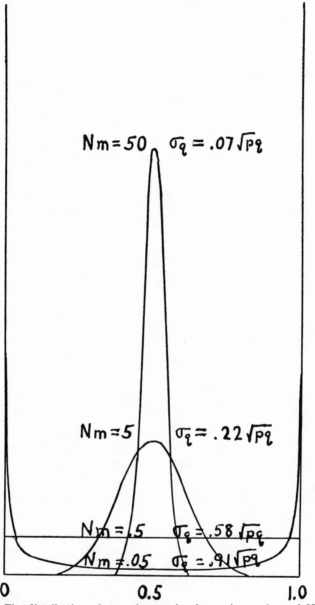

FIG. 1. The distribution of gene frequencies for various values of Nm, taking $q_t = \frac{1}{2}$ and assuming no selection. The symbol p is used for 1-q.

EFFECTIVE SIZE OF POPULATION

There appears to be the difficulty here that the number of individuals in such a form as Drosophila is so enormous that it is difficult to conceive of a limitation in numbers as having any appreciable sampling effects. However, the effective N may be very much smaller than the apparent N (Wright, 1938).

If the number of the two sexes (N_m males, N_f females) is unequal, it can be shown that effective $N = \dfrac{4N_m N_f}{N_m + N_f}$. With unequal numbers, the effective size of population depends more on the smaller number than on the larger number. Thus with N_m males but an indefinitely large number of females, $N = 4N_m$.

Again, different parents may produce widely different numbers of young. If σ^2_κ is the variance in number of gametes contributed by individuals to the following generation in a population (N_0) that is maintaining the same numbers ($\bar{\kappa} = 2$), $\sigma^2_\kappa = \dfrac{\Sigma(\kappa - 2)^2}{N_0}$

$$N = \frac{4N_0 - 2}{2 + \sigma^2_\kappa}$$

The effective size of population is twice as great as the apparent in the highly artificial case in which each parent contributes just two gametes. Effective and apparent size of population are the same if the number of gametes contributed by different parents vary at random (Poisson distribution). If, as would often be the case, most of the offspring come from a small percentage of the mature individuals of the parental generation, the effective size would be much less than the apparent size.

A population may vary tremendously in numbers from generation to generation. If there is a regular cycle of a few generations (N_1, N_2 . . . N_n) an approximately equivalent constant population number can be found.

$$N = \frac{n}{\sum\limits_{x=1}^{n} [1/N_x]}$$

This is controlled much more by the smaller than by the larger numbers. Thus if the breeding population in an isolated region increases ten-fold in each of six generations during the summer (N_0 to $10^6 N_0$) but falls at the end of winter to the same value, N_0, the effective size of population ($N = 6.3N_0$) is relatively small.

In such a cycle, certain individuals in favorable locations are likely to start reproduction earlier than others, perhaps getting a start of a whole generation. In a rapidly breeding form, these few individuals would contribute overwhelmingly more than the average to all later generations. Thus, by a combination of the two preceding principles, the effective size of population may be very small indeed.

The possible evolutionary significance of periodic reduction in the size of natural populations has been discussed by a number of authors. Elton (1934) especially has maintained that chance deviations in the characteristics of survivors at the time of least numbers may have important effects of this sort.

An important case arises where local populations are liable to frequent extinction, with restoration from the progeny of a few stray immigrants. In such regions the line of continuity of large populations may have passed repeatedly through extremely small numbers even though the species has at all times included countless millions of individuals in its range as a whole (*cf*. Fig. 2).

Such mutations as reciprocal translocations that are very strongly selected against until half fixed seem to require some such mechanism to become established. There is an exceedingly deep valley in the surface $\overline{W}$ representing the mean adaptive value in populations with given frequencies of old and new chromosomes, and the term $\overline{W}^{2N}$ in the formula for the joint chromosome frequencies is so small, where N consists of more than some half-dozen individuals that fixation is virtually impossible. Yet translocations have been noted between Drosophila species (*e.g.*, *D. pseudoobscura* and *D. miranda*, Dobzhansky and Tan, 1936) although they are far less common than inversions. The difficulty referred to here does not, of course, apply in species that reproduce vegetatively or by self-fertilization.

We have discussed various considerations that make

effective N much smaller than at first apparent. The effective amount of cross-breeding may also be much less than the actual amount of migration seems to imply. Most of the immigrants are likely to come from neighboring groups, differing less from the receiving population in gene frequency than would a random sample from the

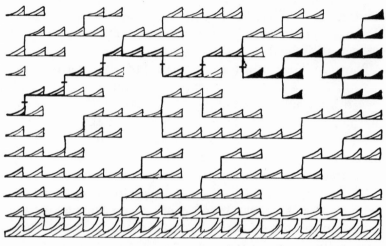

Fig. 2. Diagram of breeding structure in a species in which the populations in certain regions are liable to frequent extinction with reestablishment by rare migrants. Different territories are distinguished vertically. Generations proceed from left to right horizontally. The heavily shaded group represents a large population the entire ancestry of which has passed through small groups of migrants six times in the period shown.

species. If there is a correlation, r, between immigrants and receiving group, the m of the formula must be replaced by $m(1-r)$ if m is to continue to be the actual amount of replacement by immigration.

In the case of *Drosophila pseudoobscura*, it has been noted that Dobzhansky and Queal (1938) found variability in gene frequency among mountain forests of the Death Valley region which implied an effective value of Nm of about 5. For the species as a whole, variability is such that effective Nm must be only about one tenth as large as this (0.5).

Isolation by Distance

This last case leads to another model of breeding structure which may be of considerable importance (Wright, 1938). Suppose that a population is distributed uniformly over a large territory but that the parents of any given individual are drawn from a small surrounding region (average distance D, effective population N). How much local differentiation is possible merely from accidents of sampling? Obviously the grandparents were drawn from a larger territory (average distance $\sqrt{2}\,D$, effective population $2N$). The ancesters of generation n came from an average distance $\sqrt{n}\,D$ and from a population of average size nN. It is assumed that the variance of the ancestral range, either in latitude or in longitude, increases directly with the number of generations of ancestry.

Fig. 3 shows how the standard deviation of gene frequencies for unit territories of various effective sizes increases with distance. If $\sigma_q = .577\sqrt{q_t(1-q_t)}$ and $q_t = 1 - q_t = \frac{1}{2}$ all values of gene frequency are equally numerous ($\phi(q) = 1$). Any larger value implies a tendency toward fixation of one or the other allele in different local populations.

If the parents are drawn from local populations of effective size greater than 1,000, the situation differs little from panmixia even over enormous areas. There is considerable fluctuating local differentiation of unit territories where their effective size is of the order of 100, but not much differentiation of large regions unless effective N is much less.

Kinsey's (1929) description of the gall wasp, *Cynips pezomachoides erinacei*, conforms fairly well to the above model for the case of moderately large N. This subspecies ranges over some 500,000 square miles in northeastern United States. Both the insects and their galls may differ markedly and consistently in collections taken from different trees or small groves at short distances apart, but the same variability is found throughout the range. There is little regional differentiation in this enormous territory, although at still greater distances

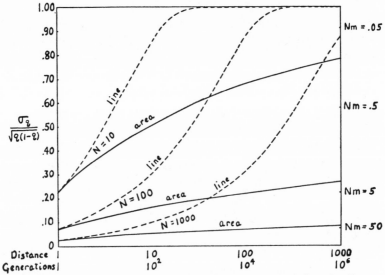

FIG. 3.   The standard deviation of the mean gene frequencies of unit random breeding territories (N = 10; N = 100; N = 1000), in relation to mean distance.   The case in which the population is distributed uniformly over an area is represented in solid lines, that in which it is distributed along one dimension by broken lines.

the species complex *C. pezomachoides* is subdivided into eight intergrading species.

In a species whose range is essentially one-dimensional (shore line, river, etc.) the ancestors of generation n come from an average distance of $\sqrt{n}\,D$ as before, but the effective size of population is $\sqrt{n}\,N$ instead of nN. Differentiation increases much more rapidly with distance than in the preceding case.   This principle was suggested in qualitative terms by Thompson (1931) in his study of differentiation within species of river fish in relation to water distance.   In weak swimmers (*e.g.*, Johnny Darters) there was marked increase in average difference in number of fin rays with increased distance in spite of a continuous distribution.   The differentiation with distance was not as rapid, however, as that in several species with discontinuous distribution (restricted to the smallest stream).   On the other hand the strong swimmers of the rivers showed little or no differentiation throughout their entire ranges.

Such uniformity in breeding structure as implied above is not likely to be closely approximated in nature. Even where there is apparent continuity of a population, it is likely that conditions vary from place to place in such a way that there is excess multiplication at certain centers separated by regions in which the species would be unable to maintain itself permanently were it not for immigration (as in the breeding structure of Figure 2). Moreover, even with complete uniformity of conditions, local differentiation should result in the accidental attainment of more adaptive complexes in some regions than in others. As before, incipient nonadaptive differentiation may lead to a more important adaptive differentiation. The centers in which population is increasing most rapidly will become increasingly isolated from each other by the mere fact that they are centers of emigration.

A process of this sort has been postulated by Sumner (1932) in the case of subspecies of Peromyscus. Within subspecies, he found statistical differentiation of most local populations which may well have been of the type due merely to distance. But at the subspecies boundaries there was typically a zone of relatively rapid change. These boundaries were not necessarily along natural barriers to migration. Sumner compared them with the distributions which would result "if a collection of spherical rubber bags were placed in rigid containers and then strongly but unequally inflated."

The breeding structure of natural populations thus is likely to be intermediate between the model of subdivision into partially isolated territories and that of local inbreeding in a continuous population. In so far as it is continuous, it is likely to be intermediate between area continuity and linear continuity.

Summing up, we have attempted to show that the breeding structure of populations has a number of important consequences with respect to speciation. Partial isolation of local populations, even if merely by distance is important, not only as a possible precursor of splitting of the species, but also as leading to more rapid evolu-

tionary change of the population as a single system and
thus more rapid differentiation from other populations
from which it is completely isolated. Local differentiation within a species, based either on the nonadaptive
inbreeding effect or on local conditions of selection or
both, permits trial and error both within series of
multiple alleles and between gene combinations and thus
a more effective process of selection than possible in a
purely panmictic population.

LITERATURE CITED

Davenport, C. B.
    1903. *The Decennial Publications,* 10: 157–176. The University of
        Chicago.
Dobzhansky, Th.
    1937. ''Genetics and the Origin of Species.'' New York: Columbia
        University Press, 364 pp.
Dobzhansky, Th., and M. L. Queal
    1938. *Genetics,* 23: 239–251.
Dobzhansky, Th., and C. C. Tan
    1936. *Zeit. Ind. Abst. Ver.,* 72: 88–114.
Elton, C. S.
    1924. *Brit. Jour. Exp. Biol.,* 3: 119–163.
Fisher, R. A.
    1930. ''The Genetical Theory of Natural Selection.'' Oxford: Clarendon
        Press, 272 pp.
Goldschmidt, R.
    1934. ''Lymantria,'' *Bibliographia Genetica,* 11: 1–186.
Haldane, J. B. S.
    1932. ''The Causes of Evolution.'' London: Harper and Bros., 235 pp.
Huxley, J. S.
    1939. ''Bijdragen tot de dierkunde,'' pp. 491–520. Leiden: E. J. Brill.
Kinsey, A. C.
    1929. Studies No. 84, 85, 86. Indiana University Studies, Vol. 16.
    1936. Indiana Univ. Publ., Science Series No. 4.
Sumner, F. B.
    1932. *Bibliographia Genetica,* 9: 1–106.
Thompson, D. H.
    1931. *Trans. Ill. State Acad. Sci.,* 23: 276–281.
Timoféëff-Ressovsky, N. W.
    1932. *Proc. 6th Internat. Cong. Genetics,* 1: 308–330.
Wright, S.
    1921. *Genetics,* 6: 111–178.
    1922. *Bull. no. 1121,* U. S. Dept. of Agr., 59 pp.
    1931. *Genetics,* 16: 97–159.
    1932. *Proc. 6th Internat. Cong. Genetics,* 1: 356–366.
    1937. *Proc. Nat. Acad. Sci.,* 23: 307–320.
    1938. *Science,* 87: 430–431.

3

Reprinted from *Amer. Naturalist* 81:114–133 (1947)

HEREDITY OF GEOGRAPHICALLY AND ECOLOGICALLY ISOLATED RACES[1]

DR. JENS CLAUSEN, DR. DAVID D. KECK AND
DR. WILLIAM M. HIESEY
CARNEGIE INSTITUTION OF WASHINGTON, STANFORD UNIVERSITY

MOST plant species are composed of races, which are aggregations of scattered local populations that have certain fundamental characteristics in common. Some of these races can be recognized on sight, because they are morphologically different; others look alike but are physiologically so distinct that they can occupy different climatic zones; still others are both morphologically and ecologically distinct. Some races are very local; others, of wider distribution. Some seem to have arisen through chance spatial isolation from other populations of the species, whereas those in ecologically different environments appear to have evolved in response to the selective effect of these environments. Geographically and ecologically isolated races are biological units just below the species level. They are of evolutionary importance, because they are probably often the forerunners of new species. Very little experimental evidence on the heredity of such races is on record. In the following account, the genetic basis will be discussed of four sets of races that exemplify kinds of intraspecific differentiation.

GEOGRAPHIC RACES IN HEMIZONIA ANGUSTIFOLIA

The coast tarweed of California, *Hemizonia angustifolia* DC., is a 10-chromosome species of the Madiinae of the sunflower family. It occupies a narrow strip on the coastal side of the outer Coast Range extending inland only as far as the coastal fog. It is composed of two major races: one occupies a coastal strip 275 miles long from northern California to south of Monterey Bay; the other starts 40 miles farther south and extends over a

---

[1] Presented by Dr. Clausen at a joint symposium of the American Society of Naturalists, the Genetics Society of America and the Society for the Study of Evolution, December 31, 1946, at Boston.

distance of 40 miles. It is separated from the northern race by the Santa Lucia Mountains, which rise precipitously from the ocean, leaving no coastal plain for this species to occupy. Geographically the two races are therefore effectively separated, but ecologically their habitats are similar.

Small but significant morphological differences separate the two races of the coast tarweed. These were studied in 11 populations from different localities of the northern race and 5 of the southern grown in a uniform garden. Some of the differences between the two races can be seen from the upper two plants in Fig. 1. The plant of the northern race, left, is of a population from a grassy hillside west of Belmont, San Mateo County, south of San Francisco on the peninsula; this race has a low and broad habit, slender and open branching, and relatively small heads. The plant of the southern race, upper right, from a population originating in fields close to the sea 15 miles north of San Simeon, San Luis Obispo County, has more erect and robust branching, and larger, more congested heads. These differences are small, as compared with the morphological characters distinguishing most species, but they are fairly consistent, and by some authors the two races, subsp. *typica* in the north, and subsp. *macrocephala* in the south, have been considered as distinct species.

The two forms are easily crossed and their hybrid is as fertile as the parents. A second generation of 1,152 plants was grown, and the segregation indicated that each of the small differences between the parents depended upon the action of multiple genes, each with a small additive effect. In this manner, the slight morphological differences between the races were resolved into even smaller steps. The recombinations of these genes produced great variation in the F_2; no two individuals were alike, and no plant exactly like either parent was recovered from this sample. The six F_2 individuals shown in Fig. 1 represent various types found. The center individual in the upper row combines the low habit of the

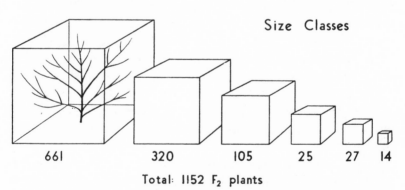

FIG. 1. Segregation in a hybrid between geographic races of *Hemizonia angustifolia*. P₁, subsp. *typica;* P₂, subsp. *macrocephala;* F₂, three vigorous and three substandard segregants. The scale is 10 cm. high. The size classes are represented by cubes, the edges of which are 50, 35, 25, 15, 10 and 5 cm., respectively.

northern race with the density of the southern, but its heads are intermediate in size. The individual in the same row to the right has the erect habit of the southern and the open branching of the northern race.

The second generation offspring were generally vigorous, although many were somewhat weaker than the parental types. All F_2 plants were classified according to their greatest dimension as represented by the size of the cubes in the lower row of Fig. 1, shown to the same scale as the plants above. More than 57 per cent. of the offspring (661 plants) were in the largest size class, ranging from 35 to 50 cm in greatest dimension, as large as the parental races. The plants of this class were similar in size to those illustrated in the upper row of the F_2.

The substandard groups, represented by the five cubes to the right, contained nearly 43 per cent. of the plants. They ranged from 35 cm down to less than 5 cm, and are represented in the lower row of the F_2. During the 7 to 8 months that these plants lived, the small individuals remained healthy and continued to flower, although there was little or no increment in their growth. Meanwhile, sister plants increased to 1,000 times the volume of the extreme dwarfs. The genes determining the rates of the physiological processes in the two races are probably not identical, for certain recombinations have resulted in upsetting balanced development. As the two races evolved, their genes became so different that they were no longer completely interchangeable without detrimental effects in the progeny.

The barriers to interbreeding between the northern and southern races of the coast tarweed are nevertheless of a much smaller order than those typical of distinct but related species. So many of the hybrid offspring are vigorous that these racial complexes are not considered to have yet reached the status of distinct species. The northern and southern races of *Hemizonia angustifolia* are therefore classified as geographic subspecies. They are not distinct ecotypes, because both occur in the same coastal zone and react very similarly. The species therefore appears to have only one ecotype but two geographic subspecies.

Evolutionarily, the two races are in the transitional stage between subspecies and full-fledged species. Many small steps were required to produce these differences, and many genes were involved, but the changes did not affect the interfertility of the races or the structure of their chromosomes. Races in such transitional stages of development are significant, because their existence indicates gradual steps in the evolution of species.

A New Genus—or Just a Subspecies?

An example of a geographically isolated race of very limited distribution is afforded by a rare plant of the sunflower family that was discovered in 1940 in the inner Coast Range of California near the quicksilver mining town of New Idria. It is a little spring-flowering annual, 5 to 15 cm tall, occurring as a small colony of some 300 individuals on a serpentine hillside. It nevertheless maintains itself there, for it was collected once before at New Idria some 40 years ago, but not classified. This plant is so unlike anything previously named that it was thought to belong to an undescribed genus. Technically it would be assigned to the Helenieae, the sneezeweed tribe, but it fits none of the known genera. There was, however, something about its vegetative characters that suggested the genera *Layia* and *Madia* of the neighboring Madiinae of the Heliantheae, the sunflower tribe, although it has no ray-florets or outer involucre, deficiencies which technically exclude it from that tribe.

In our garden this supposedly new genus with uncertain tribal affiliation was provisionally called *Roxira serpentina*, the generic name commemorating its two discoverers, Mrs. Roxana Ferris and Dr. Ira L. Wiggins, of Stanford University. It has 8 pairs of chromosomes, resembling those of *Layia*, and crossings were therefore attempted between it and 8-paired species of *Layia* and *Madia*. The *Madia* crossings were unsuccessful, but vigorous hybrids were obtained in crossings with two

Layia species. The hybrid with *Layia glandulosa* was even completely fertile, and the 8 chromosomes from the two supposedly distinct genera paired perfectly, indicating a very close evolutionary relationship.

Layia glandulosa (Hook.) H. & A., the desert *Layia*, is a species of wide distribution in sandy habitats. It occurs from Lower California to central California on the coast side of the mountains, and from Arizona to Washington in the desert regions of the Great Basin. Its common form, Fig. 2, upper left, has 8 showy, white rays and long, shining white pappus-bristles on the disk-akenes. *Roxira*, upper right, is rayless (*i.e.*, discoid), and it is a smaller and much more slender plant, with stubby and dull brown pappus scales. The F_1 hybrid, second row, is a tarweed in good standing, for it meets the technical requirements of the Madiinae, having 3 to 8 rays per head with accompanying ray-bracts that in turn enclose the ray-akenes. However, some of the heads on the same plant may have no ray-florets at all.

More than 1,200 F_2 plants were grown. They were generally more vigorous than nonhybrid forms of the desert *Layia* or than other hybrids between races of that species. The segregation was very striking, as seen in the lower half of Fig. 2. Forms with 8, 5, 3, 1 and no rays were segregated, and the rays were long, short or very short. The akene-enfolding bracts always accompanied the rays. The color and length of the disk-pappus varied from one parental extreme to the other.

The segregation for just three of the 9 to 10 characters that distinguish the parental forms are listed in Table 1. Each character was difficult to classify, because the parental differences were resolved into so many small steps that a completely graded series of variants was obtained. It was estimated that between 10 and 20 pairs of genes were possibly involved in the segregations, but both of the parental morphological types were nevertheless recovered in the F_2. Considerable genetic linkage was evident as demonstrated by the data in Table 1. For example, the short pappus typical of *Roxira* was found mainly with no, few or short rays. It appears that one or two pairs of genes may determine the presence or absence of rays and bracts, but several pairs determine the number and the length of the rays, and about three pairs the differences in length of the pappus. *Roxira* is evidently

Fig. 2. Segregation in a hybrid between *Layia glandulosa* and *Roxira serpentina*. Flower-heads of two individuals of *Layia glandulosa* (P₁), upper left, and of *Roxira* (P₂), upper right. Second row, variation in F₁. Three lower rows, segregation in F₂.

predominantly recessive as compared with *Layia glandulosa.*

Although *Roxira* has no ray-florets, it carries genes that shorten the rays of *Layia glandulosa.* Likewise, it has genes that affect the color of the rays, for 107 out of 988 F₂ plants had pale yellow rays instead of white.

Because of this genetic evidence, *Roxira serpentina* is now considered to be only a subspecies of the desert *Layia* and is to be reduced to the much less glamorous name of *Layia glandulosa discoidea.* ˙A series of systemic changes that would otherwise denote tribal differences, and which on their face value would be worthy of generic rank, have taken place in this species without affecting the interchangeability of the genes or the chromosomes. The two

TABLE 1

SEGREGATIONS IN F₂ OF *Layia glandulosa* × *Roxira serpentina*

Rays		Pappus length			Total		Approximate ratio
Number	Length	Long	Medium	Short			
8	long	42	28	..	70		
	medium	23	51	..	74	157	
	short	3	10	..	13		
							13
1–7	long	34	37	..	71		
	medium	88	363	5	456	831	
	short	51	247	6	304		
none		16	219	15		250	3
Total		257	955	26		1238	
Approximate ratio		63		1			

forms must have been separated for a long time for such differences to have evolved. ˙No form of the desert *Layia* grows with the serpentine plant, the nearest known colony being 6 miles away on the other side of the mountain range. There is no way of determining which race was first, the rare, inconspicuous one from the serpentine, or the common, showy one from sandy habitats.

Layia glandulosa discoidea has the characteristic of a relict form that in the past may have been much more widely distributed than now. Its presence on serpentine soil instead of on sand may indicate that *discoidea* is an edaphic ecotype and not merely a very local geographic race.

MARITIME AND INLAND RACES OF LAYIA PLATYGLOSSA

In contrast with the preceding two examples of geo-

graphically isolated races is another of ecologically isolated races in the tidy-tip, *Layia platyglossa* (F. and M.)
Gray. The tidy-tip is a spring-flowering annual that
adorns California hillsides during March and April.
This species, with 7 pairs of chromosomes, is common in
separated colonies throughout the Coast Ranges from the
San Francisco Bay region south to Lower California.
Farther north it occurs mainly along a narrow coastal
strip.

Layia platyglossa contains an inland and a maritime
race, shown in Fig. 3. The inland race, which is wide-

FIG. 3. Left, maritime, and right, inland races of *Layia platyglossa*, with their F₁ hybrid between them.

spread and much the more common, is early flowering
and has a distinct central leader and ascending-erect
stems. On the exposed coastal bluffs it is replaced by a
race of matted habit, without a central leader, but with
horizontal branches from the base of the plant. This
race has thick, succulent leaves, and in the experiment
garden it flowers two or three weeks later than the inland
race, and remains green much longer. The maritime
race occurs over a distance of approximately 225 miles
along the immediate coast of central California. Although intermediates occur, the two races do not lose
their identity.

The inland and coastal races of the tidy-tip cross easily, and the hybrid is completely fertile. Such hybrids are more vigorous than nonhybrids, and the increased vigor was evident through the third generation. The F_1 hybrid is shown in the center of Fig. 3 and is intermediate in most characters.

A striking segregation takes place in the second and later generations affecting all characters that distinguish

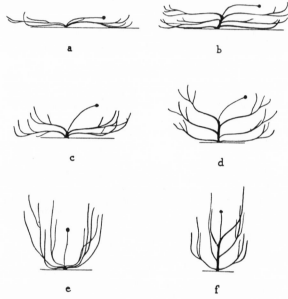

FIG. 4. Segregation in habit in F_2 of maritime × inland races of *Layia platyglossa*. The letters refer to the classes in table 2.

the parental races. The major types of growth habit found in the segregating offspring are indicated in Fig. 4 and the class frequencies of the individuals belonging to these types are listed in Table 2 together with a tabulation of earliness. Separate genes govern the presence or absence of the central leader and the horizontal or erect orientation of the branches. A counterpart of one of the recombinations predominated in one intermediate locality in the wild two miles from the coast but overlooking the ocean. It is illustrated by the plant *c* in Fig. 4 and has no central leader but merely a central peduncle and long, ascending branches.

About 3 pairs of multiple genes are responsible for the lateness of the maritime form, some 4 to 5 pairs determine the architecture of the plants, and others govern the thickness of the leaves, the number of rays and other characters.   The parental types were recovered in an F_2 population of 803 individuals, but they had not become genetically constant.   There was a fairly high degree of

TABLE 2

SEGREGATIONS IN F_2 OF MARITIME × INLAND RACES OF *Layia platyglossa*.
LETTERS IN PARENTHESES REFER TO FIGURE 4

Branching	Central leader	Earliness		Total		Approximate ratio
		Very late	± early			
horizontal	none (a)	8	38	46	69	1
	present (b)	2	21	23		
± ascending	none (c)	6	221	227	394	15
	present (d)	..	167	167		
erect	none (e)	..	203	203	340	
	present (f)	..	137	137		
Total		16	787	803		
Approximate ratio		1	63			

genetic linkage between the physiological characteristic of late flowering and the horizontal habit of the parental maritime race, as can be seen from Table 2.   This linkage tends to keep the ecologically important characteristics together, even though the two races occasionally inter-cross.

The parental forms of this cross were a maritime race from Point Joe on the Monterey Peninsula of central California and an inland race from a mesa near Etiwanda, San Bernardino County, in southern California.   Four additional hybrids between other maritime and inland populations of *Layia platyglossa* have been grown, yielding some 3,600 F_2 individuals.   Their pattern of segregation and linkage was similar to that of the hybrid here discussed.

Six F₃ populations of the Point Joe × Etiwanda cross were studied, totalling some 2,700 individuals. Because Layias are self-sterile, these were obtained from mutual pollinations between pairs of F_2 individuals, each pair composed of plants of similar growth habit. All F_3's continued to segregate a great deal, except that two cultures from F_2 plants with central leaders produced only offspring with central leaders, and one from early flowering F_2 plants was early flowering only. On the other hand, three pairs of F_2 plants without central leaders segregated forms both with and without leaders, and five pairs produced offspring that segregated very early flowering to late flowering plants. These results suggest that central leader and early flowering are probably the most easily recognizable recessive characteristics. The gene basis for the two races may be more complicated than the F_2 segregations would lead one to believe. The vigor of the F_3 populations noticeably exceeded that of the parental races, a situation very different from that prevailing in the F_2's and F_3's of hybrids between closely related species, because these are characterized by partial sterility and considerable reduction in vigor.

Hybrids between two maritime races produced only plants of maritime type. More than 1,400 F_2 plants were grown from a hybrid between a maritime *Layia platyglossa* from exposed bluffs near Bodega north of San Francisco Bay, and the previously mentioned form from Point Joe on the Monterey Peninsula. All the F_2 plants of this cross, without exception, were without central leader, were completely prostrate, succulent and late flowering. This result indicates that the genes determining the ecologically important characteristics of the maritime race from the narrow coastal strip are identically arranged in the chromosomes of the parental forms, even though these are separated by a distance of some 140 miles, including the Golden Gate channel.

Another *Layia* species has developed races strikingly parallel to the ones just described. Within a few hundred feet from the maritime *Layia platyglossa* on the

coastal bluffs near Bodega grows a late-flowering, prostrate race of *Layia chrysanthemoides* (DC.) Gray of very
similar appearance.   The erect, early flowering inland
races of both species also mimic each other, although their
floral characters differ markedly.   It is almost impossible
to cross *platyglossa* and *chrysanthemoides* with each
other, and their rare hybrids are completely sterile.
Their differences are therefore those of very distinct
species and are evolutionarily of a much higher order
than the superficially more spectacular differences between the completely interfertile coastal and inland races
of each species.

Many other species of entirely unrelated families have
produced similar pairs of inland and maritime races both
in California and other parts of the world.   The genetic
basis of these, however, has rarely been explored.   An
example parallel to those in *Layia* is found in the maritime and inland races of *Viola tricolor* L. from Denmark,
the inheritance of which has been analyzed (Clausen,
1926, pp. 16–22).   Such races are ecologically, rather than
spatially isolated.   This particular kind is a climatic race,
a special kind of an ecotype.

Altitudinal Races in Potentilla glandulosa

Climatic races of a different kind from those determined by distance from the sea are found in perennial
plant species that occupy a great range of climates.   This
is illustrated by the altitudinal races of *Potentilla glandulosa* Lindl., a member of the rose family that is common
in the western United States.   In central California this
species occurs from near the coast to 11,000 feet altitude
near the crest of the Sierra Nevada, although it is not
found in the great Central Valley.   Approximately seven
climatic races belonging to four morphologically distinct
subspecies of this *Potentilla* occupy the various climatic
zones of the transect across central California.   A great
many forms of these have been tested through the years
at the three transplant stations maintained in California

by the Carnegie Institution of Washington (Clausen, Keck and Hiesey, 1940). These stations are located at Stanford University near the coast, at Mather halfway up the Sierra Nevada, and at Timberline near the crest of this mountain range.

Lowland races of *Potentilla glandulosa* differ strikingly from alpine races both in morphological and physiological characters. For example, the robust, large-leaved, small-flowered race from the mild climate of the Coast Ranges, belonging to subspecies *typica,* is in active growth throughout the year; it is resistant to frost, and thus able to grow during the winter when the rains occur. By contrast, the dwarf, slender-stemmed, large-flowered alpines belong to subsp. *nevadensis,* remain dormant over a nine-months' winter in their natural habitat, and then spring into rapid flowering during the brief summers. When transplanted to the lowland station, the alpines are winter-dormant, but for only two or three months, and they become weakened and less floriferous. The Coast Range plants, on the other hand, are unable to survive the long, severe winter at the alpine station.

All the races of *Potentilla glandulosa* have 7 pairs of chromosomes and cross easily. They differ in a great many characters, both morphological and physiological, and although the subspecies by some authors have been recognized as distinct species, their hybrids are completely fertile and vigorous. A plant of the winter-active, self-fertile Coast Range race coming from near sea-level at Santa Barbara was crossed with a plant of the winter-dormant, self-fertile alpine race from 11,000 feet near the boundary of Sequoia National Park, in the Sierra Nevada. The F_1 was more vigorous than either parent, was fairly winter-active and highly self-fertile. A large, vigorous F_2 population was grown at Stanford and segregated for all the 11 or 12 characters that distinguish the parental races.

A striking segregation for the physiological character of winter activity was observed in this F_2. At Stanford, in mid-January, the coastal parental race has vigorously growing young stems and long leaves, and the alpine is dormant. Among 992 F₂ plants, 183 were classified as very active, having new leaves 10 to 17 cm long, 600 as moderately active and 209 as dormant. A completely intergrading series was observed, giving the impression that the segregation was governed by genes in a multiple series.

Many new forms arose through the recombination of the genes of the contrasting parental races. One of these forms, for example, combined the short internodes of the alpine with the large stem leaves of the Coast Range form, resulting in a short and compacted type with large leafy bracts in the inflorescences. About 3 per cent. of the F₂ belonged to this morphological type. Plants of this form are not found in the wild, but they are of a habit that would appear to be suitable for the extreme maritime environment, which this species has not yet been able to occupy.

An equally striking interracial hybrid of *Potentilla glandulosa* was produced between the foothill and alpine races. One parent came from the foothills of the Sierra Nevada in the scrub oak chaparral near Oak Grove, Tulare County, at an altitude of 2,500 feet. The alpine parent was from a sunny, rocky slope at 10,300 feet, above the Timberline transplant station, north of Tioga Pass in Mono County, on the east flank of the Sierra Nevada.

The foothill race, belonging to subsp. *reflexa,* occupies dry, warm slopes at lower elevations in the Sierra Nevada. It is a tall, self-fertile, large-leaved form with long, divaricately branching stems, open habit, and small, yellow, spreading to reflexed petals. Its plants are susceptible to frost and become winter-dormant even at the lowland station. They reach their best development at mid-altitude, but are unable to survive at the alpine station. The foothill parent used in this cross is shown in the center line of Fig. 5 as it grows in the gardens at Stanford and Mather. This individual was set at the alpine station seven times, but only once did it survive the first winter there.

The alpine race, in contrast, occupies habitats from around 8,500 to 11,000 feet altitude above tree-line. It is much more frost resistant than the foothill race.   The

ALPINE PARENT

FOOTHILL PARENT

Dies

F₁ HYBRID

at Stanford   at Mather   at Timberline

FIG. 5. *Potentilla glandulosa.* Responses of an individual of the alpine and one of the foothill race and their F₁ hybrid in the transplant gardens at Stanford, 100 feet, at Mather, 4600 feet, and at Timberline, 10,000 feet altitude. The height of the scale is 10 cm.

alpine parent is shown in the upper horizontal row of Fig. 5 as it grows at all three stations.

A clone of the F₁ hybrid is illustrated in the bottom row of Fig. 5.   The hybrid is intermediate in appearance, but grows vigorously and survives indefinitely at all three stations.   It is moderately self-fertile.

All the 575 F_2 individuals of this hybrid were cloned and grown simultaneously at the Stanford, Mather and Timberline transplant stations for at least five years. Detailed measurements and seasonal notes were taken annually on each individual in each environment to determine its climatic fitness.

The parents differ in at least 16 easily observed morphological and physiological characteristics, and in the F_2 a complete segregation in all these characters took place. At each station there is a great variation in vigor, but the plants that are vigorous in one environment may be weak in another, and *vice versa*. Physiological characteristics, such as earliness of flowering, frost resistance and ability to survive in specific environments, are genetically linked with morphological ones such as shape, size and color of petals. Such linkages tend to keep the climatic races distinct even where they meet and intercross. The linkage is not absolute, and many recombinations are found. The nature of the segregation is such as to indicate that each characteristic is determined by several genes. The expressions of the genes in the same individual are modified from one environment to the other. No winter-active forms were segregated in this cross between two forms differing in degree of winter dormancy.

Fig. 6 shows the reactions of three contrasting F_2 individuals in three environments, each horizontal row representing a clone. The plants at the left are those grown in the garden at Stanford, those in the middle at Mather and the ones to the right at Timberline. No two individuals in the F_2 responded to the three environments in the same way, and in this respect the F_2 was much more variable than any wild race. The very contrasting environments of the stations act as a coarse sieve, making it possible to distinguish individuals with different climatic fitnesses. The three plants illustrated represent three very different trends.

The top row shows an individual of typically alpine reactions. It survives at all three stations but is dis-

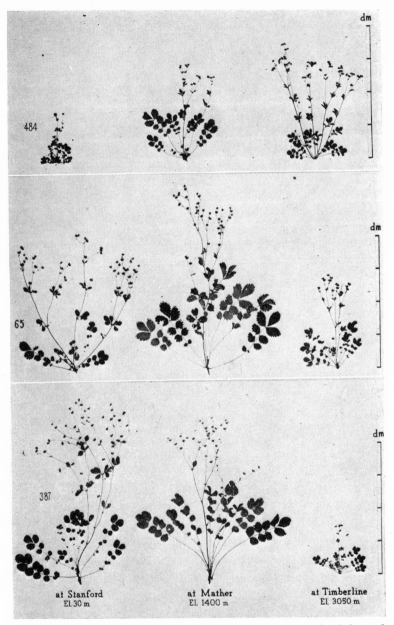

FIG. 6. Responses of three F_2 clones of the hybrid between the alpine and foothill races of *Potentilla glandulosa* at Stanford, Mather, and Timberline. Top row, best at Timberline; center row, succeeding at all three stations; and bottom row, best at Stanford.

tinctly most vigorous at Timberline. Its morphological characters, however, were recombinations of those of the foothill and alpine races.

The middle row shows a clone representing a group of individuals that survive and thrive at all three stations, showing an adaptability not matched by any of the Potentillas from the wild. This individual has the floral characters of the alpine parent and the vegetative of the foothill, except that its herbage is resistant to frost.

The lowest row is of a clone belonging to a group that, unlike either of the parental races, grows most vigorously at the lowland station. In this respect it is similar to the race native to the Coast Ranges, but differs by being winter-dormant at Stanford. Morphologically it resembles the foothill parent. The plant illustrated survives at Timberline, although growing weakly, but many other F_2's of this class die there.

A complete reshuffling of the morphological and physiological characteristics of the two parent races has taken place, resulting in the development of new forms, some of which have potentialities for superior development and others a greater capacity to survive in a diversity of environments than either parent. Half of the F_2 plants have survived for 8 years in the severe climate of the alpine station and many ripen seed there year after year. Some of these even surpass the native alpines in vigor and frost resistance. Many of those that fit the alpine climate so well have vegetative characteristics of the foothill parent.

Eighteen F_3 populations from this foothill-alpine hybrid were grown in the garden at Stanford. They consisted of 3,600 individuals obtained by self-pollinating selected F_2 plants representing very different morphological and physiological types. All these F_3 progenies continued to segregate, most of them as completely as the F_2, but two cultures approached constancy in petal size and color, and some of the others in growth habit. Hybrid vigor was maintained through the third generation.

It is evident from the F_2 and F_3 data that in this cross between a foothill and an alpine race of *Potentilla glandulosa* new climatic races are in the process of development through the recombination of the genes of the old ones. This evidence points to the importance of climatic races from contrasting environments as potential sources of gene material for the evolution of new races.

Conclusions

Both geographically and ecologically isolated races of a species are regulated through the interaction of many genes in a balanced system in harmony with their environment. The genetic and ecologic analysis of hybrids between races from contrasting environments indicates that there are deep-seated functional differences between the races, even though they may appear to intergrade by gradual steps. The differences between natural races are predominantly determined by series of genes of the multiple type, each gene having a minor but additive effect. When crossings occur between contrasting geographic or ecologic races and their genes recombine, so many new forms appear that the variability may far surpass that in the wild populations of the species.

This situation indicates that in nature there is a backlog of unutilized evolutionary resources from which races capable of fitting into many new environments could be synthesized. Hybrids from such crossings are also often superior to their parents in their ability to succeed in a wide range of environments. These facts are of importance in further clarifying the evolutionary pattern in plant life and in furnishing information of importance for those engaged in plant breeding.

LITERATURE CITED

Clausen, J.
  1926. *Hereditas*, 8: 1–156.
Clausen, J., David D. Keck and William M. Hiesey
  1940. Carnegie Inst. Washington Publ. No. 520.

4

Reprinted from *Evolution* **12**:319–336 (1958)

RAPID EVOLUTION IN *CLARKIA*

Harlan Lewis and Peter H. Raven

Introduction

Several diploid species of *Clarkia* (Onagraceae) have very limited areas of distribution (Lewis and Lewis, 1955). Most of these grow adjacent to or are surrounded by other closely related species that resemble them so closely that they would ordinarily be regarded as conspecific. Specific status is accorded to them because of reproductive isolation coupled with at least one consistent difference in external morphology. This pattern recurs with sufficient constancy to suggest that the various examples have a common explanation, with similar factors operating in each instance. This pattern suggests to us a rapid shift of the adaptive mode, such as Simpson (1944) termed quantum evolution, at the diploid specific level. The purpose of this paper is to illustrate this process by a consideration of the mode of origin of a narrow serpentine endemic, *Clarkia franciscana* Lewis and Raven (1958).

Spatial Relationship, Breeding Habit, and Morphological Differentiation

Clarkia franciscana is comprised of a single population on a serpentine outcrop just south of the Golden Gate in the Presidio in San Francisco, California. Two morphologically similar species, *C. rubicunda* and *C. amoena,* occur close by (fig. 1). Colonies of the former are found along the coast and in the valleys of the Coast Ranges from northern San Luis Obispo County to just north of San Francisco Bay in Marin County. *Clarkia franciscana* occurs, therefore, as an enclave within the area of distribution of *C. rubicunda* but does not grow intermixed with it. The closest colony of *C. rubicunda* is now at Point Lobos, San Fran-

cisco, 3.5 miles away from the population of *C. franciscana,* although it is possible that the two species may have been somewhat closer before construction in the Presidio. *Clarkia rubicunda* and *C. amoena* replace each other in central Marin County with scarcely any overlap, and the distribution of the latter continues northward along the coast and in the coastal mountains to Vancouver Island. Both *C. rubicunda* and *C. amoena* occasionally occur on serpentine, the former more frequently, perhaps because of the more common occurrence of serpentine within its range. However, neither of these is characteristically a serpentine species.

The three species are morphologically so similar that were it not for the presence of very strong barriers to gene exchange between them they would undoubtedly be considered conspecific. As living plants they are readily distinguished, however, by the color pattern and conformation of the petals. *Clarkia amoena* differs from the other two by a red spot in the center of the petal rather than at the base, and *C. franciscana* is distinguished from *C. rubicunda* by a more slender habit and smaller flowers with truncated petals (for details see Lewis and Raven, 1958). All three have the same chromosome number ($n = 7$). The closeness of the relation between *C. amoena* and *C. rubicunda* is suggested by mutants that occur in *C. rubicunda* that simulate the petal color pattern of *C. amoena* and mutants in both species that remove the petal spot (Hiorth,[1] 1940). In the absence of petal spots as indicators,

---

[1] Hiorth and Håkansson used the name *Godetia amoena* for *C. rubicunda* and *G. whitneyi* for *C. amoena.*

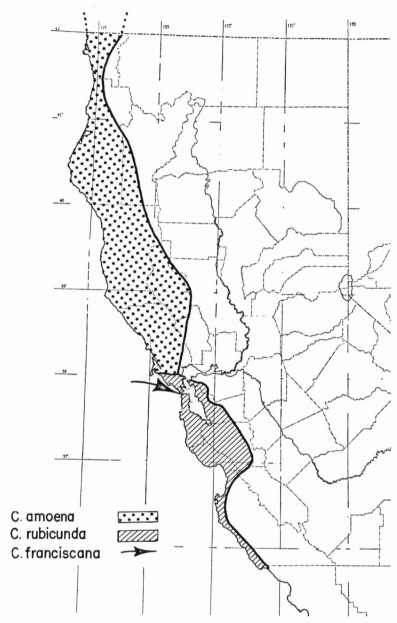

FIG. 1. Distribution of *Clarkia amoena*, *C. rubicunda*, and *C. franciscana* in California. The distribution of *C. amoena* extends northward to Vancouver Island.

the two species are indistinguishable except by test crosses. The specific status of these two taxa is shown, however, not only by the extensive study of their hybrids by Hiorth (1942, 1947) and Håkansson[1] (1947), but also by sympatric occurrence in nature. Only one mixed colony has been found (on the road to Meadow Club, 1.5 miles south of Fairfax, Marin County, *Raven 11002, 11003, 11004*) and at this site *C. rubicunda* was far more abundant than *C. amoena*. Only two hybrids were found, perhaps because of the infrequency of one of the parental species. These hybrids had petals with both a basal and central spot like the artificially produced F_1 hybrids and were apparently sterile. Visibly good pollen [2] was 2.8 per cent in the plant examined, which is comparable to that of F_1 hybrids grown in the garden (Hiorth, 1942).

Both *C. rubicunda* and *C. amoena* are protandrous and normally outcrossed by various native bees (except for an autogamous subspecies of *C. amoena* on the coast of Oregon and Washington). They are, however, self-compatible, like all species of *Clarkia*. On the other hand, *C. franciscana* is facultatively autogamous and self-pollination is undoubtedly the rule, although this species is also visited by bees.

Clarkia rubicunda and *C. amoena* occur in more or less discrete colonies varying in size from a few individuals to many thousands and separated by a few feet or as much as several miles. This colonial habit greatly restricts or effectively prevents gene exchange between colonies of the same species for indefinitely long periods of time. The size of the colonies may fluctuate from year to year. Our observations on *C. franciscana* indicate as many as 4000 individuals one year and as few as 600 another.

Clarkia franciscana is morphologically very uniform, as would be expected from its breeding habit and restricted distribution. In contrast, *C. rubicunda* and *C. amoena* are variable species comprised of modally recognizable geographic races that have been recognized formally as subspecies, two in *C. rubicunda* and five in *C. amoena* (Lewis and Lewis, 1955), as well as many locally differentiated populations which have not been accorded formal taxonomic recognition.

---

[2] Per cent of visibly good pollen given in this paper has been determined by examination of 600 grains from three buds stained in cotton blue in lactophenol.

CHROMOSOME ARRANGEMENTS AND INTRASPECIFIC FERTILITY

Different chromosome arrangements associated with high levels of sterility have invariably accompanied speciation in *Clarkia* and are frequently found within species (Lewis, 1953a). Consequently, we have examined meiosis in microsporocytes of wild individuals of the three species concerned, hybrids between populations of *C. rubicunda*, and interspecific hybrids in all combinations, to determine the kind and degree of chromosomal differentiation at each level. In addition, the extensive observations of Håkansson (1942, 1947) on meiosis in hybrids within and between *C. rubicunda* and *C. amoena* have been used to supplement our own data. Squash preparations of microsporocytes were used for all of our observations.

Meiosis was examined in five plants of *C. franciscana* grown from wild seed. These showed no meiotic irregularities of any kind and regularly formed 7 bivalents (fig. 2A). Although the sample is small, we have no doubt that this species has only one chromosome arrangement, because the population is self-pollinated and phenotypically uniform. All individuals have consistently set full complements of seeds and have had essentially 100 per cent visibly good pollen.

Meiosis in *C. rubicunda* was examined in a total of 28 plants from 7 wild populations. Like *C. franciscana*, these showed no meiotic irregularities and regularly formed 7 bivalents. Håkansson (1941, 1942) found the same regularity in progenies of this species grown from wild seeds from 6 additional populations. Taken together, these data suggest that any given population of *C. rubicunda* is characterized by one arrangement, but do not indicate whether all populations have the same arrangement. However, we have examined hybrids between 5 different populations and these hybrids have consistently shown regular bivalent pairing with no meiotic irregularities (fig.

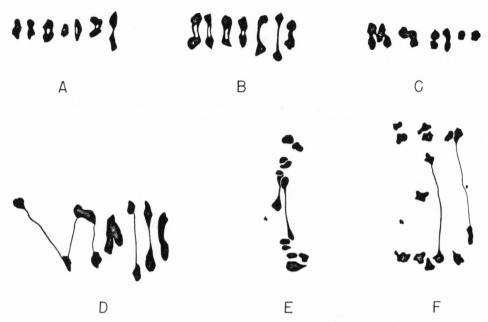

A   B   C

D   E   F

Fig. 2. Meiotic configurations in microsporocytes of the species and hybrids indicated. Camera lucida drawings × 1300. A. *Clarkia franciscana,* first metaphase showing 7 pairs. B. *C. rubicunda* (Palo Alto) × *C. rubicunda* (Stinson Beach), first metaphase showing 7 pairs. C. *C. rubicunda* (Mt. Hamilton) × *C. franciscana,* first metaphase showing a chain of 5, a chain of 3, 2 pairs, and 2 unpaired chromosomes. D. Same, showing a chain of 5, a chain of 3, and 3 pairs. E. *C. rubicunda* (Stinson Beach) × *C. franciscana,* first anaphase showing two bridges and two fragments. F. *C. amoena* (Tocaloma) × *C. rubicunda* (Palo Alto), first anaphase showing two bridges, two fragments, and a lagging chromosome.

2B). These observations also parallel those of Håkansson (1942, 1947) for hybrids between 4 different populations (other than those we have sampled), including hybrids between the coastal and interior subspecies. These 9 populations used for hybridization have come from localities distributed throughout most of the range of the species. The fact that no structural differences have been detected in any of the hybrid combinations leads us to believe that the entire species is probably characterized by a single chromosome arrangement. Commensurate with the chromosomal uniformity, all individuals of *C. rubicunda* that we have examined have been highly fertile. This has been true of all F_1 hybrids between populations as well as of plants grown from seeds collected in the wild (Lewis and Raven, 1958).

Clarkia amoena, on the other hand, is chromosomally diverse, particularly with respect to differences in arrangement of chromosome arms resulting from reciprocal translocation. Håkansson (1942) examined a total of 65 plants grown from seeds collected from 21 wild populations distributed throughout most of the range of the species. Of these, he found 30 that were structurally homozygous and regularly formed 7 pairs and 35 that were heterozygous for at least one rearrangement. All rearrangements observed were translocations except for one possible paracentric inversion. The translocation heterozygotes were of three sorts: (1) plants that regularly formed rings of 4, 6, 8, 10 or 12, which separated at first anaphase in a regular alternate manner; (2) plants that form a chain of 3 and one univalent at first metaphase, rather than a ring of 4; and (3) plants with 13 chromosomes, being heterozygous for one genome of 6 chromosomes and one of 7.

Plants in the first category with rings of 4 or 6 are found throughout much of the range of the species, but larger rings have been found only in a relatively limited area in Humboldt County, California, toward the center of the range of the species. The ring-forming heterozygotes are usually highly fertile; however, some arrangements are apparently associated with lethals. Balanced lethal systems involving rings of 6 are known in garden races (Håkansson, 1942) and comparable systems may obtain in the wild although the evidence is not conclusive.

Heterozygotes that form a chain of 3 and a univalent have been found in this species in two rather widely separated areas (northern Oregon and central California). They are also prevalent in several other species of *Clarkia* and have recently been observed in *Oenothera dentata* (Lewis *et al.*, 1958). The reason for the widespread occurrence of asynapsis of this particular sort is obscure, particularly since individuals homozygous for the altered arrangement frequently do not survive or are abnormal and sterile in *C. amoena* (Håkansson, 1944). There can be no doubt, however, that rearrangements producing this peculiar asynaptic effect in heterozygotes have occurred independently in several species and at least twice in *C. amoena*.

Genomes of six chromosomes, rather than the normal seven, have been found in five populations in central and northern California (Hiorth, 1948). These genomes are the result of translocations whereby most of one chromosome has been transferred to others followed by the loss of a relatively inert chromosome remnant (Håkansson, 1946). Hiorth and Håkansson have found that individuals homozygous for these genomes of six either do not survive or are highly sterile and show a varying but often extreme degree of asynapsis. Hybrids combining genomes of six from different populations are generally more normal in development, but meiosis is variously asynaptic, making a direct comparison of the homologies of the various genomes of 6 very difficult. However, the presence of heteromorphic bivalents and chain associations in these hybrids with 12 chromosomes indicates, with one exception, that these genomes of 6 are not of the same origin, or that the arrangement of chromosomes has been appreciably modified since their common origin. The exception is found in the 12 chromosome hybrids combining genomes of 6 from two localities about 25 miles apart (Tocaloma and Santa Rosa). These hybrids, although somewhat asynaptic, frequently had 6 pairs of chromosomes and were fairly fertile.

A bridge with an accompanying fragment, suggestive of crossing over within a heterozygous paracentric inversion, was found by Håkansson (1942) in one microsporocyte of one individual from Humboldt County. Because no other bridge-fragment configurations were observed, he has suggested that an inversion may have occurred in the anther in which the bridge-fragment was observed. However, this plant was also heterozygous for a genome of 6, which when homozygous is highly asynaptic. Consequently, chromosome association or the pattern of chiasma formation in this particular heterozygote may essentially preclude all crossing-over in a particular inverted region. The only other evidence of an inversion in *C. amoena* is in a hybrid between a plant from Kelso, Washington and one from Wildcat Road, Humboldt County, California. A single bridge with accompanying fragment was frequently seen at first anaphase in this hybrid, leaving no doubt that the parents differed by a paracentric inversion. Other individuals in the same progeny, however, showed no evidence of an inversion, indicating that one of the parents was heterozygous for the inversion. Consequently, the two populations do not differ consistently by an inversion.

The greatest frequency of structural

heterozygosity and the largest number of arrangements in wild populations of *C. amoena* are found in Humboldt County, California, and these same populations also show the greatest variation in fertility, as measured by visibly good pollen. For example, in a progeny grown from seeds collected at Shelter Cove in Humboldt County, Hiorth (1942) found differences in visibly good pollen that ranged from a mean of 96 per cent in some individuals to as low as 22 per cent in others. Other progenies from Humboldt County showed almost as great a variation. Unfortunately, however, the fertility data of Hiorth and the cytological observations of Håkansson can not be compared on a plant by plant basis.

Hybrids between populations of *C. amoena* totaling 44 individuals from 18 different hybrid combinations, involving 15 populations, were examined by Håkansson (1942). In addition, he examined many hybrids between wild and garden races. These hybrids indicate that one chromosome arrangement, designated *a* by Håkansson (*α* by Hiorth), is prevalent throughout the range of the species. This arrangement accounts for most of the structural homozygotes and is usually present as one of the arrangements in structural heterozygotes. This same arrangement *a*, in combination with a genome of *Clarkia lassenensis* (Eastw.) Lewis and Lewis, has given rise to the allotetraploid species *Clarkia gracilis* (Piper) Nels. and Macbr. (Håkansson, 1942, as *Godetia nutans;* Lewis and Lewis, 1955). All other arrangements found in *C. amoena* are apparently local and are found primarily, and in some cases exclusively, as heterozygotes.

The fertility of interpopulational hybrids of *C. amoena* is generally high, even in crosses between the various subspecies (Hiorth, 1942), with two notable exceptions. Hybrids involving individuals from Humboldt County populations often show a marked and significant reduction in fertility, whether crossed to one another or to individuals from distant areas. To a somewhat lesser extent, the same is true of hybrids involving plants from the vicinity of Springfield, Oregon. However, the Humboldt populations, as indicated above, are notably variable in chromosome arrangement and in fertility, and the same is apparently true to some extent in the Springfield population (Hiorth, 1942). In no instance was an interpopulational hybrid found to be as sterile as some of the individuals grown from wild seeds collected in Humboldt County.

In summation, then, *Clarkia amoena* is a widespread species that is chromosomally variable but which, at the same time, is characterized by one arrangement that occurs as a common element throughout the species. In addition it carries an undetermined number of arrangements that differ from the standard arrangement (*a*) by one or more translocations. But these arrangements are local and a number of them are lethal or sterile as homozygotes and form heterozygotes with reduced fertility. The prevalence of these arrangements suggests, however, that they may have an adaptive value in the genetic system. Individuals are occasionally found that are heterozygous for a paracentric inversion but these are apparently very rare and, consequently, probably do not play an important role in the genetic system. In contrast to *C. amoena, C. franciscana* and *C. rubicunda* are each characterized by a single chromosomal arrangement.

INTERSPECIFIC HYBRIDS

Interspecific hybrids between *Clarkia franciscana, C. rubicunda* and *C. amoena* were made in all combinations in order to determine the fertility of the hybrids (Lewis and Raven, 1958), and especially to study chromosome homologies and differences in chromosome arrangement as indicated by meiotic pairing in microsporocytes of the hybrids. All of the F_1 hybrids are highly sterile and we have grown no subsequent generations. Reference to hybrids refers, therefore, to the F_1 in every instance.

TABLE 1. *Meiosis in microsporocytes of hybrids between* Clarkia franciscana *and* Clarkia rubicunda

Configurations at first metaphase *

Chain of 5	Chain of 4	Chain of 3	Bivalents	Univalents	Number of cells
1		1	3		42
1		1	2	2	11
1		1	1	4	1
1			4	1	23
1			3	3	4
1			2	5	2
	1	1	3	1	1
	1	1	2	3	1
	1		5		2
	1		4	2	1
		2	4		13
		2	3	2	9
		2	2	4	1
		1	5	1	8

Frequency of bridges at first anaphase

Number of bridges with accompanying fragments	Number of cells
0	34
1	31
2	13
3	3
4	1

* Numbers indicate frequency of indicated configurations.

Hybrids between *C. franciscana* and *C. rubicunda* have been obtained using plants from four different wild populations of the latter species. No differences were observed between reciprocal crosses. Inasmuch as all *C. rubicunda* plants used as parents were homozygous for the same chromosome arrangement and the *C. franciscana* plants were homozygous for another arrangement, meiosis was expected to be comparable in all of the hybrids, as indeed it was. We have, therefore, combined observations from six different progenies in preparing the summary shown in table 1.

The maximum association of chromosomes at meiotic first metaphase in the hybrids between *C. franciscana* and *C. rubicunda,* as well as the most prevalent association, is a chain of 5, a chain of 3, and 3 pairs (fig. 2D), indicating that the parental genomes differ by at least three large translocations involving four pairs of chromosomes. The maximum possible association may be a ring of 8 and 3 pairs, not realized in our observations. The genomes of *C. franciscana* and *C. rubicunda* also differ by at least four paracentric inversions, as indicated by four bridges and four accompanying fragments at first anaphase in the same cell. As shown in table 1, first anaphase bridges with fragments (fig. 2E) were observed in more than half of the cells. No double bridges and no second anaphase bridges were observed, indicating that double crossing-over does not ordinarily occur within chromosome arms heterozygous for inversions.

Additional undetected structural differences are probably present and, together with those observed, may account for the frequent occurrence of associations of chromosomes less than the maximum. By an examination of table 1, we see that the five chromosomes that formed a chain of 5 in 71 per cent of the cells formed a chain of 3 and a pair in 14 per cent, a chain of 3 and 2 univalents in 8 per cent, 2 pairs and a univalent in 5 per cent, and a chain of 4 and a univalent in about 2 per cent of the cells examined. The three chromosomes that formed a chain of 3 in 73 per cent of the cells were found as a pair and a univalent in 23 per cent of the cells and as 3 univalents in 4 per cent. The six chromosomes that formed 3 pairs in 85 per cent of the cells appeared as 2 pairs and 2 univalents in 14 per cent of the cells (fig. 2C) and as 1 pair and 4 univalents in one cell. The mean frequency of univalents at first metaphase is 0.9 per cell. This observed variation in chromosome association, probably caused in large measure by structural differences, undoubtedly accounts for much, and perhaps all, of the sterility of the hybrids.

The sterility of the hybrids between C. franciscana and C. amoena probably has a similar basis. Unlike C. rubicunda, C. amoena is chromosomally highly variable, as indicated above. We therefore selected parental plants that regularly formed 7 bivalents. Two plants of C. amoena from different populations were used and these may have been homozygous for different arrangements because the two progenies showed different chromosome associations. One hybrid combination, in which the C. amoena parent came from eastern Humboldt County, California, formed a chain of 5, 4 pairs, and an unpaired chromosome as the maximum and most frequent association. The other hybrid combination, in which the C. amoena parent came from Willets, Mendocino County, California, formed a maximum association of a chain of 4 and 5 pairs, although the most frequent association was 6 pairs and 2 unpaired chromosomes.

The variation in chromosome association in these hybrids is comparable to that described for hybrids between C. franciscana and C. rubicunda, and the mean frequency of univalents is 2.1 per cell, which is more than twice as great as in the hybrids between C. franciscana and C. rubicunda. This suggests that the genomes of C. franciscana and C. amoena may differ by a great many individually undetected rearrangements that interfere with chromosome pairing and chiasma formation. These genomes do differ by at least two paracentric inversions, as is indicated by two bridges with accompanying fragments in the same first anaphase cell, but many more inversions may be concealed by the reduced pairing in the hybrid.

Hybrids between C. amoena and C. rubicunda have been studied by a number of investigators who have consistently found them to have very low fertility (Rasmuson, 1921; Chittenden, 1928; Hiorth, 1942; Lewis and Raven, 1958). Meiosis in these hybrids has been described several times (Chittenden, 1928; Håkansson, 1931, 1942, 1947). The observations have varied in detail even in hybrids involving the same combination of genomes. For example, meiosis in a hybrid between C. rubicunda from a wild population and a garden race of C. amoena homozygous for the a arrangement has been described by Håkansson (1942) as often having 7 pairs, although far more frequently having 6 pairs and 2 univalents or 5 pairs and 4 univalents. No multivalents were observed. However, in the same cross he later (Håkansson, 1947) observed a chain of 5 in some cells, a ring or a chain of 4 in some, a chain of 4 and a chain of 3 in others, and frequently two chains of 3. Inversion bridges were only rarely observed. On the basis of the observations of Håkansson, Hiorth (1947) has suggested that the maximum expected association of chromosomes between C. rubicunda and the a arrangement of C. amoena is a ring of 6 plus a ring of 4 and two pairs.

We have examined one progeny of

hybrids between *C. amoena* from Willets, Mendocino County, California, and *C. rubicunda* from Lands End, San Francisco. Since both of the parents were structural homozygotes that regularly formed 7 pairs at meiosis, the hybrids would be expected to be equivalent in respect to chromosome association. We found chromosome association to be highly variable within any one plant, as was true of *C. franciscana* × *C. rubicunda* and *C. amoena* × *C. franciscana*. However, of the two plants examined in detail, one showed a much higher association of chromosomes than the other. The maximum as well as the most frequent association in one of the plants was a chain of 6, a ring or chain of 4, and two pairs, one of which was a ring bivalent. This is very close to the maximum association predicted by Hiorth. The four chromosomes capable of forming a ring did so in about 25 per cent of the cells. In the remainder of the cells they formed, in decreasing sequence, a chain of 4, two pairs, or a chain of 3 and a univalent. The mean frequency of univalents was 0.5 per cell. In the other plant, the maximum association observed was a chain of 5, 4 pairs, and a univalent, with the most frequent association being a chain of 3, 5 pairs, and a univalent. In neither plant was a cell with 7 pairs observed. The reason for the difference in chromosome association is obscure. Genetic asynapsis, known to be prevalent in *C. amoena* (Håkansson, 1944), may be a factor, or the hybrids may be very sensitive to small differences in the external environment, although our hybrids were grown at the same time under essentially uniform conditions.

Inversion bridges with accompanying fragments were observed in 6 out of 79 first anaphase cells in the plant that showed the greater degree of chromosome association, and one of the 6 cells showed two bridges with fragments (fig. 2F). No bridges were observed at second anaphase. The frequency of bridges observed by Håkansson (1947) was ap-parently much lower, which may indicate that different *C. amoena* arrangements are involved, but is more likely a reflection of the lower degree of chromosome association in his material.

In summary, *Clarkia franciscana* differs from *C. amoena* by at least two translocations and two paracentric inversions, and from *C. rubicunda* by at least three translocations and four inversions: *Clarkia amoena* and *C. rubicunda* differ by at least three translocations and two inversions. These observations might be taken as evidence that *C. franciscana* is chromosomally more similar to *C. amoena* than to *C. rubicunda* and that *C. amoena* is more similar to *C. franciscana* than to *C. rubicunda*. However, we believe just the contrary. The number of structural differences that have been detected represents a minimum and many more may be present. The detection of structural differences in *Clarkia* hybrids depends upon synapsis of homologous segments followed by chiasma formation. In the present instance the mean frequency of univalents (2.1 per cell) in hybrids between *C. amoena* and *C. franciscana* is more than twice the value (0.9 per cell) observed in hybrids between *C. rubicunda* and *C. franciscana*, indicating a higher degree of pairing and chiasma formation in the latter. Consequently, we believe that the low level of detected structural rearrangements in the hybrids between *C. franciscana* and *C. amoena* is a function of decreased pairing which is probably attributable to a number of undetected structural differences. In the same manner, the low frequency of univalents (0.5 per cell) in one hybrid between *C. amoena* and *C. rubicunda* suggests that the genomes of these species are structurally very similar to each other. This is also suggested by the frequent occurrence of rings of chromosomes at meiosis in this hybrid, whereas only chains are found in the other two hybrid combinations. Considering all of the cytological evidence, we conclude that *C. franciscana* is chromosomally more similar to *C. rubicunda* than to *C. amoena,* and *C. rubicunda* is probably even more similar to *C. amoena* than to *C. franciscana.*

DISCUSSION

We have shown that *Clarkia franciscana,* which is confined to a single serpentine hillside, occurs as an enclave within the area of distribution of *C. rubicunda,* and that *C. rubicunda* is replaced geographically, with very little overlap, by a third species, *C. amoena.* All three species are so similar morphologically that were it not for data obtained from hybridization they undoubtedly would be considered conspecific. Hybrids between any two of these species have very low fertility as a consequence of meiotic irregularities that are attributable in large measure, if not entirely, to structural differences in their chromosomes. The problem is to explain the limited distribution of *C. franciscana,* the phylogenetic relationship between the species concerned, and the origin of the chromosomal differentiation that has led to speciation.

A highly restricted distribution, such as that of *C. franciscana,* may represent a relictual fragment of a once more prevalent species, or may be indicative of a relatively recent origin. The latter seems probable in the case of *C. franciscana* because of its autogamous breeding habit; because of its close similarity to *C. rubicunda,* which grows near by; and because of the specialized habitat that it occupies.

Autogamy has arisen repeatedly in *Clarkia* and in 10 species it is characteristic of at least some populations. In no instance is there evidence that outcrossing races have been derived from autogamous races. This suggests that the forerunner of *C. franciscana* was an outcrossing population like *C. rubicunda* or *C. amoena.*

The serpentine habitat suggests that *C. franciscana* has been derived from adjacent relatives that grow facultatively on serpentine. Non-serpentine races could,

presumably, be derived from serpentine races, but the autogamous breeding habit of *C. franciscana* strongly suggests that it is derivative. Similar patterns of differentiation that can be interpreted the same way are known to occur in other genera, notably *Streptanthus* (Kruckeberg, 1957). The morphological similarity and spatial relationship of *S. niger,* a very restricted autogamous serpentine endemic, to its widespread outcrossing relatives closely parallels the situation described for *C. franciscana* and its close relatives. In both instances the narrow serpentine endemics are surely derivative and probably of recent origin.

The very restricted distribution of *C. franciscana* may be due not only to a relatively recent origin but also to its genetic uniformity and special adaptation to a particular habitat. The genetic uniformity is probably attributable primarily to inbreeding, perhaps augmented by occasional reduction in the size of the population to a few individuals. The autogamy in turn may be adaptive in maintaining genotypes particularly adapted to the serpentine habitat. A species, such as *C. franciscana,* comprised of uniform genotypes adapted to a particular habitat, would be expected to have little chance of success as a migrant, as Mason (1950) has inferred, unless a comparable habitat is widely prevalent. Serpentine habitats are, however, relatively common in the Coast Ranges of California and given time a species such as *C. franciscana* might occupy a number of sites. On the other hand, since serpentine habitats have been available in this same area throughout the Cenozoic, the possibility can not be excluded that *C. franciscana* is not recent but was once a more widely distributed species with autogamous races growing on serpentine, of which only one population remains.

The evidence indicates to us that *C. franciscana* has probably arisen very recently, perhaps *in situ,* from either *C. rubicunda* or *C. amoena;* and, on the basis of morphology and spatial relationship, *C. rubicunda* is the more likely parent. The morphological traits that characterize *C. franciscana,* except those associated with its autogamous breeding habit, are found individually in some plants of *C. rubicunda* at various places throughout its range, but never in the combination found in *C. franciscana.* This suggests that the distinctive genotype of *C. franciscana* could have been derived from variation in *C. rubicunda,* and subsequently maintained by structural rearrangement of the chromosomes. The origin of the chromosomal differences poses a problem, because both *C. rubicunda* and *C. franciscana* are apparently chromosomally uniform. Before considering chromosomal differentiation between these two species, however, we should consider the relationship of *C. amoena* to each of them.

Clarkia amoena is probably much older than either of the other two species on the basis of morphological, ecological, and chromosomal evidence. It is morphologically and ecologically more diverse than the others and is comprised of both selfing and outcrossing races. It is chromosomally variable and various presumably adaptive polymorphic systems have been developed in different parts of its range. Furthermore, it occupies more northern and generally more mesic sites, which also suggests greater antiquity because a modal sequence of adaptation to drier habitats has been shown to have occurred in the course of evolution in *Clarkia* (Lewis, 1953b). In addition, *C. amoena* is one of the parents of the allotetraploid species *C. gracilis,* which itself is a polytypic species with a relatively large area of distribution (Lewis and Lewis, 1955). Although no one of these observations is conclusive in itself, taken together they strongly suggest that *C. amoena* is relatively much older and perhaps ancestral to both *C. rubicunda* and *C. franciscana.*

Assuming that *C. amoena* is in fact ancestral to the other two species, morphological and geographical considerations suggest a linear sequence of origin from *C. amoena* to *C. rubicunda* to *C. franciscana.* Hybrid fertility as well as cytological observations reinforces this hypothesis. Fertility, as indicated by visibly good pollen, does not provide an infallible indication of the degree of structural differences between genomes of *Clarkia* (Lewis and Roberts, 1956), but in the present instance cytological observations in respect to univalent frequencies in the hybrids are in agreement with the pollen data. Together these observations indicate that *C. amoena* is more closely related to *C. rubicunda* than to *C. franciscana,* that *C. rubicunda* is more closely related to *C. amoena* than to *C. franciscana,* and that *C. franciscana* is more closely related to *C. rubicunda* than to *C. amoena.* The evidence strongly suggests, therefore, that derivation has been in sequence rather than independently from *C. amoena* for if the latter were true, one would expect *C. franciscana* and *C. rubicunda* to differ chromosomally from each other to a greater extent than either differs from *C. amoena.*

To account for the chromosomal differences between the species, any one of three processes, alone or in combination, is possible: (1) rearrangements arose one by one in different populations or groups of populations which gradually became differentiated to their present degree; (2) chromosome rearrangements gradually accumulated as variation within a species which later became fragmented with the result that the variable elements were sorted out into various combinations; (3) differentiation resulted from a rapid and major reorganization of the chromosomes. These possibilities will be discussed in turn.

Chromosome rearrangements have occasionally become fixed and characteristic of a population or group of populations in *Clarkia.* For example, two populations of *C. biloba,* each of which consists only of structurally homozygous individuals, may differ by a translocation as shown by a ring of four in their hybrids (Roberts and Lewis, 1955; Lewis and Mathew, unpubl.). Differentiation by a translocation has also apparently occurred between populations of *C. amoena* (Saanich and Otter Crest, Håkansson, 1942). Yet, even though some populations have become differentiated by one chromosome arrangement, it is difficult to account for the number of differences that characterize *C. franciscana, C. rubicunda,* and *C. amoena* by a one-by-one accumulation of chromosome alterations, because the colonial habit of these species greatly restricts or effectively prevents gene exchange between them for indefinitely long periods. Consider, for example, the present situation in regard to *C. franciscana* and *C. rubicunda.* *Clarkia franciscana* could easily become further differentiated chromosomally from *C. rubicunda* because *C. franciscana* is apparently limited to one population. On the other hand, a new highly adapted arrangement that might occur in *C. rubicunda* would stand small chance indeed of becoming characteristic of all populations. Consequently, if a one-by-one accumulation of structural rearrangements does account for the present differences between *C. franciscana* and *C. rubicunda,* the rearrangements must have occurred at a time when *C. rubicunda* essentially consisted of an interbreeding population or a series of populations between which gene exchange was frequent. But if chromosomal differences arose and gradually accumulated under such conditions, it seems very surprising that *C. rubicunda* has not continued to spawn chromosomal rearrangements that are differentially represented in different populations. Consequently, we see little evidence to suggest that a gradual one-by-one accumulation of chromosome rearrangements has been of primary importance in producing the differences between these species.

Second, Stebbins (1950, p. 247) has suggested that a chromosomally variable species in which the different chromosome arrangements are associated with adaptive gene combinations may be preadapted to the formation of new, chromosomally differentiated species, under conditions of geographical isolation and differential selection. He cites *C. amoena (Godetia whitneyi)* as a possible example of a species that is breaking up into chromosomally differentiated populations under these conditions. If so, *C. rubicunda* and *C. franciscana* might represent chromosomally homomorphic end products of such a process. Populations of *C. amoena* do show geographical differences in frequency and kinds of chromosome arrangement and many of the populations or groups of populations are effectively isolated geographically and occupy different habitats. There is no evidence, however, that the existing polymorphism has given rise to genetically isolated, homomorphic races. Despite population-to-population differences in the frequency of any given arrangement, one chromosome arrangement is found throughout essentially the entire range of the species and is usually one member of any given structural heterozygote (Håkansson, 1946). Furthermore, the companion arrangement is frequently lethal when homozygous. Consequently, one must suppose that many and perhaps most of the chromosome arrangements that have accumulated in *C. amoena* are adapted only as heterozygotes and hence are obligate components of adaptive systems of chromosomal polymorphism. The derivation of homomorphic, genetically isolated chromosomal races would require the collapse of the polymorphic system. Collapse of systems of chromosome polymorphism has been suggested by White (1957) as a probable explanation for multiple differences in the chromosomes found between many species of animals, because the kinds of rearrangements that characterize chromosome polymorphism in a particular group are generally the same kinds that distinguish species within that group.

The local collapse of chromosome polymorphism in *C. amoena* to produce different monomorphic populations is conceivable. However, the collapse of existing polymorphism in *C. amoena* would not produce differences of the kind and number that distinguish it from *C. rubicunda* and *C. franciscana*. The chromosomal differences between these species include translocations and inversions, both of which occur as variable elements in *C. amoena*. However, translocation heterozygotes found in wild populations of *C. amoena*, or those derived from interpopulational crosses within that species, usually show catenations that not only include all of the interchanged chromosomes but also have a regular alternate disjunction. In contrast, the translocations by which *C. franciscana*, *C. rubicunda*, and *C. amoena* differ from one another behave very differently as heterozygotes. Rings or chains that involve all of the interchanged chromosomes are found in low frequency or often not at all. Associations that are formed vary in number of chromosomes from cell to cell and frequently do not dissociate in a regular manner. Consequently, the translocations that characterize the different species are structurally of a different sort from those found within species, unless the difference in their behavior is due to genetic factors determining chromosome association and orientation on the spindle. Translocations that persist as variable elements in *C. amoena* and other species of *Clarkia* involve the exchange of large segments or perhaps entire chromosome arms; in contrast, those by which the species differ may have originated as short or unequal interchanges, or, if initially comparable to translocations found within species, have subsequently been altered by additional interchanges or inversions. Inasmuch as genetic asynapsis in varying degrees is known to occur in *C. amoena* (Håkansson, 1946), as well as other species of *Clarkia*, the variable association of chromosomes in the interspecific hybrids

may be attributable to such factors. However, if so, they are apparently inoperative in the triploid hybrid between autotetraploid *C. amoena* and *C. rubicunda* (Håkansson, 1941). We are inclined, therefore, to consider chromosome repatterning as the principal factor responsible for the variable association of chromosomes in the interspecific hybrids. Support for this explanation comes from the number of inversions by which these species differ, which is far greater than could be accounted for by the collapse of any known polymorphic system in *Clarkia*.

Inversions of a size and position to be detected by bridge-fragment configurations, resulting from crossing over within the inversion, are very rare in *Clarkia*. Examination of meiosis of several thousand wild individuals, or those grown from wild seed, has revealed only two individuals that were probably heterozygous for a paracentric inversion: one in *C. amoena*, discussed above, and the other in *C. dudleyana* (Snow, 1957). Furthermore, bridge-fragment configurations have been observed in hybrids between colonies in only two species, *C. amoena* (Håkansson, 1942) and *C. biloba* (Lewis and Mathew, unpubl.). This low frequency of inversion heterozygotes stands in marked contrast to the observation that *C. franciscana* differs from *C. rubicunda* by at least four paracentric inversions and that *C. franciscana* and *C. amoena*, as well as *C. amoena* and *C. rubicunda*, differ by at least two.

Finally, this leaves for consideration a rapid reorganization of the chromosomes, which we believe affords the most likely explanation of the kind and degree of chromosomal differentiation between the species under consideration, especially the origin of *C. franciscana* from *C. rubicunda*. Chromosome arrangement tends to be very stable in *Clarkia*, despite the known occurrence of translocations in some individuals of about half of the diploid species. Not only are there a number of chromosomally homomorphic species, such as *C. rubicunda,* occupying a variety of habitats, but even those species, such as *C. amoena* and *C. unguiculata,* which are chromosomally extremely polymorphic, have one arrangement that is characteristic of the species and occurs in high frequency throughout its range, except perhaps for occasional colonies (Håkansson, 1946; Mooring, 1958).

High levels of spontaneous chromosome breakage have been very instructive in demonstrating a possible mechanism for rapid reorganization of genomes which may permit rapid transition from one stable arrangement to a very different one. Extremely high levels of breakage, such as those exhibited by certain *Bromus* hybrids (M. S. Walters, 1957), are so excessive that the probability of producing a functionally reorganized genome may be effectively zero. Of greater evolutionary significance are probably mutator genes, or genotypes, with a level of effect perhaps comparable to that of *hi* extracted from a wild population of *Drosophila melanogaster* by Ives (1950). From this stock a number of chromosome rearrangements were obtained (Hinton, Ives, and Evans, 1952) and many others were probably not detected. A number of reports of spontaneous chromosome breakage are now on record for various plant genera including *Tradescantia* (Giles, 1940; Darlington and Upcott, 1941), *Hyacinthus, Tulipa* (Darlington and Upcott, 1941), *Paris* (Haga, 1953), *Paeonia* (J. L. Walters, 1956), and in hybrids between *Allium cepa* and *A. fistulosum* (Emsweller and Jones, 1938). In all instances, save *Paeonia,* a high level of chromosome breakage was found to be correlated with a visible repatterning of the chromosomes, as observed in pollen mitoses, and in the case of the *Allium* hybrid, more or less fertile lines with altered chromosome arrangements were obtained by selection from among the progeny of the F_1. Most authors reporting spontaneous breakage have suggested that fragmentation was genotypically controlled, and a specific genetic effect has been demonstrated in maize (McClintock, 1951, 1953) in which chromosomes tend to form breaks at the *Ds* (dissociation) locus in the presence of *Ac* (activator) at another locus. The frequent translocation of *Ds* and *Ac* suggests that other breaks are also associated with this genotype. The evolutionary effect of genotypes producing high levels of breakage depends on a great many factors, such as the extent of chromosome breakage, the fortuitous coincidence of the adaptedness of a particular genotype to a particular habitat, and the breeding habit of the organism.

Although a number of authors have recognized the importance of mutator genotypes as a potential source of genome reorganization, most of them (Goldschmidt is a notable exception) have visualized the process to consist of the rejection or incorporation, one at a time, of each alteration. Such a process could, of course, lead to extensive repatterning of the chromosomes over a period of time. But this would require that the mutator genotype remain in the population for a prolonged time or recur periodically. Although neither of these possibilities can be excluded, the absence of chromosomal differentiation in *C. rubicunda* suggests to us that the shift from one chromosomally stable state to another, represented by *C. franciscana,* was fairly rapid and attributable to a mutator genotype, producing many chromosome breakages, which was probably soon eliminated from the population in which it occurred as a consequence of its disruptive effect on the adaptedness of the population. The vast majority of reorganized genomes resulting from such a mutator genotype would undoubtedly be poorly adapted under any circumstances, both in heterozygous and homozygous condition, and consequently would be expected to be rapidly eliminated from the population. Occasionally, however, an extensively reorganized genome might be associated with a genotype especially well adapted to a particular site, for example, a serpentine slope, and might persist to the exclusion of its progenitors, including the mutator genotypes that led to the original chromosomal instability. Self-compatibility, characteristic of all species of *Clarkia,* would facilitate the establishment and maintenance of homozygotes. Consequently, we believe that the transition to *C. franciscana* from *C. rubicunda* and probably to *C. rubicunda* from *C. amoena* was a rapid one illustrative of speciation by what Goldschmidt (1940, p. 206) has called systemic mutation and of a sort that Simpson (1944, p. 206) has called quantum evolution.

The systemic mutations of Goldschmidt differ from the present example in that Goldschmidt visualized a fundamentally different developmental process accompanying chromosome reorganization, which would result in macroevolution. In the present instance, close morphological similarity of the species and the normal development of their hybrids, except for meiosis, indicate that development has not been greatly altered by extensive reorganization of the chromosomes. This does not, however, preclude the possibility that the structurally very different genomes may have very different evolutionary potentials, not just because hybrid sterility has produced independently evolving lines, but because of inherent differences in chemical reorganization. From such differences in potential might come the macroevolution envisioned by Goldschmidt.

A rapid reorganization of the chromosomes is not unique to the species we have discussed; comparable patterns of differentiation are frequent in *Clarkia.* Two examples that have been studied in detail will be reviewed briefly (*C. biloba* —*C. lingulata,* Lewis and Roberts, 1956; *C. unguiculata*—*C. exilis,* Vasek, 1958).

Clarkia lingulata has demonstrably been derived from *C. biloba australis* that grows adjacent to it. Both taxa are normally outcrossed and each is chromo-

somally homomorphic. They differ in external morphology only in the shape of the petals, although their genomes differ by at least one paracentric inversion, a translocation, and quantitatively by an additional pair of chromosomes in *C. lingulata.* The translocation by which they differ usually forms a ring with an orientation and dissociation of chromosomes that results in a high proportion of nonviable meiotic products in the hybrid. The additional chromosome of *C. lingulata* is comprised of parts of two chromosomes of *C. biloba* and consequently joins together in the hybrid two pairs of chromosomes to form a chain of 5, which also results in a high proportion of nonviable products. Although the number of chromosomal differences is not great, to account for their gradual accumulation in the population that became *C. lingulata* requires a series of highly improbable events. Paracentric inversions of a size and position to be detected by crossing-over within heterozygotes are, as we have indicated, very rare in *Clarkia.* Although populations may occasionally become differentiated for such inversions, the establishment in the same population of a translocation that greatly reduced fertility as a heterozygote is quite unlikely, if the events are independent. The chromosome that was added is the product of a translocation; to assume that this translocation and duplication occurred independently in the same population in which a rare inversion and a heterozygously maladapted translocation became fixed is compounding a series of improbabilities to the point of incredulity. On the other hand, if the chromosomal differences are causally related, the phenomenon becomes understandable. One possibility is that these multiple differences were introduced simultaneously into the population by interspecific hybridization (see discussion in Lewis and Roberts, 1956). Another possibility, which we believe is more likely, is that a genotype conducive to chromosomal breakage arose, and perhaps persisted for several generations, in a population of *C. biloba australis,* and that the new genome of *C. lingulata* is the result.

The relationship of *Clarkia exilis* to *C. unguiculata* has many features in common with the other examples. *Clarkia exilis,* a species of relatively limited distribution which is facultatively autogamous and grows adjacent to *C. unguiculata,* is morphologically as similar to *C. unguiculata* as *C. franciscana* is to *C. rubicunda.* Like the latter pair of species, *C. exilis* and *C. unguiculata* have the same chromosome number. *Clarkia unguiculata* is chromosomally polymorphic (Lewis, 1951; Mooring, 1958) and to some extent so is *C. exilis* (Vasek, 1958). The translocation heterozygotes in both of these species, however, regularly form catenations that include all of the chromosomes involved and disjunction is regular. In contrast, the two species differ by at least 3 translocations and these, as in the case of hybrids between *C. franciscana, C. rubicunda,* and *C. amoena,* form catenations in the hybrid which are highly variable in the number of chromosomes and dissociate in an irregular manner. This, together with the frequent occurrence of univalents, suggests that *C. unguiculata* and *C. exilis* differ by a number of structural rearrangements that have not been individually detected.

Ancestral and derivative species grow adjacent to each other in all of the examples discussed. This suggests to us that differentiation has been very recent because the areas of distribution of *Clarkia* species are certainly not static. This is graphically illustrated by the present distribution of the known parents of alloploid species (Lewis and Lewis, 1955). Pairs of species that must have grown in the same area when their alloploid derivatives were formed often do not grow with each other today. Furthermore, these alloploid species are probably of recent origin, because chromosome pairing in hybrids between the alloploid and its parental species often indicates that no structural change has

occurred in the genomes since the alloploid was formed (Lewis, unpubl.). Many of the distribution patterns that we observe in California have resulted undoubtedly from migrations, expansion and contraction of areas of distribution during pluvial and interpluvial periods of the Pleistocene. If *C. franciscana, C. lingulata,* and similar derivatives were in existence and hence participated in such migrations, one would not expect invariably to find the derivatives adjacent to the parental species, or as enclaves within them. Such considerations lead us to believe that derivatives such as *C. franciscana* and *C. lingulata* are more recent than the climax of the last glacial advance about 12,000 years ago and are probably much more recent.

Summary

Clarkia franciscana consists of a single population on a serpentine slope in the Presidio at San Francisco, California, where it occurs as a reproductively isolated enclave within the area of distribution of *C. rubicunda,* to which it is morphologically most similar. It is also closely related to *C. amoena,* which geographically replaces *C. rubicunda* farther north. All three species are diploid ($n = 7$), and *C. franciscana* and *C. rubicunda* are each characterized by a single chromosome arrangement, whereas *C. amoena* is chromosomally variable. However, the differences in chromosomal arrangement between *C. franciscana* and the other two species is shown to be far greater and of a different sort from that ordinarily found as variation within species of *Clarkia.* The kind and degree of chromosomal differentiation accompanying the relatively minor differences in morphology, together with geographical position, suggest that *C. franciscana* may have had its origin *in situ* from *C. rubicunda* as a consequence of a rapid reorganization of the chromosomes due to the presence, at some time, of a genotype conducive to extensive chromosome breakage. A similar mode of origin by rapid reorganization of the chromosomes is suggested for the derivation of other species of *Clarkia*. In all of these examples the derivative populations grow adjacent to the parental species, which they resemble closely in morphology, but from which they are reproductively isolated because of multiple structural differences in their chromosomes. The spatial relationship of each parental species and its derivative suggests that differentiation has been recent.

The repeated occurrence of the same pattern of differentiation in *Clarkia* suggests that a rapid reorganization of chromosomes has been an important mode of evolution in the genus. This rapid reorganization of the chromosomes is comparable to the systemic mutations proposed by Goldschmidt as a mechanism of macroevolution. In *Clarkia,* we have not observed marked changes in physiology and pattern of development that could be described as macroevolution. Reorganization of the genomes may, however, set the stage for subsequent evolution along a very different course from that of the ancestral populations.

Acknowledgments

We gratefully acknowledge the assistance we have had from stimulating discussions with several of our colleagues and from a critical review of the manuscript by Carl Epling, G. Ledyard Stebbins, and Richard Snow. We do not imply, however, that they agree with the ideas we have expressed or the conclusions we have drawn. Any errors of interpretation are entirely our own.

Financial support has been provided by a grant from the National Science Foundation and field studies by the junior author were conducted with the aid of a grant from the American Association for the Advancement of Science awarded to him by the California Academy of Science. We are grateful to these agencies for this support.

Literature Cited

CHITTENDEN, R. J. 1928. Notes on species crosses in *Primula, Godetia, Nemophila,* and *Phacelia.* Jour. Genetics, **19** : 285–314.

DARLINGTON, C. D., AND M. B. UPCOTT. 1941. Spontaneous chromosome change. Jour. Genetics, **41** : 297–338.

EMSWELLER, S. L., AND H. A. JONES. 1938. Crossing-over, fragmentation and formation of new chromosomes in an *Allium* species hybrid. Bot. Gaz., **99** : 729–772.

GILES, N. 1940. Spontaneous chromosome aberrations in *Tradescantia.* Genetics, **25** : 69–87.

GOLDSCHMIDT, R. 1940. The Material Basis of Evolution. Yale University Press, New Haven, Conn.

HAGA, T. 1953. Meiosis in *Paris.* II. Spontaneous breakage and fusion of chromosomes. Cytologia, **18** : 50–66.

HÅKANSSON, A. 1931. Chromosomenverkettung bei *Godetia* und *Clarkia.* Ber. d. Deutsch. Bot. Ges., **49** : 228–234.

——. 1941. Zur Zytologie von *Godetia*-Arten und -Bastarden. Hereditas, **27** : 319–336.

——. 1942. Zytologische Studien an Rassen und Rassenbastarden von *Godetia whitneyi* und verwandten Arten. Lunds Univ. Årsskrift N. F. Avd. 2. 38. Nr. 5. 70 pp.

——. 1944. Studies on a peculiar chromosome configuration in *Godetia whitneyi.* Hereditas, **30** : 597–612.

——. 1946. Meiosis in hybrid nullisomics and certain other forms of *Godetia whitneyi.* Hereditas, **32** : 495–513.

——. 1947. Contributions to a cytological analysis of the species differences of *Godetia amoena* and *G. whitneyi.* Hereditas, **33** : 235–260.

HINTON, T., P. T. IVES, AND A. T. EVANS. 1952. Changing the gene order and number in natural populations. EVOLUTION, **6** : 19–28.

HIORTH, G. 1940. Eine Serie multipler Allele für Blutenzeichnungen bei *Godetia amoena.* Hereditas, **26** : 441–453.

——. 1942. Zur Genetik und Systematik der *amoena*-Gruppe der Gattung *Godetia.* Zeit. f. Vererb., **80** : 565–569.

——. 1947. Zur Genetik des Artbastardes *Godetia amoena* × *G. whitneyi.* Züchter **17/18** : 109–121.

——. 1948. Zur Genetik der Monosomen von *Godetia whitneyi.* Zeit. f. Vererb., **82** : 230–275.

IVES, P. T. 1950. The importance of mutation rate genes in evolution. EVOLUTION, **4** : 236–252.

KRUCKEBERG, A. R. 1957. Variation in fertility of hybrids between isolated populations of the serpentine species, *Streptanthus glandulosus* Hook. EVOLUTION, **11** : 185–211.

LEWIS, H. 1951. The origin of supernumerary chromosomes in natural populations of *Clarkia elegans*. EVOLUTION, **5**: 142–157.

———. 1953a. The mechanism of evolution in the genus *Clarkia*. EVOLUTION, **7**: 1–20.

———. 1953b. Chromosome phylogeny and habitat preference in *Clarkia*. EVOLUTION, **7**: 102–109.

———, AND M. LEWIS. 1955. The genus *Clarkia*. Univ. Calif. Publ. Bot., **20**: 241–392.

———, AND P. H. RAVEN. 1958. *Clarkia franciscana*, a new species from central California. Brittonia, **10**: 7–13.

———, P. H. RAVEN, C. S. VENKATESH, AND H. L. WEDBERG. 1958. Observations of meiotic chromosomes in the Onagraceae. Aliso, **4**: 73–86.

———, AND M. R. ROBERTS. 1956. The origin of *Clarkia lingulata*. EVOLUTION, **10**: 126–138.

MASON, H. 1950. Migration and evolution in plants. Madroño, **12**: 161–169.

McCLINTOCK, B. 1951. Chromosome organization and genic expression. Cold Spring Harbor Symp. Quant. Biol., **16**: 13–47.

———. 1953. Induction of instability at selected loci in maize. Genetics, **38**: 579–599.

MOORING, J. R. 1958. A cytogenetic study of *Clarkia unguiculata*. I. Translocations. Amer. Jour. Bot. **45**: 233–242.

RASMUSON, H. 1921. Beiträge zu einer genetischen Analyse zweier *Godetia*-Arten und ihrer Bastarde. Hereditas, **2**: 143–289.

ROBERTS, M. R., AND H. LEWIS. 1955. Subspeciation in *Clarkia biloba*. EVOLUTION, **9**: 445–454.

SIMPSON, G. G. 1944. Tempo and Mode in Evolution. Columbia Univ. Press, New York.

SNOW, R. 1957. Evolution in *Clarkia dudleyana*. Ph.D. Thesis (unpubl.). Univ. Calif., Los Angeles, Library.

STEBBINS, G. L. 1950. Variation and Evolution in Plants. Columbia Univ. Press, New York.

VASEK, F. C. 1958. The relationship of *Clarkia exilis* to *Clarkia unguiculata*. Amer. Jour. Bot. **45**: 150–162.

WALTERS, J. L. 1956. Spontaneous meiotic chromosome breakage in natural populations of *Paeonia californica*. Amer. Jour. Bot., **43**: 342–354.

WALTERS, M. S. 1957. Studies of spontaneous chromosome breakage in interspecific hybrids of *Bromus*. Univ. Calif. Publ. Bot., **28**: 335–447.

WHITE, M. J. D. 1957. Some problems of chromosome evolution and speciation in animals. Surv. Biol. Prog., **3**: 109–147. Academic Press, New York.

5

Reprinted from *Amer. Naturalist* **102**:193-205 (1967)

PROTEIN DIFFERENCES IN DROSOPHILA.
IV. A STUDY OF SIBLING SPECIES*

JOHN L. HUBBY and LYNN H. THROCKMORTON

Department of Biology, University of Chicago, Chicago, Illinois 60637

INTRODUCTION

Sexually isolated but morphologically very similar species have been described in most classes of animals. They appear to be especially abundant among invertebrates, notably among the insects, and among the fishes. Two alternative interpretations of the significance of the morphological similarity between sibling species are current. One interpretation regards their close morphological similarity to be the result of, and to reflect, a high degree of genic identity between them. This view has been criticized by Mayr (1963), who pointed out that sibling species may be no different from other kinds of species, being qualitatively and quantitatively as genetically distinct from each other as morphologically distinct species are. He says (p. 57), "All the available evidence indicates that sibling species show the same number of genetic differences as do other closely related species." He holds that their high degree of morphological similarity is a consequence of developmental homeostasis and not of genetic similarity.

These two viewpoints are very different in their implications relative to the amount of genetic change involved during speciation. The first interpretation is consistent with the assumption that arrival at species status may entail only a small amount of genetic change. Proponents of the second alternative (Mayr, 1963; Dobzhansky, 1959) are quite explicit in stating that a major reorganization of the gene pool accompanies speciation. But what constitutes a major reorganization? We infer, perhaps erroneously, that such a reorganization implies a replacement of alleles at a majority of the loci of each species. The major argument supporting reorganization rests on the assertion that genes are so coadapted that a change in a single gene precipitates a change in others; these likewise precipitate still further changes, and so on. This "domino" effect is sweep-

* The work reported was supported in part by a grant from the Public Health Service (GM 11216).

ing in its consequences. To change one locus is to change many. Also, natural selection places a high premium on the phenotype; development is, therefore, highly canalized (Waddington, 1957), and many different genotypes can and do "produce" indistinguishable phenotypes. In some instances adaptation requires the preservation of phenotypic constancy and, inevitably, cannot occur without genetic change. These cases would result in sibling species little different morphologically but sharply divergent genetically. In other instances adaptation requires a phenotypic change and also the usual extensive genetic change—hence, the existence of an array of species of varying degrees of difference phenotypically, but which are *all* different genetically. Earlier (Throckmorton and Hubby, 1963), we pointed out some of these problems. Here we wish to focus attention only on one central question: Does divergence to the species level of differentiation *require* a massive change in the gene pool, or can this involve change in just a few of the many thousands of loci?

In the area of species genetics, methods are being developed that allow exploration of the alternative possibilities. We presented one such approach (Hubby and Throckmorton, 1965) in our study of the electrophoretic properties of soluble proteins from nine species of the virilis group of *Drosophila*. That study, which included several clusters of sibling species, demonstrated the possibility that a high degree of genetic similarity existed between sibling species. Simpler and more precise single fly assays for specific enzymes and for hemolymph proteins have been developed in this laboratory and elsewhere (Hubby and Lewontin, 1966; Lewontin and Hubby, 1966). The number of assays applicable to single flies continues to grow rapidly, and with each technical advance more and more of the refractory questions of species genetics become open to analysis. For this study we have used seven different assays to disclose genetic variants at an average of 18 loci per species. We have used nine pairs of sibling species, and each pair has been matched by a third, generally morphologically distinct, species from the same species group or subgroup as the sibling pair. We seek evidence for the amount of genetic identity between sibling species, between each sibling and its morphologically distinct close relative, and between the various triads themselves. We ask whether any sibling pair shows evidence of only slight genetic differentiation. We also ask whether sibling pairs, on the average, show less genetic divergence between them than do nonsibling pairs. Other questions develop as these are pursued.

MATERIAL AND METHODS

Twenty-seven species of *Drosophila* were used in this investigation. These constituted nine triads (a sibling pair plus one close relative) of species drawn from six species groups and representing three subgenera. They are listed in Table 1.

Electrophoretic techniques and the enzyme and protein assays have been described in detail previously (Hubby, 1963; Hubby and Lewontin, 1966).

TABLE 1

SPECIES OF *Drosophila* USED IN THIS STUDY

TRIAD	SPECIES DESIGNATION	SPECIES	NUMBER*
	Genus: *Drosophila*		
	Subgenus: *Drosophila*		
	Species Group: repleta		
1	Sibling *a*	*arizonensis*	2156.4
	Sibling *b*	*mojavensis*	2533.1
	Other relative	*mulleri*	1815.2
2	Sibling *a*	*mercatorum*	2507.7
	Sibling *b*	*paranaensis*	H378.6
	Other relative	*peninsularis*	2303.3
3	Sibling *a*	*hydei*	2360.30
	Sibling *b*	*neohydei*	H207.26
	Other relative	*eohydei*	H62.52
4	Sibling *a*	*fulvimacula*	H435.7
	Sibling *b*	*fulvimaculoides*	H163.31
	Other relative	*limensis*	1529.2a
	Species Group: melanica		
5	Sibling *a*	*melanica*	1720.3
	Sibling *b*	*paramelanica*	2017.9
	Other relative	*nigromelanica*	2160.12
	Subgenus: *Sophophora*		
	Species Group: melanogaster		
6	Sibling *a*	*melanogaster*	Oregon-R
	Sibling *b*	*simulans*	H48.3
	Others species	*takahashii*	2363.4
	Species Group: saltans		
7	Sibling *a*	*saltans*	H180.40
	Sibling *b*	*prosaltans*	H303.3
	Other species	*emarginata*	H158.2
	Species Group: willistoni		
8	Sibling *a*	*willistoni*	2267.9
	Sibling *b*	*paulistorum*	1925.21
	Other relative	*nebulosa*	H88.5
	Subgenus: *Pholadoris*		
	Species Group: victoria		
9	Sibling *a*	*victoria*	1865.3
	Sibling *b*	*lebanonensis*	1733.1
	Other relative	*pattersoni*	2093.3

* University of Texas accession number.

In every assay the species from each triad were placed together on a single gel for comparison. The supernatant from a single-fly homogenate was used in each pocket of a 12-pocket gel. The supernatants were distributed according to the following format: pockets 1, 5, and 12, control (*D. melanogaster*, Oregon-R [Ore-R]); pockets 2, 6, and 7, sibling *a*; pockets 3, 8, and 9, sibling *b*; pockets 4, 10, and 11, closely related species. The assays performed were (1) esterase, (2) larval hemolymph proteins, (3) malate dehydrogenase, (4) α-glycerol phosphate dehydrogenase, (5) glucose-6-phosphate dehydrogenase, (6) acid phosphatase, and (7) leucine aminopeptidase. The mobilities of enzymes and hemolymph proteins were calculated relative to the variant seen in the control. The use of a single laboratory strain per species, and the low number of individuals examined, precluded establishing the degree of polymorphism for these species. This problem is discussed later in this paper and will be the subject of future publications. Side-by-side comparisons between species of different triads were made only when variants of very similar mobility were encountered.

RESULTS

From the esterase assay approximately five sites of activity were seen per comparison. Approximately nine larval hemolymph proteins could be detected. Each of the remaining assays showed one site of strong activity. Thus, we could study approximately 19 different proteins in each comparison. The number of sites investigated per species is given in Table 2. It ranged from a high of 23 for *mojavensis* to a low of 13 for *nebulosa*.

TABLE 2

THE DISTRIBUTION OF PROTEIN TYPES AMONG SPECIES OF EACH TRIAD

TRIAD	SPECIES	TOTAL SITES	CATEGORY					
			I	IIa	IIb	III	I + III	II + III
1	arizonensis	19						
	mojavensis	23	8	0	2	1	9	2.0
	mulleri	16						
2	mercatorum	20						
	paranaensis	21	11	2	2	2	13	4.0
	peninsularis	17						
3	hydei	18						
	neohydei	16	7	0	1	1	8	1.5
	eohydei	16						
4	fulvimacula	20						
	fulvimaculoides	22	10	3	2	3	13	5.5
	limensis	19						
5	melanica	21						
	paramelanica	19	5	2	2	1	6	3.0
	nigromelanica	23						
6	melanogaster	19						
	simulans	17	9	3	0	0	9	1.5
	takahashii	21						
7	saltans	21						
	prosaltans	19	7	1	2	2	9	3.5
	emarginata	21						
8	willistoni	15						
	paulistorum	14	1	1	2	2	3	3.5
	nebulosa	13						
9	victoria	15						
	lebanonensis	14	9	0	0	3	12	3.0
	pattersoni	14						
Average.............		18.3	7.4	1.3	1.4	1.7	9.1	3.2
Average as % total sites..............			40.4	7.1	7.7	9.3	49.7	17.5

NOTE—The category designations are explained in the text. The total number of proteins shared between siblings is given in the column headed "I + III." The total number of proteins shared between a species and a nonsibling relative is given in the column headed "II + III."

For comparisons between members of each triad, we may place proteins in one of four categories. Those proteins that show identical electrophoretic mobility between members of a sibling pair are placed in category I. Those proteins that show identical electrophoretic mobility between sibling a and the close relative are placed in category IIa. Those that show identical electrophoretic mobility between sibling b and the close relative are placed in category IIb. Those that show identical electrophoretic mobility between all three members of the triad are placed in category III. Thus, the number of proteins in category I plus the number of proteins in category III equal the total number of proteins in common between the members of the sibling pair. The number in category IIa plus the number in category III equal the total number of proteins in common between sibling a and the close relative, and so on. The numbers in the column headed "II + III" in Table 2 were computed by averaging the values for categories IIa and IIb and then adding this average to the value for category III. The bottom line of Table 2 shows the average value for each category calculated as a percentage of the average number of sites per species.

TABLE 3

Maximum and Minimum Percentage Similarity between Species

Triad	Species	Category					
		I	IIa	IIb	III	I + III	II + III
1	arizonensis	42.1	0.0	12.5	6.3	48.4	12.6
	mojavensis	34.8	0.0	8.7	4.3	39.1	8.7
	mulleri						
2	mercatorum	55.0	11.8	11.8	11.8	66.8	23.6
	paranaensis	52.4	10.0	9.5	9.5	61.9	19.3
	peninsularis						
3	hydei	43.8	0.0	6.3	6.3	50.1	9.5
	neohydei	38.9	0.0	6.3	5.6	44.5	8.8
	eohydei						
4	fulvimacula	50.0	15.8	10.5	15.8	65.8	29.0
	fulvimaculoides	45.5	15.0	9.1	13.6	59.1	25.7
	limensis						
5	melanica	26.3	9.5	10.5	5.3	31.6	15.3
	paramelanica	23.9	8.7	8.7	4.3	28.2	13.0
	nigromelanica						
6	melanogaster	52.9	15.8	0.0	0.0	52.9	7.9
	simulans	47.4	14.3	0.0	0.0	47.4	7.2
	takahashii						
7	saltans	36.8	4.8	10.5	10.5	47.3	18.2
	prosaltans	33.3	4.8	9.5	9.5	42.8	16.7
	emarginata						
8	willistoni	7.1	7.7	15.4	15.4	22.5	27.0
	paulistorum	6.7	6.7	14.3	13.3	20.0	23.8
	nebulosa						
9	victoria	64.3	0.0	0.0	21.4	85.7	21.4
	lebanonensis	60.0	0.0	0.0	20.0	80.0	20.0
	pattersoni						
Average.		42.0	7.3	8.6	11.6	52.3	18.3
		38.1	6.6	7.3	8.9	47.0	15.9

Note.—Triad numbers are from Table 1. Category designations are as in Table 2. Maximum values are given in the top line for each triad and minimum values in the bottom line. The maximum estimate is calculated using the number of sites seen in the species of the comparison having the lowest number of sites. The minimum estimate is based on the species having the highest number of sites.

The data from Table 2 are represented in percentage form in Table 3. We have provided two estimates of the percentage of total proteins showing identical mobility between two species. A maximum estimate is based on the number of sites seen in the species of the comparison showing the lowest number of sites. The minimum estimate is based on the number of sites seen in the species of the comparison showing the highest number of sites. The average maximum and minimum percentage for each category is given at the bottom of the table. Approximately 40% of a sibling's proteins are shared only with the other sibling (I), about 8% are shared only with the other relative (II), and about 9% are shared jointly by all members of the triad (III). As an overall average, members of a sibling pair have 50% of their proteins in common (I + III), while nonsibling members of a triad share only about 18% of their proteins. The highest maximum percentage identity (I + III) between any of the sibling pairs was seen for *victoria* and *lebanonensis* of triad 9 (Table 3, column 6). This value is 85.7%. The next highest was between *mercatorum* and *paranaensis* of triad 2 (66.8%) and between *fulvimacula* and *fulvimaculoides* of triad 4 (65.8%). This value ranged downward to a low of 22.5% for *willistoni* and *paulistorum* in triad 8.

It is also possible to make comparisons between species and triads on an individual enzyme basis. Such comparisons can be made most accurately for the five assays recorded in Table 4. The mobility differences evident in the table were verified by side-by-side comparison of doubtful forms. These comparisons can be summarized as shown in Table 5. The different enzymes existed in from 13 to 27 different forms each, with an average of 18.6 variants per enzyme. On the average, only 11.8% (Table 5, last column) of these variants were shared between members of two or more triads. Out of the 36 possible pairwise comparisons between the nine different triads (Table 5, line 5), an average of 5.8, or 16.1%, of the potential matches were realized, whereas 25.2% of the possible matches *within* triads were realized (line 4), and 48.9% of the possible matches within *sibling pairs* were realized (line 3). There were 351 possible comparisons between individual species, and of these only 5.9% (line 6) showed bands with identical mobility on comparison. It should, perhaps, be pointed out again that we did not make all of the possible side-by-side comparisons on gels. Side-by-side comparisons were made only when bands of very similar mobility were involved.

DISCUSSION

As discussed in several previous publications (Hubby, 1963; Hubby and Throckmorton, 1965; Hubby and Lewontin, 1966; Lewontin and Hubby, 1966), we make a number of assumptions in dealing with data of this sort. For example, we view single sites of enzymatic activity or of protein staining on a gel as representing the product of a single locus. This is a simplification, and we are well aware that two, and rarely perhaps even more, structural genes may contribute polypeptide subunits to a

TABLE 4

RELATIVE MOBILITIES OF FIVE ENZYMES FOR EACH SPECIES

TRIAD	SPECIES	ENZYME				
		MD	AGPD	G-6-PD	AP	LAP
1	*arizonensis*	1.39	1.00	0.50/0.56	0.85	1.42
	mojavensis	1.36	1.00	0.50/0.56	0.64	1.42
	mulleri	1.42	1.00	0.49/0.53	0.82	1.38
2	*mercatorum*	1.73	0.93	0.54	0.89	1.08
	paranaensis	1.84	1.03	0.54	0.89/1.00	1.08
	peninsularis	2.00	1.00	0.57	0.85	1.58
3	*hydei*	1.41	1.11	0.45	1.00	1.00
	neohydei	1.41	1.11	0.45	1.00	1.30
	eohydei	1.58	1.11	0.59	1.03	1.10
4	*fulvimacula*	2.10	1.00	0.39	1.06	1.24
	fulvimaculoides	1.70	1.00	0.37	0.75	1.24
	limensis	1.40	1.00	0.42	0.85	1.55
5	*melanica*	1.11	0.95	0.93	1.03	1.07
	paramelanica	0.80	0.89	0.92	1.03	1.27
	nigromelanica	1.20	0.82	1.03	1.60	1.50
6	*melanogaster*	1.00	1.00	1.00	1.00	1.00
	simulans	1.00	1.07	0.96	1.03	0.92
	takahashii	1.26	1.13	0.86	1.03	0.00
7	*saltans*	1.31	0.97	0.68	1.04	1.13
	prosaltans	1.05	1.00	0.68	1.04	1.13
	emarginata	1.11	1.00	....	1.12	1.00
8	*willistoni*	0.98	0.96	0.68	1.40	1.55
	paulistorum	1.11	0.99	0.68	1.30	1.30
	nebulosa	1.11	0.99	0.44	1.60	1.35
9	*victoria*	1.26	0.87	0.63	....	1.58
	lebanonensis	1.26	0.87	0.63	....	1.58
	pattersoni	1.26	0.90	....	....	1.54

NOTE.—Abbreviations are as follows: MD, malate dehydrogenase; AGPD, α-glycerol phosphate dehydrogenase; G-6-PD, glucose-6-phosphate dehydrogenase; AP, acid phosphatase; LAP, leucine aminopeptidase

migrating entity. This simplification is tolerable since it tends to bias our results toward an underestimate of the amount of genetic identity between two species, and for the purposes of this discussion an underestimate is preferred. Any mobility difference we do establish clearly represents a change in a structural gene. Identical mobility probably reflects identical base sequences in structural genes, and the probability that it does increases as the number of other features in common increases. That is to say, identical mobility between members of a species group more probably represents identical base sequences than does identical mobility between species of different species groups, and so on. Third, we assume that the array of assays involved in our procedure assesses an unbiased sample of the structural genes of the organisms concerned and that this itself is an unbiased sample of the total genome of the organism. It is possible that all of the proteins investigated are soluble proteins and so are not representative of so-called structural *proteins*. It is also possible that some genetic elements (as in genetic control systems, perhaps) are not well typified by the products of structural genes. In either of these cases, our sample of the

TABLE 5

SUMMARY OF DATA FROM TABLE 4

LINE	COMPARISON	ENZYME					AVERAGE	AVERAGE (%)
		MD	AGPD	G-6-PD	AP	LAP		
1	Number of different forms	19	14	20	13	27	18.6	....
2	Number of forms shared between groups	2	1	1	4	3	2.2	11.8
3	Matches/possible matches within sibling pairs	3/9	4/9	7/9	4/9	4/9	4.4/9	48.9
4	Matches/possible matches within triads	6/27	12/27	7/27	4/27	5/27	6.8/17	25.2
5	Matches/possible between triads	4/36	10/36	1/36	6/36	8/36	5.8/36	16.1
6	Matches/possible matches between species of different triads	6/108	38/108	4/108	14/108	8/108	14/108	13.0
7	Matches/possible matches between all species	12/351	50/351	11/351	18/351	13/351	20.8/351	5.9

NOTE.—Abbreviations are as in Table 4. Computations are based on pairwise comparisons. There are nine sibling pairs and therefore nine possible pairwise comparisons within sibling pairs. There are nine triads, and therefore there are 27 possible pairwise comparisons *within* triads, etc.

genome would be biased, but in which direction we do not know. In the latter instance, it may be pointed out that the number of sites assayed varied from 13 to 23 (Table 2) in the different species. The absence of activity on a gel is not necessarily evidence for change in a structural gene. The gene may be present in the organism but inactive, or it may be present and active but not sufficiently active (or not active in enough cells) to be detected in our single-fly assays. If cases such as the latter were the result of changed control loci, we have indeed assayed control loci as well as structural gene loci, but these have been assayed in an undiscriminating manner. This reflects back on the first point made earlier, that we over-simplify when we treat each site as representing a single locus, and it tends to reinforce our interpretation that our methods are strongly biased to understimate the actual amount of genetic identity between species. We may construct a single example to illustrate this last point.

Consider the summary line of averages at the bottom of Table 2. This has been calculated as *number of identical sites/average number of sites*. If we assume one locus per site, this translates to *number of identical loci/average number of loci*, and we calculate that the average sibling pair has 49.7% of its loci occupied by identical alleles while the average nonsibling pair has 17.5% of its alleles in common. If we change our assumption and say that each site represents two loci and that every change detected represents a change in *only one* of these loci, then our calculation becomes the following: for average identity between sibling pairs, 9.1 + 18.3/18.3 + 18.3 = 0.749; and for average identity between nonsibling pairs, 3.2 + 18.3/18.3 + 18.3 = 0.587. Thus, we would estimate that sibling pairs had about 75% of their genetic material in common, on the average, instead of the much lower estimate of 48.7% that we are accepting as the basis for this discussion. Similarly, the estimate of maximum amount of genetic identity between siblings (Table 3, line 6, triad 9) becomes 90% (12 + 15/15 + 15) instead of the lower 85.7% based on the more conservative assumptions. The bias in our estimate becomes more extreme as the amount of identity declines, which is again as we would wish it for the following discussion.

Not surprisingly, our triads are of quite diverse sorts. In the first type (Table 3, triads 1, 3, and 6) the siblings have much in common only with each other (category I), but only one of the siblings shows any category II proteins shared only with the close relative. In one case, triad 6, no single site showed identical mobilities for all three species. In a second type of triad (2 and 4;5 and 7), the siblings show mostly category I proteins, and the remainder of their proteins are distributed more or less equally among categories II and III. Triads 2 and 4 (drawn from subgroups of the repleta group) differ from triads 5 and 7 (drawn from species groups) primarily in that the siblings of the latter case show less similarity to each other (20–30% as opposed to approximately 50% [Tables 1 and 3]). A third type of triad is seen in triad 8, made up of species from the willistoni group. Here the siblings show no more similarity to each other than to the close relative. Indeed, *paulistorum* appears to have more in common with *nebulosa* than with its own sibling, *willistoni*. Triad 9 represents a fourth type of triad, since its siblings are very similar to each other (64.3% category I proteins), show no category II proteins, and yet show a relatively high number (21.4%) of category III proteins. We suspect that this latter case reflects the consequences of passive divergence during geographical isolation. The two siblings, *victoria* and *lebanonensis*, are found on different continents (southwestern United States and Lebanon, respectively; *pattersoni* is from Lebanon), and their populations may have been separated by events of the Pleistocene. Since we cannot characterize a species by one small sample, speculation from our results to the consequences of geographical isolation is not permitted.

Turning our attention from the triads to the sibling pairs, we find one, *victoria* and *lebanonensis*, of triad 9 (Table 3, I + III), with 85.7% of their proteins in common, followed by two sibling pairs from the repleta group (triads 2 and 4), with around 65% in common. At the opposite extreme, we note the siblings *paulistorum* and *willistoni* with only around 20% of their genetic material in common. We interpret these results to indicate that speciation does not *require* a change in a large number of gene loci. Our present results correspond closely with, and tend to confirm, those from our earlier work with species of the virilis group (Hubby and Throckmorton, 1965), where we estimated a change of about 20% during speciation and subsequent divergence. In other respects also, the results closely parallel each other. If the virilis data is recalculated after the method used here, category I + III (total proteins in common between siblings) ranges from a high of 82% to a low of 32%, with an average of 56%. Category II + III (total proteins in common between nonsiblings) ranges from a high of 41% to a low of 34%, with an average of about 39%. The average similarities are somewhat higher in the virilis data, but the highest value is much the same as in our present study (82%, to our present 85%).

Our present results also indicate that, on the average, a high amount of similarity in gross morphology is paralleled by a high degree of similarity at the protein, and hence the genetic, level. Sibling species average 50% in common while nonsiblings average only approximately one-third as much (18%) in common (Tables 2 and 3). If identical mobilities were randomly distributed among the species of our comparisons, we would expect concordances in the ratio of 9/27/36/108/351, or 1/3/4/12/39 (Table 5, column 8, lines 3–7). Instead, this ratio approximates 4/7/6/14/21, and it is clearly biased by common descent. The greatest deviations from random expectation are for comparisons between the species considered taxonomically most similar.

We do not intend to ignore the fact that similarity in gross morphology and similarity at the protein (genetic) level do not *necessarily* go hand in hand. The sibling species, *willistoni* and *paulistorum*, show only 22.5% of their sites having identical mobilities. Similarly, *melanica* and *paramelanica* show only 31.6% identical mobilities. Obviously, a balanced view of sibling species must present them as being comprised of a spectrum of forms ranging from some pairs with high levels of genetic identity to others with low levels. It is important to be aware that extensive changes in structural genes can occur without concommitant morphological divergence. Mayr (1963) has stressed the dangers of drawing genetic inferences too freely from limited aspects of gross morphology. It is equally important, however, to recognize that sometimes and at some levels morphological and genetic similarities are quite parallel with each other. You cannot view similar morphologies and assert that they evidence similar genotypes. Neither can you assert the contrary, that they certainly evidence dissimilar genotypes. It is important for advancing evolutionary theory that we achieve an understanding of how, why, and when species status might be achieved with small, perhaps numerically negligible, amounts of genetic change. Extensive reorganization of a gene pool does not seem to be requisite to speciation. We are not yet certain just how slight the reorganization can be.

Before turning to the problem of sampling and polymorphism, we should note that the proteins and enzymes in our study illustrate a second, and expected, feature of genetic differentiation. They do not all appear to have changed at the same rate. For example, glucose-6-phosphate dehydrogenase is represented by a unique form of the enzyme in eight of the nine triads studied. On the other hand, with the α-glycerol phosphate dehydrogenase assay, proteins of common mobility are seen from five out of nine triads. This suggests the possibility that this latter enzyme has retained the same structure over long periods of evolutionary time, whereas glucose-6-phosphate dehydrogenase has been much more liable. The remaining three enzymes are intermediate in some respects, and the evidence from Tables 4 and 5 may be construed as indicating not only differential rates of evolution between the different enzymes but also different rates of evolution for the same protein in different evolutionary lineages.

If all species of *Drosophila* are as polymorphic as is *D. pseudoobscura* (Hubby and Lewontin, 1966; Lewontin and Hubby, 1966), then there is a definite bias in our present data. For individual species comparisons, this bias can only be removed through an intensive survey of wild populations of the species in question. Such surveys are presently underway for *pseudoobscura* and *persimilis* and for the species of the virilis group. Until these works are completed, we can only note the direction of bias and the probable consequences for comparisons of the type undertaken here. The study of *pseudoobscura* showed a majority (11 out of 18) of loci to be monomorphic. The remaining loci were polymorphic, and some were highly so. Thus, when a comparison is based on only a single sample from each entity (culture, population, species), the accuracy of the results will depend upon the proportion of the loci actually monomorphic in each entity. If two populations are compared, and if both are completely monomorphic for the loci compared, one individual from each population will tell the whole story. If two species are compared, and if each is highly polymorphic, a single individual, or a single strain, or even a single population from each species, will tell only a part of the story. When comparisons are made between polymorphic populations, the lower the number of comparisons, the lower the probability that identical alleles in both will be detected. That is to say, comparisons between single individuals, or between single samples, tend to exaggerate the differences between populations.

We based our study on single samples and on a low number of individuals from each sample. This was expedient. If our results are in error, we wish them to show less genetic identity between species than actually exists. As far as we can judge, polymorphism, and the other major factors noted earlier, all tend to bias downward our estimates of genetic identity. We have already noted the alternative to entertaining bias of this sort in our data. A completely definitive comparison between species requires a tremendous amount of time and effort, and any justifiable shortcut is welcome. We have reason to think that the shortcut will not strongly distort the pattern of genetic relationships between species. The published data of Lewontin and Hubby (1966) for *pseudoobscura* indicate a relatively, and unexpectedly, high degree of polymorphism for that species. From these data we can calculate the probability that two strains drawn from that species will have a particular allele in common. That probability proves to be 0.8862 when averaged over all loci. Approximately one time out of 10 such sampling would have failed to detect genetic identity. Obviously, the distortion from this factor to data such as ours in small, and, since we would expect it to be distributed proportionally to all categories, it is not serious. If the amount of polymorphism seen in *pseudoobscura* is average for the genus, we have not erred greatly.

With these considerations in mind, we wish to emphasize that our results indicate a considerable amount of genetic identity between species. On the average, this identity is higher where it might be expected. Where exceptions appear they are of considerable interest in their own right. As we know from the extensive investigations of Dobzhansky et al. (1964), members of the willistoni group reflect in other characteristics an evolutionary situations of surprising complexity. Our results conform. They show a pattern for the willistoni triad that is at one end of a spectrum of patterns extending at the opposite extreme to the conservative pattern of the victoria triad. We think that this overall pattern is real and that the diversity reflects a highly significant diversity in evolutionary modes and adaptive strategies. Verifying, defining, and extending these patterns of diversity will require much work. Relating them to evolutionary histories and present ecologies will require still more. Perhaps when that work is finished we will be able to speak with confidence of the modes of speciation and the properties of gene pools.

SUMMARY

Nine triads of species of the genus *Drosophila*, each triad composed of a pair of sibling species and a form closely related but morphologically distinct, were studied using electrophoretic techniques at an average of 18 loci per species. The sibling pairs, on the average, shared proteins with identical mobility 50% of the time, while a sibling and a morphologically distinct form shared proteins with identical mobility only 18% of the time. One sibling pair shared proteins with identical mobility 85% of the time. These findings are discussed with special reference to "the reorganization of the gene pool" during speciation.

LITERATURE CITED

Dobzhansky, Th. 1959. Evolution of genes and genes in evolution. Cold Spring Harbor Symp. Quant. Biol. 24:15–30.

Dobzhansky, Th., Lee Ehrman, O. Pavlovsky, and B. Spassky. 1964. The superspecies *Drosophila paulistorum*. Nat. Acad. Sci., Proc., 51:3–9.

Hubby, J. L. 1963. Protein differences in Drosophila. I *Drosophila melanogaster*. Genetics 48:871–879.

Hubby, J. L., and L. Throckmorton. 1965. Protein differences in Drosophila. II. Comparative species genetics and evolutionary problems. Genetics 52:203–215.

Hubby, J. L., and R. C. Lewontin. 1966. A molecular approach to the study of genic heterozygosity in natural populations. I. The number of alleles at different loci in *Drosophila pseudoobscura*. Genetics 54:577–594.

Lewontin, R. C., and J. L. Hubby. 1966. A molecular approach to the study of genic heterozygosity in natural populations. II. Amount of variation and degree of heterozygosity in natural populations of *Drosophila pseudoobscura*. Genetics 54:595–609.

Mayr, E. 1963. Animal species and evolution. Belknap, Cambridge, Mass. 797 p.

Throckmorton, L. H., and J. L. Hubby. 1963. Toward a modern synthesis of evolutionary thought. Science 140:628–631.

Waddington, C. H. 1957. The strategy of the gene. Allen & Unwin, London.

6

Reprinted from *Proc. Nat. Acad. Sci.* 71:2843–2847 (1974)

Two Types of Molecular Evolution. Evidence from Studies of Interspecific Hybridization

(mammals/frogs/proteins/regulation/maternal–fetal immunology)

A. C. WILSON*†‡, L. R. MAXSON*, AND V. M. SARICH*

* University of California, Berkeley, Calif.; † Weizmann Institute of Science, Israel, and University of Nairobi, Kenya

Communicated by Bruce N. Ames, April 25, 1974

ABSTRACT   To assess the significance of macromolecular sequence differences among species, we compared the serum albumins of 81 pairs of vertebrate species capable of producing viable hybrids. Micro-complement fixation experiments showed that the average difference between the albumins within such pairs was only 3 immunological distance units for placental mammals (31 pairs), but 36 units for frogs (50 pairs). Albumin immunological distance is strongly correlated with other measures of genetic distance, including those made with DNA annealing techniques. It therefore seems likely that mammalian species pairs capable of hybridization are far more similar at the macromolecular sequence level than is the case for most hybridizable frogs.

We think the most likely explanation for the marked molecular restriction on hybridization among mammals is that the ratio of regulatory evolution to protein evolution is higher for mammals than for frogs. Mammals may have experienced unusually rapid regulatory evolution; indeed, this could be the factor responsible for their unusually rapid anatomical evolution.

There may be two major types of molecular evolution. One is the process of protein evolution, which goes on at about the same rate in all species. The other is a process whose rate is variable and which is responsible for evolutionary changes in anatomy and way of life. We propose that evolutionary change in regulatory systems accounts for evolution at and beyond the anatomical level.

This proposal emerges from attempts to explain the observation that protein evolution and anatomical evolution can proceed independently (1–3). This independence is illustrated by protein and anatomical studies on frogs and mammals. Frogs (Anura) are an ancient group that has undergone much protein evolution (1, 2, 4–7) but little anatomical evolution during its 150-million-year history. Although there are thousands of frog species living today, they are all rather alike in anatomy and way of life. By contrast, the placental mammals, which are only 75 million years old, have undergone extensive anatomical evolution. The diversity in anatomy and way of life represented by bats, whales, sloths, and people is unparalleled among frogs. Yet placental mammals have experienced less protein evolution than frogs have. While the rate of protein evolution is similar in the two groups, their rates of anatomical evolution differ greatly (1, 2). This remarkable contrast between protein evolution and anatomical evolution implies that protein evolution may not be at the basis of anatomical evolution.

‡ To whom requests for reprints may be addressed at the Dept. of Biochemistry, University of California, Berkeley, Calif. 94720.

For the idea that evolutionary changes in regulatory systems may provide the basis for anatomical evolution, we are indebted to Wolpert (8), Britten and Davidson (9, 10), and above all, Ohno (11, 12). Accordingly, we suggest that the rapid anatomical evolution exhibited by placental mammals is attributable to rapid evolutionary changes in their developmental regulatory systems. Evidence in support of this idea is now presented.

Our evidence comes from studies on interspecific hybridization. For the past several years we have been comparing the blood proteins, albumin, transferrin, and hemoglobin, of a great variety of vertebrate species (1, 2, 7, 13–23) including numerous pairs of frog and of mammal species known to be capable of producing viable interspecific hybrids. This enabled us to estimate how similar the proteins of the parental species are in those cases where successful interspecific hybridization can occur. Hence, one can examine the problem of what relationship, if any, exists between hybridization potential and degree of protein sequence difference among species. At first thought, it might seem obvious that degree of protein similarity between the parental species should be a major factor affecting the probability of successful development of an interspecific zygote. The more similar the proteins of two species, the more likely it is, one might expect, that their genomes would be compatible enough to permit development of viable hybrids. However, our results do not fulfill this expectation. Mammals that can hybridize with each other differ only slightly at the protein level, whereas frogs that differ substantially in protein sequence hybridize readily. In order to explain this contrast, we review evidence suggesting that the principal molecular barriers to interspecific hybridization are regulatory differences between the parental genomes. Rapid regulatory evolution in mammals may account for both their rapid anatomical evolution and their rapid evolutionary loss of the potential for interspecific hybridization.

MATERIALS AND METHODS

Protein Purification and Antiserum Production. Serum or plasma samples were obtained from 31 pairs of mammalian species and 50 pairs of frog species known to produce viable interspecific hybrids. Albumin was purified from many of these species, usually by preparative polyacrylamide gel electrophoresis (2, 7, 13) and then injected into groups of three to six rabbits (of the New Zealand White or the Dutch Belted varieties). After a 3-month period of immunization by published methods (2, 14), antisera were collected and pooled in

Proc. Nat. Acad. Sci. USA 71 (1974)

inverse proportion to their micro-complement fixation titers. Transferrin was purified by Rivanol precipitation, ammonium sulfate fractionation of the supernatant, and preparative polyacrylamide gel electrophoresis (15). Hemoglobin was purified from hemolysates by polyacrylamide electrophoresis alone. The immunization procedure used for hemoglobin and transferrin was essentially the same as for albumin.

Measurement of Immunological Distance. Amino-acid sequence differences between proteins were measured immunologically. Each antiserum pool was tested for reactivity with the unpurified albumin present in serum from various species. Reactivity was measured by the quantitative micro-complement fixation method (24). The results are given in immunological distance units, which are defined elsewhere (14, 20, 24, 25). Immunological distance (y) is generally related to percent difference in amino-acid sequence (x) by the equation $y \cong 5x$ (24–28). For the particular case of albumin, there is direct empirical evidence that each unit of immunological distance is roughly equivalent to one amino acid substitution (23). Although micro-complement fixation measures only the approximate degree of sequence difference between homologous proteins, it is superior to conventional chemical methods in speed and economy (16, 24, 25).

Albumin Immunological Distance as a Measure of Genetic Distance. We worked mainly with serum albumin, not only because of our considerable experience with the study of species differences in this protein (1, 2, 7, 13–23), but also because albumin evolves faster than most other proteins. Whereas the average rate of protein evolution is 1 amino-acid substitution per 100 residues per 10^7 years (29–31), that of albumin appears to be twice as fast (13). Albumin is also nearly twice as large as the average protein, having about 580 amino acids in a single polypeptide chain (32). For these reasons, it is a useful protein for detecting sequence differences among closely related species.

Although we studied primarily albumin, protein evolution proceeds with sufficient regularity (22) to make us confident that species whose albumins differ greatly will also differ

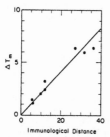

Fig. 1.   Relationship between DNA evolution and albumin evolution in primates. The albumins of various species of catarrhine primates (i.e., humans, apes, and Old World monkeys) were compared by the micro-complement fixation method. Each immunological distance value plotted is the average of two reciprocal measurements. The nonrepeated fraction of the total genome DNA was also compared, using the same primate species and the methods described by Kohne *et al.* and Hoyer *et al.* (34, 35). The ΔT_m values plotted are taken from refs. 34 and 35; ΔT_m is thought to be related linearly to percentage difference in nucleotide sequence (34, 35).

TABLE 1.   *Albumin differences within 31 pairs of placental mammal species that hybridize*

Pair	Immunological distance between albumins[*]
Primates	
Cercocebus albigena × *C. galeritus*	10
Cercocebus torquatus × *Macaca fascicularis*	5
Cercocebus torquatus × *Macaca nemestrina*	5
Cercocebus torquatus × *Mandrillus sphinx*	6
Cercopithecus aethiops × *C. mona*	4
Cercopithecus aethiops × *Macaca mulatta*	8
Cercopithecus cephus × *Erythrocebus patas*	5
Cynopithecus niger × *Macaca fascicularis*	4
Mandrillus sphinx × *Papio anubis*	4
Papio anubis × *P. cynocephalus*	0
Papio anubis × *P. hamadryas*	0
Papio anubis × *P. papio*	0
Papio cynocephalus × *P. hamadryas*	0
Papio cynocephalus × *P. papio*	0
Papio hamadryas × *P. papio*	0
Papio hamadryas × *P. ursinus*	0
Papio hamadryas × *Theropithecus gelada*	0
Papio papio × *P. ursinus*	0
Lemur fulvus × *L. macaco*	6
Carnivora	
Felis catus × *Felis libyca*	0
Canis familiaris × *C. latrans*	2
Canis familiaris × *C. lupus*	0
Ursus americanus × *U. arctos*	0
Ursus arctos × *Thalarctos maritimus*	3
Arctocephalus pusillus × *Zalophus californicus*	8
Perissodactyla	
Equus asinus × *E. caballus*	4
Equus burchelli × *E. caballus*	8
Artiodactyla	
Bison bison × *Bos taurus*	1
Cervus canadensis × *C. elaphus*	2
Odocoileus hemionus × *O. virginianus*	5
Odocoileus hemionus × *Axis axis*	8
Mean	3

* Values taken from ref. 19 and from Sarich (unpublished work). These results were obtained with antisera against the purified albumins of the following species: *Bison bison, Bos taurus, Canis familiaris, Cercocebus galeritus, Cercopithecus aethiops, Cervus canadensis, Equus caballus, Felis catus, Lemur fulvus, Macaca mulatta, Odocoileus hemionus, Papio anubis, Ursus americanus,* and *Zalophus californicus.*

substantially at other loci as well. Electrophoretic measures of genetic distance (33), for example, correlate strongly ($r = 0.8$) with immunological distances among the albumins of the same species. If two species differ electrophoretically at 50% of their loci, the immunological distance between their albumins is usually about 22 units (V. M. Sarich, L. R. Maxson, M. -C. King, K. Keeler, and A. C. Wilson, paper presented at the annual meeting of the Society for the Study of Evolution, Houston, Texas, December 1973).

Genetic distance can also be estimated from DNA hybridization experiments; the best method is to measure the melting (denaturation) temperature of heteroduplexes formed by an-

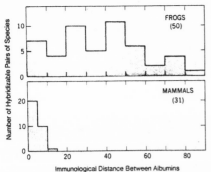

FIG. 2. Immunological distances between the serum albumins of species pairs capable of producing hybrids. The numbers of pairs are given in parentheses.

nealing non-repeated DNA sequences and to subtract it from the melting temperature of the homoduplexes. By comparing the albumins of the same species whose DNAs were so compared (34, 35), we find that there is a very strong correlation ($r = 0.9$) between melting temperature difference (ΔT_m) and albumin immunological distance. This is illustrated in Fig. 1. Hence we believe the immunological distance results given below are indicative of the overall degree of sequence resemblance among the genomes of the species compared.

RESULTS

Serum Albumin. Table 1 gives the results of the albumin comparisons for 31 pairs of placental mammal species. Gray (36) reports that every one of these pairs can produce viable, full-term interspecific offspring. The albumins of these pairs generally differ by about 3 units (range 0–10), which corresponds to a sequence difference of about 0.6%. It appears that if the albumin sequence difference found within a pair of mammalian species exceeds 2% (i.e., 10 units), the pair is very unlikely to produce a viable hybrid.

Sharply contrasting with the mammal results are the frog results given in Table 2. The 50 pairs of frogs listed are reported to produce interspecific offspring that successfully metamorphose from tadpole to adult (37–40). Yet the albumin differences within these pairs average 37 units (range 0–91), which is about 10 times greater than the average for hybridizable mammal pairs. Indeed, 42 of the 50 frog pairs§ showed albumin differences greater than those within any of the mammal pairs in Table 1. Fig. 2 summarizes the albumin results and illustrates the frog–mammal contrast.

Other Proteins. The large molecular differences within hybridizable frog pairs are not unique to albumin. Immunological comparison of the hemoglobins of several of the *Hyla*

§ The low number of frog values in the mammalian range (0–10 units) may result from the fact that frog populations differing from one another by 0–10 units of albumin immunological distance are rarely (except in the case of *Bufo* species) considered as separate species and hence did not fall within our purview. Thus the wide range of within-pair immunological distance values (0–91 units) found for frogs may be more significant than the average (36 units) in the comparison with mammals.

pairs in Table 2 showed immunological distances averaging half of the corresponding albumin immunological distances (7). This is consistent with the finding in other vertebrate groups, including mammals, that albumin generally evolves twice as fast as hemoglobin (13).

The small differences found within hybridizable mammal species pairs are also not unique to albumin. Fibrinopeptides, which are known to evolve extremely fast (31), do not differ much within hybridizable species pairs. We calculated that the average sequence difference between the fibrinopeptides of 13 such pairs is 1.8 amino-acid substitutions (a 5% sequence difference). In addition, we have obtained information on transferrins, which are known to evolve faster than albumin but slower than fibrinopeptides (V. M. Sarich, J. E. Cronin, E. M. Prager, and A. C. Wilson, unpublished work). The transferrins of 21 of the species pairs listed in Table 1 differ by an average of 8 units of immunological distance (a 1.6% sequence difference). Hence there is a parallel between the relative rates of evolution of the three polypeptides and the relative magnitudes of the sequence differences within pairs of hybridizable species. Accordingly, the 3 polypeptides give a consistent picture of the degree of amino-acid sequence difference within the various species pairs.

In summary, it appears that, as a general rule, protein sequence differences within mammalian pairs capable of hybridization are an order of magnitude smaller than the corresponding frog differences.

DISCUSSION

Regulatory hypothesis

We propose that the marked restriction on interspecific hybridization among mammals occurs because mammals, in contrast to frogs, have experienced rapid evolutionary change in the systems regulating expression of genes. If two species have very different mechanisms for regulating gene expression during embryonic development, it is unlikely that a healthy adult hybrid organism could develop. The hypothesis that the chief molecular barriers to development of hybrid organisms are regulatory ones is consistent with observations on somatic cell hybrids as well as the phenomenon of allelic repression in organismal hybrids.

Somatic Cell Hybrids Versus Organismal Hybrids. Somatic cells from extremely different animals can hybridize and grow well for many generations (41). Bird cells, for example, hybridize readily with those of mammals. Yet, at the protein level, the average degree of sequence difference within a pair of mammal species capable of organismal hybridization is at least 100 times smaller than that between birds and mammals. It is even possible for invertebrate cells to hybridize with those of mammals (42), despite sequence differences which are undoubtedly greater than those between birds and mammals.

Cell hybridization between distantly related species is much easier than organismal hybridization because cell hybrids are exempt from the requirement to develop into an organism. The process of embryonic development involves activation of most of the genes that were inactive in the sperm and egg (43, 44). For successful development of an interspecific zygote, the two regulatory systems (contributed by the egg and sperm genomes) controlling the expression of such genes must be compatible. As somatic cell hybrids are less subject to such a

TABLE 2. *Albumin differences within 50 pairs of frog species that hybridize*

Pair	Immunological distance between albumins*
Bufo	
B. boreas × *B. alvarius*	25
B. boreas × *B. americanus*	30
B. boreas × *B. arenarum*	61
B. boreas × *B. calamita*	46
B. boreas × *B. coccifer*	49
B. boreas × *B. cognatus*	20
B. boreas × *B. compactilis*	24
B. boreas × *B. ibarrai*	43
B. boreas × *B. marmoreus*	46
B. boreas × *B. mazatlanensis*	42
B. boreas × *B. microscaphus*	23
B. boreas × *B. perplexus*	46
B. boreas × *B. punctatus*	4
B. boreas × *B. speciosus*	25
B. boreas × *B. spinulosus*	54
B. boreas × *B. terrestris*	29
B. boreas × *B. valliceps*	36
B. boreas × *B. viridis*	58
B. boreas × *B. woodhousei*	27
B. cognatus × *B. compactilis*	3
B. cognatus × *B. punctatus*	24
B. cognatus × *B. woodhousei*	19
B. marinus × *B. arenarum*	4
B. marinus × *B. paracnemis*	0
B. woodhousei × *B. americanus*	2
B. woodhousei × *B. hemiophrys*	3
B. woodhousei × *B. microscaphus*	5
B. viridis × *B. calamita*	45
Hyla and *Pseudacris*	
H. chrysoscelis × *H. cinerea*	42
H. chrysoscelis × *H. femoralis*	52
H. chrysoscelis × *H. gratiosa*	34
H. chrysoscelis × *H. squirella*	35
H. cinerea × *H. arborea*	57
H. cinerea × *H. avivoca*	45
H. cinerea × *H. squirella*	31
H. femoralis × *H. arenicolor*	63
H. femoralis × *H. cinerea*	66
H. femoralis × *H. gratiosa*	51
H. femoralis × *H. squirella*	54
H. gratiosa × *H. squirella*	42
H. regilla × *P. triseriata*	70
H. crucifer × *P. triseriata*	70
H. crucifer × *P. nigrita*	91
P. brachyphona × *P. nigrita*	38
P. brachyphona × *P. ornata*	76
Rana	
R. pipens × *R. capito*	10
R. pipiens × *R. palustris·*	17
R. pipiens × *R. areolata*	21
R. temporaria × *R. japonica*	29
Xenopus	
X. laevis × *X. mulleri*	18
Mean	36

* Values taken from refs. 2 and 7 and from Maxson (unpublished work). These results were obtained with antisera against the purified albumins of the following species: *Bufo boreas, B. cog-*

requirement, it is understandable that cell hybridization, but not organismal hybridization, can take place between extremely distantly related species.

Breakdown of Gene Regulation in Organismal Hybrids. Additional evidence that interspecific differences in developmental regulatory systems may be the major barrier to organismal hybridization comes from studies on gene expression in organismal hybrids. In the fish hybrids, *Lepomis* × *Micropterus*, for example, the glucose-6-phosphate dehydrogenase present is encoded exclusively by the paternal allele; expression of the maternal allele is completely repressed (45). Such allelic repression is indicative of a breakdown in gene regulation. A converse example is provided by alcohol dehydrogenase in quail × chicken hybrids; here, the maternal allele is expressed while expression of the paternal allele is delayed or suppressed totally (46). Similar observations have been reported for other cases of hybridization between distantly related species (see ref. 45 for a review). Indeed, at some loci in such hybrids, neither the maternal nor the paternal allele is expressed (45).

Allelic repression is most often encountered in extreme hybrids. Three of the eight loci tested in the *Lepomis* × *Micropterus* hybrids exhibited this phenomenon (45). Allelic repression is reported to be less common in hybrids between taxonomically very similar species (45). Thus, the extent of allelic repression may be correlated with taxonomic distance between the parental species. This leads one to expect that hybrids between very distantly related species could not develop because the breakdown in gene regulation would be so extensive.

We are impressed with the regulatory hypothesis because it explains why mammals have experienced both rapid anatomical evolution and rapid evolutionary loss of the potential for interspecific hybridization. However, it is important to be aware that an alternative hypothesis may explain the restriction on hybridization among placental mammals.

Immunological hypothesis

This hypothesis appeals to immunological interaction between the mammalian mother and fetus. Such interaction has been the subject of several reviews (e.g., 47, 48). According to this hypothesis, if the proteins of the placental mother and fetus differed as much in sequence as does the average frog species pair in Table 2, the mother would make antibodies against the hybrid fetus, thereby causing abortion. Obviously this phenomenon cannot occur in most frogs, as both fertilization and embryonic development take place outside the mother in the great majority of species, including all those in Table 2. This hypothesis has the corollary that if lethal immunological interaction between mother and fetus were circumvented, hybrids between mammalian species pairs as distinct in protein sequence as the frog pairs of Table 2 should be obtainable. The consequence is staggering, as this would mean that mammalian species pairs with albumin immunological distances of up to 50 units would often be similar enough at the molecular level to form viable hybrids once the postulated immuno-

natus, B. marinus, B. viridis, B. woodhousei, Hyla cinerea, H. crucifer, H gratiosa, H. femoralis, H. regilla, H. squirella, Pseudacris brachyphona, Rana pipiens, R. temporaria, and *Xenopus laevis.* The antisera to *B. cognatus, B. marinus,* and *B. woodhousei* were supplied by Dr. S. Guttman.

logical barrier were eliminated. Such pairs of mammals include: (*1*) Any pair of anthropoid primates (17–19), e.g., man and monkey; (*2*) Any pair of arctoid carnivores (14), e.g., dog and seal; (*3*) Any pair of pecoran artiodactyls (V. M. Sarich, A. Bennett, and A. C. Wilson, unpublished albumin studies), e.g., sheep and giraffe.

Elimination of the hypothetical immunological barrier can in principle be achieved, for example, by use of immunosuppressants or by growing the fetus *in vitro*. In fact, immunosuppressive experiments have already been attempted with two interspecific crosses in which the hybrid fetus normally dies during pregnancy. These are the goat × sheep cross (49) and the ferret × mink cross (50). No significant improvement in hybrid survival resulted from such treatment. Given continued rapid progress in both our understanding of the immune response and the development of *in vitro* fetal growth techniques (51), it should soon be possible to conduct more definitive tests of the immunological hypothesis. Until this is done, the available evidence (49, 50) leads us to think that the immunological hypothesis is probably incorrect.

Conclusions

We therefore propose that (*a*) the chief molecular barriers to interspecific hybridization are the regulatory system differences between the maternal and paternal genomes, which must function in concert if an interspecific zygote is to develop, and (*b*) anatomical evolution is due chiefly to regulatory system changes, macromolecular sequence changes usually being rather inconsequential.

Further evidence consistent with the regulatory hypothesis will appear in the next issue of these PROCEEDINGS (53). That evidence, derived from studies on chromosomal evolution in frogs and mammals, will focus attention on the phenomenon of gene rearrangement as a possible means of achieving new systems of regulation.

We thank R. Falk, J. Gerhart, W. Lidicker, E. Penhoet, C. Richards, S. Salthe, M. Soller, J. Wahrman, D. Wake, A. Walker, and F. Wilt for advice. We also thank the many people who supplied specimens for this work. This work was supported by a fellowship from the J. S. Guggenheim Foundation and by grants from the National Institutes of Health and the National Science Foundation. A preliminary account of these findings has appeared (52).

1. Wallace, D. G., Maxson, L. R. & Wilson, A. C. (1971) *Proc. Nat. Acad. Sci. USA* 68, 3127–3129.
2. Wallace, D. G., King, M.-C. & Wilson, A. C. (1973) *Syst. Zool.* 22, 1–13.
3. Turner, B. J. (1974) *Evolution* 28, in press.
4. Cei, M. (1972) *The Serological Museum, Bulletin No. 48*, 1–4.
5. McCarron, K. & Volpe, E. P. (1973) *Experientia* 29, 626–628.
6. Baldwin, T. O. & Riggs, A. (1974) *J. Biol. Chem.* 249, in press.
7. Maxson, L. R. (1973) Ph.D. Thesis in Genetics, University of California, Berkeley, and California State University, San Diego.
8. Wolpert, L. (1959) *J. Theor. Biol.* 25, 1–47.
9. Britten, R. J. & Davidson, E. H. (1971) *Quart. Rev. Biol.* 46, 111–133.
10. Davidson, E. H. & Britten, R. J. (1973) *Quart. Rev. Biol.* 48, 565–613.
11. Ohno, S. (1972) *J. Human Evol.* 1, 651–662.
12. Ohno, S. (1973) *Nature* 244, 259–262.
13. Wallace, D. G. & Wilson, A. C. (1972) *J. Mol. Evol.* 2, 72–86.
14. Sarich, V. M. (1969) *Syst. Zool.* 18, 286–295 and 416–422.
15. Sarich, V. M. (1973) *Nature* 245, 218–220.
16. Sarich, V. M. & Wilson, A. C. (1966) *Science* 154, 1563–1566.
17. Sarich, V. M. & Wilson, A. C. (1967) *Proc. Nat. Acad. Sci. USA* 58, 142–148.
18. Sarich, V. M. & Wilson, A. C. (1967) *Science* 158, 1200–1203.
19. Sarich, V. M. (1970) in *Old World Monkeys*, eds. Napier, J. R. & Napier, P. H. (Academic Press, New York), pp. 175–226.
20. Gorman, G. C., Wilson, A. C. & Nakanishi, M. (1971) *Syst. Zool.* 20, 167–185.
21. Sarich, V. M. (1972) *Biochem. Genet.* 7, 205.
22. Sarich, V. M. & Wilson, A. C. (1973) *Science* 179, 1144–1147.
23. Maxson, L. R. & Wilson, A. C. (1974) *Science*, in press.
24. Champion, A. B., Prager, E. M., Wachter, D. & Wilson, A. C. (1974) in *Biochemical and Immunological Taxonomy*, ed. Wright, C. A. (Academic Press, London), pp. 397–416.
25. Prager, E. M. & Wilson, A. C. (1971) *J. Biol. Chem.* 246, 5978–5989 and 7010–7017.
26. Prager, E. M., Arnheim, N., Mross, G. A. & Wilson, A. C. (1972) *J. Biol. Chem.* 247, 2905–2916.
27. Rocha, V., Crawford, I. P. & Mills, S. E. (1972) *J. Bacteriol.* 111, 163–168.
28. Wilson, A. C. & Prager, E. M. (1974) in *Lysozyme*, eds., Osserman, E., Canfield, R. & Beychok, S. (Academic Press, New York), pp. 127–141.
29. King, J. L. & Jukes, T. H. (1969) *Science* 164, 788–798.
30. Dayhoff, M. O., ed. (1972) *Atlas of Protein Sequence and Structure, 5* (National Biomedical Research Foundation, Silver Spring, Md.).
31. Dickerson, R. E. (1971) *J. Mol. Evol.* 1, 26–45.
32. Brown, J. R., Low, T., Beherns, P., Sepulveda, P., Barker, K. & Blakeney, E. (1971) *Fed. Proc.* 30, 1240 abstr.
33. Selander, R. K. & Johnson, W. E. (1973) *Annu. Rev. Ecol. Syst.* 4, 75–91.
34. Kohne, D. E., Chicson, J. A. & Hoyer, B. H. (1972) *J. Human Evol.* 1, 627–644.
35. Hoyer, B. H., van de Velde, N. W., Goodman, M. & Roberts, R. B. (1972), *J. Human Evol.* 1, 645–650.
36. Gray, A. P. (1972) *Mammalian Hybrids* (Commonwealth Agricultural Bureaux, Farnham Royal, Bucks., England) 2nd ed.
37. Blair, W. F., ed. (1972) *Evolution in the Genus Bufo* (University of Texas Press, Austin).
38. Ralin, D. B. (1970) Ph.D. Thesis, University of Texas, Austin.
39. Moore, J. A. (1955) *Advan. Genet.* 7, 139–182.
40. Blackler, A. W. & Gecking, C. A. (1972) *Develop. Biol.* 27, 385–394.
41. Ephrussi, B. (1972) *Hybridization of Somatic Cells* (Princeton University Press, Princeton, New Jersey).
42. Zepp, H. D., Conover, J. H., Hirschhorn, K. & Hodes, H. L. (1971) *Nature* 229, 119–121.
43. Davidson, E. H. (1968) *Gene Activity in Early Development* (Academic Press, New York).
44. Church, R. B. & Brown, I. R. (1972) in *Problems and Results in Differentiation*, ed. Ursprung, H. (Springer-Verlag, New York), Vol. 3, pp. 11–24.
45. Whitt, G. S., Childers, W. F. & Cho, P. L. (1973) *J. Hered.* 64, 55–61.
46. Ohno, S. (1969) in *Heterospecific Genome Interaction*, ed. Defendi, V. (Wistar Institute Press, Philadelphia), pp. 137–150.
47. Beer, A. E. & Billingham, R. E. (1971) *Advan. Immunol.* 14, 1–84.
48. Clarke, A. G. & Hetherington, C. M. (1972) *J. Reprod. Fert., Suppl.* 15, 99–118.
49. Hancock, J. L., McGovern, P. T. & Stamp, J. T. (1968) *J. Reprod. Fert., Suppl.* 3 29–36.
50. Chang, M. C., Pickworth, S. & McGaughey, R. W. (1969) in *Comparative Mammalian Cytogenetics*, ed. Benirschke, K. (Springer-Verlag, New York), pp. 132–145.
51. Hsu, Y.-C. (1973) *Develop. Biol.* 33 403–411.
52. Maxson, L. R., Sarich, V. M. & Wilson, A. C. (1973) *Genetics* 74 s. 176 abstr.
53. Wilson, A. C., Sarich, V. M. & Maxson, L. R. (1974) *Proc. Nat. Acad. Sci. USA* 71, in press.

7

Copyright © 1974 by the Society for the Study of Evolution

Reprinted from *Evolution* **28**:576–592 (1974)

GENETIC DIFFERENTIATION DURING THE SPECIATION PROCESS IN *DROSOPHILA*[1,2]

Francisco J. Ayala, Martin L. Tracey,[3] Dennis Hedgecock, and Rollin C. Richmond[4]

Evolution consists of changes in the genetic constitution (gene pool) of populations. The process of evolution may be seen in two ways—which have been called *anagenesis* and *cladogenesis* (Rensch, 1960). Changes occurring within a given phylogenetic line as time proceeds, are anagenetic evolution. They result in increased adaptation to the environment, and often reflect changes of the physical or biotic conditions of the environments. Cladogenesis occurs when a phylogenetic lineage splits into two or more independently evolving lineages. The great diversity of the living world is the result of cladogenetic evolution, which results in adaptation to a greater variety of niches, or ways of life. Among cladogenetic processes, the most decisive one is speciation, the process by which one species splits into two or more species. Species are groups of populations reproductively isolated from any other such groups. Species are independent evolutionary units. Adaptive changes occurring in an individual or population may be extended to all members of the species by natural selection; however, they cannot be passed on to different species. One of the most important questions in evolutionary genetics is the amount of genetic differentiation occurring in the speciation process.

Speciation may occur by a variety of processes. In sexually reproducing organisms speciation most generally occurs according to the model of "geographic speciation." Two main stages may be recognized in this process. First, allopatric populations of the same species become genetically differentiated, mostly as a consequence of their adaptation to different environments. This genetic differentiation can only occur if the populations are geographically separated for some time, and there is no or very little migration between them. The second stage takes place when genetically differentiated populations come into geographic contact. If the gene pools of two populations are sufficiently different, progenies from interpopulational crosses are likely to have less fitness than progenies from intrapopulational crosses. Mating preferences are affected by genes. Alleles that decrease the probability of mating with individuals of a different population will, then, be selected against, while alleles increasing the probability of intrapopulational mating will be favored by natural selection. Eventually, the process may result in two reproductively isolated populations, and thus two different species.

The question, "how much genetic differentiation occurs in the process of speciation," must be unfolded into two separate questions concerning the two stages of the process. The first question concerns the genetic differentiation occurring between allopatric populations that are likely to give rise to different species if and when they become, at least partially, sympatric. The second question refers to the amount of genetic differentiation taking place after sympatry, when the populations become reproductively isolated.

---

[1] This is paper number XII in a series: "Enzyme variability in the *Drosophila willistoni* group."

[2] Supported by NSF grant GB32895.

[3] Present address: Dept. of Biology, Brock University, St. Catherines, Ontario, Canada.

[4] Address: Department of Zoology, University of Indiana, Bloomington, Indiana.

FIG. 1. The known geographic distribution of four sibling species of the *Drosophila willistoni* group.

THE PROCESS OF SPECIATION: A PARADIGM

The *willistoni* group of *Drosophila* consists of at least 15 closely related species endemic to the New World tropics. Six species are siblings, morphologically nearly indistinguishable, although the species of individual males can be identified by slight but diagnostically reliable differences in their genitalia. Two sibling species are narrow endemics: *D. insularis* Dobzhansky in some islands in the Lesser Antilles, and *D. pavlovskiana* Kastritsis & Dobzhansky in Guyana. Four other siblings, namely *D. willistoni* Sturtevant, *D. paulistorum* Dobzhansky & Pavan, *D. equinoxialis* Dobzhansky, and *D. tropicalis* Burla & da Cunha, have wide and largely overlapping distributions through Central America, the Caribbean, and much of continental South America (Fig. 1; see also Spassky et al., 1971).

Some sibling species consist of at least two subspecies. Populations of *D. willistoni* west of the Andes near Lima, Peru, belong to *D. w. quechua* Ayala, while east of the

Fig. 2. The known geographic distribution of the semispecies of *Drosophila paulistorum*.

Andes and elsewhere the subspecies is *D. w. willistoni*. Incipient reproductive isolation in the form of partial hybrid sterility exists between these two subspecies. Laboratory crosses between *D. w. willistoni* females and *D. w. quechua* males yield fertile males and females. Crosses between *D. w. quechua* females and *D. w. willistoni* males from continental South America east of the Andes produce fertile females but sterile males. Laboratory tests show no evidence of sexual isolation between the subspecies (Ayala and Tracey, 1973).

Two subspecies are also known in *D. equinoxialis*: *D. e. caribbensis* Ayala in Central America north of Panama, and in the Greater Antilles; and *D. e. equinoxialis*

in eastern Panama and continental South America. Laboratory crosses between the two subspecies yield fertile females but sterile males, independently of the subspecies of the male parent. Like in *D. willistoni*, there is no sexual isolation in the laboratory between the subspecies of *D. equinoxialis* (Ayala et al., 1974a).

Evolutionary divergence beyond the taxonomic category of subspecies, but with incomplete achievement of speciation, exists in a third sibling species, *D. paulistorum*. This "species" consists of six semispecies, or incipient species, named Centroamerican, Transitional, Andean-Brazilian, Orinocan, Interior, and Amazonian (Spassky et al., 1971). Reproductive isolation between semispecies is, in some cases, complete; two and even three semispecies coexist sympatrically in many localities (Fig. 2). Laboratory crosses between the semispecies generally yield fertile females but sterile males. Sexual isolation is essentially complete between some semispecies, particularly when sympatric populations are tested. Gene flow among the semispecies is nevertheless possible, particularly via populations of the Transitional semispecies.

Five increasingly divergent levels of cladogenesis can be recognized in the *D. willistoni* group:

1) *Between geographic populations of the same taxon.*

2) *Between subspecies.*—These are allopatric populations that exhibit incipient reproductive isolation in the form of partial hybrid sterility. If populations of two subspecies were to come into geographic contact, intersubspecific matings would leave fewer fertile descendants than intrasubspecific matings. Therefore, natural selection would favor the development of reproductive isolating mechanisms between the subspecies. Whether two species would ultimately result, or one subspecies be absorbed (by introgression) or eliminated (by competition), we of course do not know. The subspecies are allopatric populations in the first stage of the speciation process.

3) *Between the semispecies of* D. paulistorum.—The process of speciation is being completed between the semispecies. Sexual isolation is nearly complete in many cases. Some semispecies are sympatric in many localities. The semispecies are populations in the second stage of the speciation process.

4) *Between sibling species.*—In spite of their morphological similarity, the sibling species are completely reproductively isolated. Study of genetic differentiation between them will show how much genetic differentiation may occur after speciation without noticeable morphological diversification.

5) *Between morphologically distinguishable species of the same group.*—D. nebu-

losa is a close relative of *D. willistoni* and its siblings, but can be easily distinguished from them by external morphology. Comparison of *D. nebulosa* with the siblings will show how much genetic differentiation occurs at this level of evolutionary divergence.

Thirty years of intensive study have provided a great body of information concerning the evolutionary biology of the *D. willistoni* group. Their geographic distribution and relative abundance is reasonably well known (see Spassky et al., 1971, for a recent summary). Much information is also available concerning the reproductive affinities and incompatibilities within and between species (Dobzhansky and Mayr, 1944; Burla et al., 1949; Dobzhansky et al., 1957; Dobzhansky and Spassky, 1959; Carmody et al., 1962; Ehrman, 1965; Ayala and Tracey, 1973; Ayala et al., 1974a). Studies of salivary gland chromosomes have uncovered a large number of inversion polymorphisms (Dobzhansky, 1950; da Cunha et al., 1953; Kastritsis, 1969). The relationships between the chromosomal polymorphisms and certain ecological parameters have also been the subject of intensive studies (da Cunha et al., 1959, and references therein).

Drosophila willistoni and its relatives are excellent materials to study genetic differentiation in the process of speciation. Techniques of gel electrophoresis and selective staining of enzymes permit one to quantify, at least to a first approximation, the amount of genetic variation within and between populations. We report here our results of a study started in 1965.

METHODS TO MEASURE GENETIC DIFFERENTIATION

The techniques of gel electrophoresis and enzyme assay permit the identification of allelic variation at single gene loci. The most important point is that loci can be selected for study without *a priori* knowledge of whether or not they are variable within or between populations. Therefore, the results from a moderate number of enzyme loci can be extended to the whole genome of the organisms, since the loci studied may be assumed to represent a random sample of the genome with respect to allelic variation. Several potential sources of bias in such extrapolations have been pointed out (Lewontin and Hubby, 1966; Ayala et al., 1970). Particularly important is that not all allelic variation is detectable by electrophoresis; thus, the amount of genetic variation within a taxon or of genetic differentiation between taxa is probably underestimated. Another serious difficulty is that only one kind of gene can be studied, namely structural genes coding for soluble proteins and enzymes.

Our techniques of starch gel electrophoresis have been described elsewhere (Ayala et al., 1972a, 1974a). We have studied a total of 36 loci coding for enzymes. The enzymes studied, and the symbols for the genes which encode them, are as follows: acid phosphatase (*Acph*, 2 loci); adenylate kinase (*Adk*, 2 loci); alcohol dehydrogenase (*Adh*, 1 locus); aldehyde oxidase (*Ao*, 2 loci); aldolase (*Ald*, 2 loci); alkaline phosphatase (*Aph*, 1 locus); esterase (*Est*, 6 loci); fumarase (*Fum*, 1 locus); glucose-6-phosphate dehydrogenase (*G6pdh*, 1 locus); glutamate-oxaloacetate transaminase (*Got*, 1 locus); glyceraldehyde-3-phosphate dehydrogenase (*G3pdh*, 1 locus); α-glycerophosphate dehydrogenase (*αGpdh*, 1 locus); hexokinase (*Hk*, 3 loci); hydroxybuterate dehydrogenase (*Hbdh*, 1 locus); isocitrate dehydrogenase (*Idh*, 1 locus); leucine aminopeptidase (*Lap*, 1 locus); malate dehydrogenase (*Mdh*, 1 locus); malic enzyme (*Me*, 2 loci); octanol dehydrogenase (*Odh*, 2 loci); phosphoglucomutase (*Pgm*, 1 locus); tetrazolium oxidase (*To*, 1 locus); triose phosphate isomerase (*Tpi*, 1 locus); xanthine dehydrogenase (*Xdh*, 1 locus).

Our sampling techniques are generally as follows. Immediately upon arrival of the wild-collected flies to our laboratory, males are used for electrophoresis. The females are placed in individual cultures; one F_1 progeny from each wild female is studied for each enzyme. Thus, we are sampling

two wild genomes for each wild fly collected in nature. In the case of *D. pavlovskiana*, *D. insularis*, and the Centroamerican semispecies of *D. paulistorum*, no new samples were obtained during the period of our electrophoretic studies; the allelic frequencies for these three taxa are based only on the study of several stocks kept in the laboratory for several years. We have assumed that four wild genomes are sampled per stock. For all other taxa we have sampled from several hundred to several thousand wild genomes, on the average, for each of the 36 loci. The average sample size per locus is 4,983 ± 636 for *D. willistoni*, 1,731 ± 229 for *D. tropicalis*, 2,356 ± 238 for *D. equinoxialis*, 1,277 ± 258 for *D. paulistorum*, and 412 ± 43 for *D. nebulosa*. We have studied only one wild population of *D. w. quechua*; in all other taxa (except *D. pavlovskiana* and *D. insularis* and the Centroamerican semispecies) we have studied at least 10, and generally many more, different local populations. To estimate genetic similarity and genetic distance between taxa, we have pooled all samples available for each taxon. Generally, little genetic differentiation exists between local populations. Thus, very nearly the same results are obtained whether the local samples of a given taxon are pooled, or whether comparisons are made between all local populations of the taxa being compared and the results of these comparisons are averaged.

To quantify genetic differentiation between taxa we have used two statistics: *I*, genetic similarity; and *D*, genetic distance (Nei, 1972). Briefly, if *X* and *Y* are two populations, the mean genetic similarity per locus between them is:

$$I = I_{xy}/(I_x \cdot I_y)^{1/2}, \qquad (1)$$

where I_{xy}, I_x and I_y are the arithmetic means, over all loci, of $\Sigma_{x_i y_i}$, $\Sigma_{x_i}^2$ and $\Sigma_{y_i}^2$; with x_i and y_i being the frequencies of the *i*th allele in populations *X* and *Y*, respectively.

The average genetic distance per locus is

$$D = -\log_e I. \qquad (2)$$

103

TABLE 1. *Average genetic similarity, $\bar{I}$, and genetic distance, $\bar{D}$, between local populations of various taxa of the* Drosophila willistoni *group*.

Taxon	$\bar{I}$	$\bar{D}$
D. w. willistoni	0.986 ± 0.005	0.014 ± 0.005
D. tropicalis	0.960 ± 0.005	0.041 ± 0.005
D. e. equinoxialis	0.977 ± 0.003	0.023 ± 0.003
D. e. caribbensis	0.975 ± 0.004	0.026 ± 0.004
D. paulistorum		
Transitional	0.906 ± 0.026	0.101 ± 0.028
Andean-Brazilian	0.969 ± 0.007	0.031 ± 0.006
Interior	0.968 ± 0.007	0.033 ± 0.007
Amazonian	0.960 ± 0.005	0.042 ± 0.005
Average	0.951 ± 0.015	0.052 ± 0.017
Grand average	0.970 ± 0.006	0.031 ± 0.007

If it is assumed that codon substitutions within a locus occur independently from each other, and that the number of allelic substitutions per locus follows a Poisson distribution, D may be interpreted as a measure of the average number of electrophoretically detectable allelic substitutions per locus that have accumulated since the two populations separated from a common ancestral one.

GENETIC DIFFERENTIATION BETWEEN TAXA

1) *Local populations.*—Little genetic differentiation exists between local populations of the same taxon in the *D. willistoni* group. Allelic frequencies in different geographic localities have been previously described for *D. nebulosa* and the four widely distributed sibling species, including several subspecies and semispecies (Ayala et al., 1971, 1972*a*, *b*, 1974*a*, *b*; Richmond, 1972; Ayala and Tracey, 1973, 1974). A summary of average genetic similarity, *I*, and genetic distance, *D*, between local populations of various taxa is given in Table 1. Within each taxon, all possible comparisons between pairs of localities have been made; the values given are the averages of these pairwise comparisons. The number of different local populations compared ranges from 23 in *D. tropicalis* to 42 in *D. willistoni*. The distribution of loci relative to

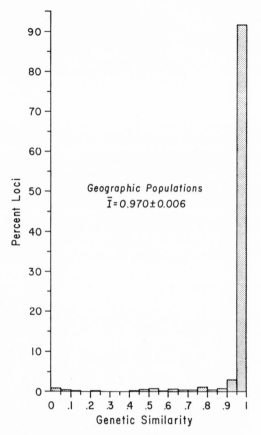

FIG. 3. Frequency distribution of loci relative to genetic similarity when local populations of the same species are compared. $\bar{I}$ is the mean genetic similarity with its standard error.

genetic similarity is shown in Figure 3. At most loci (92%), geographic populations have essentially identical allelic frequencies ($I = 0.95–1.00$); at a few loci, however, some local populations have substantially different, and even totally different, genetic constitutions.

Geographic populations of the Transitional semispecies of *D. paulistorum* are genetically more differentiated ($D = 0.101 \pm 0.028$) than those of any other semispecies ($\bar{D} = 0.035 \pm 0.003$ for the other three semispecies in Table 1). This is not surprising. Studies of chromosomal polymorphisms, sexual isolation and hybrid sterility, have shown that the Transitional semispecies consists of a very heterogeneous

TABLE 2. *Genetic similarity,* I, *and genetic distance,* D, *between subspecies of the* Drosophila willistoni *group.*

Subspecies	I	D
D. w. willistoni- D. w. quechua	0.808	0.214
D. e. equinoxialis- D. e. caribbensis[1]	0.782	0.246
Average	0.795 ± 0.013	0.230 ± 0.016

[1] The average I and $\bar{D}$ of all pairwise comparisons between local populations of these two subspecies are 0.755 ± 0.006 and 0.255 ± 0.008, respectively.

group of populations (Spassky et al., 1971, and references therein).

Drosophila willistoni has the most extensive geographic distribution among the sibling species, yet it is geographically little differentiated ($D = 0.014 \pm 0.005$). Genetic differentiation among local populations is greatest in *D. tropicalis* ($D = 0.041 \pm 0.005$), while *D. equinoxialis* is intermediate ($D = 0.023 \pm 0.003$, and 0.026 ± 0.004 for the *equinoxialis* and *caribbensis* subspecies, respectively). These results are again in agreement with previous observations based on reproductive relationships and other information (Petit and Ehrman, 1969; Ayala et al., 1974b).

2) *Subspecies.*—We have studied genetic variation in two pairs of subspecies, *D. w. willistoni-D. w. quechua* and *D. e. equinoxialis-D. e. caribbensis.* These subspecies represent groups of allopatric populations in the first stage of geographic speciation. Crosses between the subspecies always yield fertile females but sterile males in *D. equinoxialis* (Ayala et al., 1974a). In *D. willistoni* both sexes are fertile in F_1 hybrid progenies when the male parent is *quechua*, but hybrid males are in most cases sterile when the male parent is *willistoni* (Ayala and Tracey, 1973). There is, however, no sexual isolation between the subspecies either in *D. willistoni* or *D. equinoxialis.* Thus, if populations of two different subspecies would come into geographic contact, matings would at first occur at random, but natural selection would favor the development of sexual isolation between them.

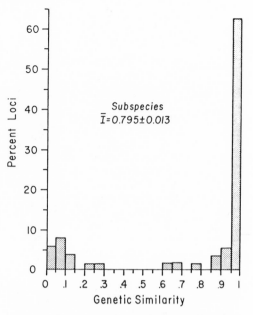

FIG. 4. Frequency distribution of loci relative to genetic similarity for comparisons between subspecies. $\bar{I}$ is the mean genetic similarity with its standard error.

Table 2 shows the amount of genetic differentiation between the subspecies. On the average, 23 allelic substitutions for every 100 loci have occurred in a pair of subspecies since their separation from a common ancestor. The genetic distance between the two subspecies of *D. willistoni* is 0.214, that is, about 15 times greater than the genetic distance between local populations of the same subspecies (0.014). The genetic distance between the *D. equinoxialis* subspecies is 0.246, ten times greater than the average distance between geographic populations of the same subspecies (0.025). A great deal of genetic differentiation has occurred in the process of evolutionary divergence between the subspecies.

There is greater genetic differentiation between the subspecies of *D. equinoxialis* than between the subspecies of *D. willistoni.* This agrees well with their reproductive differentiation, since intersubspecific hybrid males are always sterile in *D. equinoxialis*, but in *D. willistoni* they are sterile

TABLE 3. *Genetic similarity (above diagonal), and genetic distance (below diagonal) between pairs of semispecies of* Drosophila paulistorum.

	Centro-american	Transitional	Andean-Brazilian	Amazonian	Orinocan	Interior
Centroamerican	—	0.957	0.932	0.859	0.811	0.880
Transitional	0.043	—	0.935	0.838	0.820	0.862
Andean-Brazilian	0.071	0.067	—	0.844	0.848	0.881
Amazonian	0.152	0.176	0.170	—	0.827	0.875
Orinocan	0.209	0.198	0.165	0.189	—	0.929
Interior	0.127	0.149	0.127	0.134	0.074	—

only when the male parent belongs to the *willistoni* subspecies.

The distribution of genetic distances among loci is shown in Figure 4. Nearly complete genetic differentiation ($I < 0.15$) occurs at 18% of the loci. The allelic frequencies are essentially identical ($I \geqslant 0.95$) at 63% of the loci (versus 92% of the loci when populations of the same subspecies are compared).

3) *Semispecies.*—The semispecies of *D. paulistorum* are groups of populations in the second stage of speciation; reproductive isolation between them is being completed by natural selection. Laboratory crosses between the semispecies yield fertile females but sterile males, with the exception of some crosses of Transitional × Centroamerican and Orinocan × Interior, which produce fertile progenies of both sexes. Sexual isolation between the semispecies ranges from very little to nearly complete. The average "index of sexual isolation" in 90 combinations of strains of different subspecies is 0.728 ± 0.053 (Ayala, 1974, calculated from Carmody et al., 1962; the "index" is 0 when matings occur at random, and 1 when sexual isolation is complete). Generally, the Transitional strains exhibit less sexual isolation from the other semispecies (average index = 0.632 ± 0.076) than the latter from each other (average index = 0.871 ± 0.036). Most interestingly, the degree of sexual isolation between strains of the same pair of semispecies is higher between sympatric than between allopatric strains (Ehrman, 1965). This is precisely what is expected if natural selec-

tion is strengthening sexual isolation between sympatric semispecies. Two or three semispecies are sympatric in many localities (Fig. 2).

A matrix of genetic similarities (above the diagonal) and genetic distances (below the diagonal) between the semispecies is given in Table 3. The most similar semispecies are Centroamerican and Transitional ($D = 0.043$); the Orinocan and Interior semispecies are also genetically quite similar to each other ($D = 0.074$). These results agree very well with the analyses of Richmond (1973) and with previous information based on chromosomal polymorphisms (Kastritsis, 1969), biometrical differentiation (Pasteur, 1970), and reproductive isolation (Dobzhansky et al., 1969; Ayala et al., 1974*b*). The distribution of loci relative to genetic distance is given in Figure 5. This distribution is similar to that of the subspecies (Fig. 4), except that there is a larger proportion of loci with intermediate degrees of differentiation between the semispecies.

The values of I and D between the semispecies reported here are less reliable than those obtained for other levels of evolutionary divergence. Our studies of the Centroamerican semispecies were made exclusively with stocks kept in the laboratory for several years. Fresh samples of the other semispecies were obtained at various stages of our survey, but only 15 loci were studied in most of these samples while about 20 other loci were studied later using a few laboratory stocks. Recently, fresh samples of the semispecies Amazonian, Orinocan,

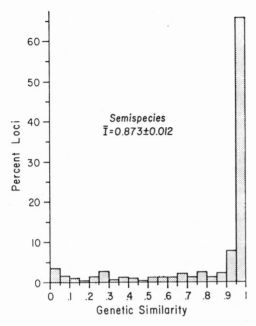

FIG. 5. Frequency distribution of loci relative to genetic similarity for comparisons between the semispecies of *Drosophila paulistorum*. *Ī* is the mean genetic similarity with its standard error.

and Interior were collected in Venezuela; 32 enzyme loci were studied in these samples. The average genetic differentiation between populations of different semispecies in the Venezuelan samples is as follows: $\bar{I} = 0.798 \pm 0.026$, $\bar{D} = 0.226 \pm 0.033$ (Ayala et al., 1974b). We shall use these values as representative of the average genetic differentiation between the semispecies.

The average genetic distance between subspecies is 0.230 ± 0.016 (Table 2); between semispecies is 0.226 ± 0.033. The process of speciation is being completed between the semispecies. It appears that the development of sexual isolation does not require the change of a large fraction of the genome of the populations.

4) *Sibling species.*—Different species have independently evolving gene pools. After speciation is completed, species are likely to continue diverging genetically. The sibling species of the *D. willistoni* group are genetically very different as shown in Table 4. Their morphological similarity is not due to little genetic differentiation. The average genetic similarity between two sibling species is 0.475 ± 0.037; the average genetic distance is 0.750 ± 0.078.

We have obtained very extensive electrophoretic data for each of the four widely distributed sibling species. However, only a few laboratory stocks of *D. pavlovskiana* and *D. insularis* were available for study. The electrophoretic information concerning the latter two species is, therefore, less reliable than the rest. If comparisons involving *D. pavlovskiana* and *D. insularis* are not included, the mean values are $\bar{I} = 0.563 \pm 0.023$, $\bar{D} = 0.581 \pm 0.039$. On the average, 58.1 allelic substitutions for every 100 loci have occurred in each pair of these sibling species since their divergence from a common ancestor.

The distribution of loci relative to genetic similarity between sibling species is depicted in Figure 6. At about 40% of the

TABLE 4. *Genetic similarity (above diagonal), and genetic distance (below diagonal) between sibling species of the* Drosophila willistoni *group. When subspecies or semispecies occur, the average values between each one of them and the other species are given.*

	D. willistoni	D. tropicalis	D. equinoxialis	D. paulistorum	D. pavlovskiana	D. insularis
D. willistoni	—	0.663	0.522	0.594	0.596	0.344
D. tropicalis	0.413	—	0.514	0.545	0.496	0.414
D. equinoxialis	0.656	0.665	—	0.540	0.537	0.336
D. paulistorum	0.524	0.609	0.621	—	0.795	0.299
D. pavlovskiana	0.518	0.701	0.633	0.232	—	0.280
D. insularis	1.070	0.883	1.091	1.208	1.273	—

Average genetic similarity = 0.475 ± 0.037; average genetic distance = 0.740 ± 0.078.

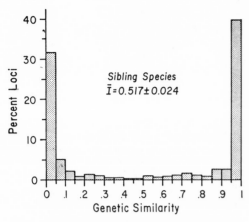

FIG. 6. Frequency distribution of loci relative to genetic similarity between sibling species. $\bar{I}$ is the mean genetic similarity with its standard error.

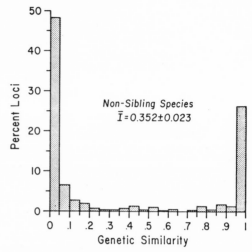

FIG. 7. Frequency distribution of loci relative to genetic similarity between morphologically distinguishable species. $\bar{I}$ is the mean genetic similarity with its standard error.

loci, any two species have essentially identical distributions of allelic frequencies; at about 32% of the loci the sibling species have essentially non-overlapping genetic configurations.

5) *Morphologically different species.*— *D. nebulosa* is morphologically easily distinguishable from the sibling species of the *willistoni* group, although closely related to them. Table 5 gives the I and D values for comparisons between each of the sibling species and *D. nebulosa*. The average values are $\bar{I} = 0.352 \pm 0.023$, $\bar{D} = 1.056 \pm 0.068$. On the average, about one allelic substitution per locus has taken place between *D. nebulosa* and each of the siblings, since they diverged from a common ancestral popula-

tion. As expected, *D. nebulosa* is genetically more different from the siblings than these are from each other.

The distribution of loci with respect to genetic similarity for comparisons of the sibling species with *D. nebulosa* is shown in Figure 7. As in the comparisons between siblings the distribution is strongly bimodal, but the mode near $I = 0$ is now greater (48% of the loci), and the mode near $I = 1$ (26% of the loci) is smaller than for the siblings.

PHYLOGENY OF THE
D. WILLISTONI GROUP

We have studied allelic variation at 36 loci in 14 taxa of the *D. willistoni* group. The information in the matrix of genetic distances between the 14 taxa can be used to build a dendrogram of genetic relationships. We have used Wagner's method (Farris, 1972) to derive the most likely dendrogram. The method maximizes the information contained in the matrix of genetic distances. Briefly, we have started with the two genetically most similar taxa (the Transitional and Centroamerican semispecies of *D. paulistorum*) and added one

TABLE 5. *Genetic similarity, I, and genetic distance, D, between morphologically different species of the* Drosophila willistoni *group. When subspecies or semispecies occur, the average value between each one of them and* D. nebulosa *is given.*

Species compared to D. nebulosa	I	D
D. willistoni	0.267	1.325
D. tropicalis	0.391	0.939
D. equinoxialis	0.426	0.854
D. paulistorum	0.367	1.006
D. pavlovskiana	0.344	1.066
D. insularis	0.319	1.144
Average	0.352 ± 0.023	1.056 ± 0.068

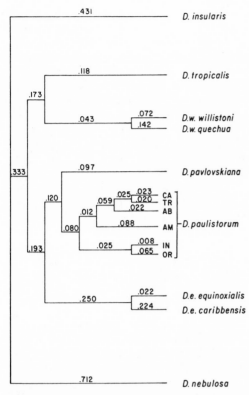

FIG. 8. Dendrogram showing the probable phylogenetic relationships based on genetic differentiation at 36 gene loci in 14 taxa of the *Drosophila willistoni* group. The vertical distances between neighboring taxa are roughly proportional to their genetic distances. The numbers are the genetic distances between consecutive nodes, or between a node and a taxon.

TABLE 6. *Average genetic similarity, $\bar{I}$, and genetic distance, $\bar{D}$, between taxa of various levels of evolutionary divergence in the* Drosophila willistoni *group.*

Taxonomic level	$\bar{I}$	$\bar{D}$
Local populations	0.970 ± 0.006	0.031 ± 0.007
Subspecies	0.795 ± 0.013	0.230 ± 0.016
Semispecies	0.798 ± 0.026	0.226 ± 0.033
Sibling species	0.563 ± 0.023	0.581 ± 0.039
Non-sibling species	0.352 ± 0.023	1.056 ± 0.068

of the *D. willistoni* group as inferred from studies of reproductive isolation, chromosomal polymorphisms, morphological biometry, sexual behavior, and geographic distribution. The agreement between our results and their inferences is essentially complete. Figure 3 of Spassky et al. (1971) shows hierarchical groupings identical with those of our Figure 8. Among the semispecies of *D. paulistorum*, Centroamerican, Transitional and Andean-Brazilian are most closely related, with Transitional being intermediate; Interior and Orinocan are also closely related to each other. *D. pavlovskiana* is most closely related to *D. paulistorum*. (When *D. pavlovskiana* was first collected it was considered to be a new semispecies: see Kastritsis and Dobzhansky, 1966.) *D. equinoxialis* is more closely related to *D. paulistorum* (and *D. pavlovskiana*) than to any other sibling species. *D. insularis* is genetically most similar to *D. tropicalis*; this supports the speculation of Spassky et al. (1971) that *D. insularis* may be an insular offshoot of *D. tropicalis*.

DISCUSSION

We have studied genetic differentiation at 36 loci coding for enzymes in natural populations of 14 taxa of the *Drosophila willistoni* group. Five levels of evolutionary divergence can be recognized: geographic populations, subspecies, semispecies, sibling species, and morphologically different species. Table 6 summarizes our results. Very little genetic differentiation exists between geographic populations. On the average, genetic distance between local populations

taxon at a time, using as criterion of best fit the satisfaction of the triangle inequality. The dendrogram obtained is depicted in Figure 8. The genetic distances between branching points or between a taxon and a branching point are written in the Figure. The vertical distances between neighboring taxa has been adjusted to be roughly proportional to their genetic distance. If it is assumed that genetic differentiation over time occurs at a rate which is constant *on the average*, the dendrogram gives a representation of the phylogenetic relationships between the taxa.

Spassky et al. (1971) discussed the evolutionary relationships between taxa is $\bar{D} = 0.031 \pm 0.007$. *D. w. willistoni* is the taxon least ($\bar{D} = 0.014 \pm 0.005$) and *D. tropicalis* is the taxon most differentiated geographically ($\bar{D} = 0.041 \pm 0.005$).

Incipient reproductive isolation in the form of partial hybrid sterility exists between the subspecies of *D. willistoni* and *D. equinoxialis*. The subspecies are groups of populations in the first stage of species formation, according to the model of geographic speciation. If populations of two subspecies were to come into geographic contact, individuals mating with members of their own subspecies would have greater fitness than individuals mating with members of the other subspecies. If there are genes affecting the probability of intra-subspecific matings, allelic variants increasing such probability would be selected for. Therefore, natural selection would favor the development of reproductive isolation between the subspecies. We cannot, of course, be sure whether two species would ultimately develop, or whether a hybrid population would result. Yet, the subspecies represent the type of differentiated allopatric populations that might give rise to different species upon sympatry, according to the model of geographic speciation. The subspecies show a substantial degree of genetic divergence. On the average, 23 electrophoretically detectable allelic substitutions for every 100 loci have occurred in a pair of subspecies since their divergence from a common ancestral population. This is nearly ten times as much genetic differentiation as is found between geographic populations of the same subspecies. Our results indicate that much genetic differentiation takes place during the first stage of the speciation process.

On the other hand, little genetic differentiation seems to take place in the second stage of speciation. Our results suggest that the development of complete reproductive isolation may not require allelic changes in a large fraction of the genome. The average genetic distance between the semispecies of *D. paulistorum* is not significantly different from the average genetic distance between subspecies. Sexual isolation is the fundamental mechanism maintaining reproductive isolation between the *Drosophila* species. Some semispecies have achieved nearly complete sexual isolation and can coexist sympatrically. Perhaps sexual isolation may develop by change of only a few genes affecting the courtship and mating behaviors of the populations. This hypothesis is strengthened by the observation that the correlation between the indices of genetic similarity given in Table 3 and the isolation coefficients of Carmody et al. (1962) is not significant ($r = -0.486$, $p > 0.10$; see also Richmond, 1973).

Dobzhansky (1956) has speculated that the evolution of external morphology has reached in the genus *Drosophila* a high degree of perfection and that the adaptive evolution proceeds largely through physiological channels. Our results corroborate this hypothesis. In spite of complete reproductive isolation, and thus separate evolutions, the sibling species of the *D. willistoni* group have remained morphologically very similar. Yet, genetically the sibling species are very different. On the average, 58 electrophoretically detectable allelic substitutions for every 100 loci have accumulated in a pair of sibling species since the start of their evolutionary divergence. This is, indeed, a great deal of genetic change.

Drosophila nebulosa is morphologically easily distinguishable from the sibling species, and differs from them in the inversion polymorphisms of the chromosomes, in sexual behavior, and in ecology. These differentiations are accompanied by substantial differentiation in the genes coding for soluble proteins. About one electrophoretically detectable allelic substitution per locus has occurred between *D. nebulosa* and each sibling species during their separate evolutions. This is approximately twice as much genetic change as has occurred between any two sibling species. Once the process of speciation is completed, genetic divergence is likely to increase with time.

TABLE 7. *Mean (and range) genetic similarity between taxa of various levels of evolutionary divergence.*

Organisms	Number of species	Number of loci	Taxonomic level			Index	Source
			Subspecies	Semispecies	Species		
Mammals:							
Dipodomys	11	18	—	—	.61(.31–.89)	Rogers[1]	Johnson and Selander (1971)
Sigmodon	2	23	—	—	.76(.76–.77)	Rogers	Johnson et al. (1972)
Mus	1	41	.84(.82–88)	—	—	Nei[2]	Calculated from Selander et al. (1969)
Peromyscus	16	21	—	—	.66(.34–.99)	Rogers	Avise et al. (1974)
Thomomys	1	27	.84(.83–86)	—	—	Rogers	Patton et al. (1972)
Reptiles and amphibians:							
Anolis	4	23	—	—	.21(.16–.29)	Rogers	Webster et al. (1972)
Sceloporus	1	20	.79(.73–84)	—	—	Rogers	Hall and Selander (1973)
Taricha	3	18	.87(.77–90)	—	.63(.50–.77)	Nei	Hedgecock and Ayala (1974)
Fish:							
Lepomis	10	14	—	—	.54(.37–.79)	Rogers	Avise and Smith (1974a,b)
Drosophila groups:							
virilis	9	37	.65	—	.44(.28–.79)	—[3]	Hubby and Throckmorton (1965)
obscura	11	22	—	—	.29(.15–.74)	—[3]	Lakovaara et al. (1972)
bipectinata	4	24	.91(.90–92)	—	.79(.68–.96)	Nei	Calculated from Yang et al. (1972)
mesophragmatica	6	24	—	—	.50(.30–.77)	Rogers	Nair et al. (1971)
several groups	27	13–23	—	—	.35(.08–.87)	—[3]	Hubby and Throckmorton (1968)
willistoni	7	36	.80(.78–81)	.80(.77–.82)	.45(.27–.79)	Nei	This report

[1] Rogers (1972).
[2] Nei (1972).
[3] Calculated as the proportion of loci in which the most common allele is the same in the two taxa being compared.

Table 7 gives a summary of a survey of electrophoretic studies of genetic differentiation between taxa below the genus category. Different indices of genetic similarity are used by different authors, and thus the results are not fully comparable. In general, for a given set of data, Rogers' (1972) coefficient of genetic similarity gives a lower numerical value than Nei's (1972) coefficient. The trend in Table 7 is clear; the overall amount of genetic differentiation at different taxonomic levels is approximately of the same magnitude in the *D. willistoni* group as in other organisms studied. In every case, a substantial amount of genetic differentiation exists between subspecies. Species have different configurations of allelic frequencies at between one and two thirds of their loci. The study of genetic divergence in the *D. willistoni* group as well as all the studies reported in Table 7 are based on allelic differences detectable by electrophoresis. Only a fraction of all allelic differences are detectable by electrophoresis (Lewontin and Hubby, 1966; Ayala et al., 1970). It is likely that the overall amount of genetic differentiation between taxa is greater, perhaps much greater, than the values given in the Table indicate.

A suggestive result appears in the dendrogram shown in Figure 8. There are two pairs of subspecies. In each pair, one of the subspecies (*D. w. willistoni* and *D. e. equinoxialis*) has a wider geographic distribution than the other (*D. w. quechua* and *D. e. caribbensis*, respectively). It is interesting that in both cases, the less extensively distributed subspecies is genetically more different from other sibling species than the most widespread subspecies. In the fork leading to the two subspecies of *D. willistoni*, the amount of genetic change in the *quechua* branch is about twice that in the *willistoni* branch (0.142 versus 0.072). In the case of *D. equinoxialis*, nearly ten times as much genetic differentiation seems to have occurred in the branch leading to *caribbensis* as in the branch leading to *equinoxialis* (0.224 versus 0.022). It is

tempting to speculate that the narrowly distributed subspecies are offshoots of the widely distributed ones. These offshoots may have resulted from successful colonizations of new territories. Greater amounts of genetic change are likely to occur in populations becoming adapted to new habitats than in those remaining in the old territories. Alternatively, the greater genetic differentiation of the more recent subspecies may be due to the "founder effect" (Mayr, 1963), if they were established with only a few colonists, followed perhaps by "population flush" according to Carson's (1968, 1971) model. In any case, the evidence indicates that the rate of genetic change over time is not necessarily the same in different phyletic lines. The apparent constancy of evolutionary rates over long periods of evolution observed by certain authors (King and Jukes, 1969; Kimura and Ohta, 1972) may simply be due to the law of large numbers; that is, the result of averaging over long periods of time, variable rates of genetic change. However, when no other information is available and long periods of time are involved, it is reasonable to assume that *average* rates of genetic change are approximately constant. The degree of genetic differentiation may, then, be assumed to be inversely related to the degree of phylogenetic proximity.

SUMMARY

We have studied allelic variation at 36 gene loci coding for enzymes in natural populations of 14 taxa of the *Drosophila willistoni* group. Five different levels of evolutionary divergence can be recognized in these taxa. The average amounts of genetic differentiation, D, between populations are for each level as follows: geographic populations, 0.031 ± 0.007; subspecies, 0.230 ± 0.016; semispecies, 0.226 ± 0.033; sibling species, 0.581 ± 0.039; morphologically different species, 1.056 ± 0.068. D may be interpreted as the number of electrophoretically detectable allelic substitutions per locus that have accumulated during the evolution of two taxa since they separated from a common ancestor.

The model of geographic speciation recognizes two stages in the formation of species. In the first stage, allopatric populations become genetically sufficiently different for natural selection to favor the development of reproductive isolation between the populations if they were to come into geographic contact. The second stage occurs after sympatry when reproductive isolation is being completed. Two pairs of subspecies in the *D. willistoni* group represent populations in the first stage of speciation. On the average about 0.23 allelic substitutions per locus have accumulated in the separate evolutions of the subspecies. The second stage of the speciation process can be recognized in the semispecies of *D. paulistorum*. Genetic differentiation is not significantly greater, on the average, between semispecies than between subspecies. Thus, our results indicate that a substantial degree of genetic differentiation occurs during the first stage of speciation, but little change is required during the second stage when reproductive isolation is being completed.

Species are independent evolutionary units, and thus they continue to diverge genetically through time. In spite of their morphological similarity, any two sibling species have accumulated, on the average, about 0.58 allelic substitutions per locus during their separate evolutions; and about twice as many allelic substitutions have accumulated in the evolution of morphologically distinguishable species.

ACKNOWLEDGMENT AND DEDICATION

This study was started under the inspiration of Professor Theodosius Dobzhansky. During the long years of accumulation and analysis of data, we obtained much encouragement, information and advice from his seemingly unlimited wisdom. We express our thanks and dedicate this paper to Professor Dobzhansky on the occasion of his approaching 75th birthday.

LITERATURE CITED

AVISE, J. C., AND M. H. SMITH. 1974a. Biochemical genetics of sunfish. I. Geographic variation and subspecific intergradation in the bluegill, *Lepomis macrochirus.* Evolution 28:42–56.

——. 1974b. Biochemical genetics of sunfish. II. Genic similarity between hybridizing species. Amer. Natur., 108:458–472.

AVISE, J. C., M. H. SMITH, AND R. K. SELANDER. 1974. Biochemical polymorphism and systematics in the genus *Peromyscus.* VI. Systematic relationships in the *boylii* species group. J. Mammalogy 55:751–763.

AYALA, F. J., C. A. MOURÃO, S. PÉREZ-SALAS, R. RICHMOND, AND T. DOBZHANSKY. 1970. Enzyme variability in the *Drosophila willistoni* group. I. Genetic differentiation among sibling species. Proc. Nat. Acad. Sci. 67:225–232.

AYALA, F. J., J. R. POWELL, AND T. DOBZHANSKY. 1971. Polymorphisms in continental and island populations of *Drosophila willistoni.* Proc. Nat. Acad. Sci. 68:2480–2483.

AYALA, F. J., J. R. POWELL, AND M. L. TRACEY. 1972b. Enzyme variability in the *Drosophila willistoni* group. V. Genic variation in natural populations of *Drosophila equinoxialis.* Genet. Res. 20:19–42.

AYALA, F. J., J. R. POWELL, M. L. TRACEY, C. A. MOURÃO, AND S. PÉREZ-SALAS. 1972a. Enzyme variability in the *Drosophila willistoni* group. IV. Genic variation in natural populations of *Drosophila willistoni.* Genetics 70:113–139.

AYALA, F. J., AND M. L. TRACEY. 1973. Enzyme variability in the *Drosophila willistoni* group. VIII. Genetic differentiation and reproductive isolation between two subspecies. J. Heredity 64:120–124.

——. 1974. Genic differentiation within and between species of the *Drosophila willistoni* group. Proc. Nat. Acad. Sci. 71 (*in press*).

AYALA, F. J., M. L. TRACEY, L. G. BARR, AND J. G. EHRENFELD. 1974a. Genetic and reproductive differentiation of the subspecies, *Drosophila equinoxialis caribbensis.* Evolution 28:24–41.

AYALA, F. J., M. L. TRACEY, L. G. BARR, J. F. McDONALD, AND S. PÉREZ-SALAS. 1974b. Genetic variation in natural populations of five *Drosophila* species and the hypothesis of the selective neutrality of protein polymorphisms. Genetics (*in press*).

BURLA, H., A. B. DA CUNHA, A. R. CORDEIRO, T. DOBZHANSKY, C. MALOGOLOWKIN, AND C. PAVAN. 1949. The *willistoni* group of sibling species of *Drosophila.* Evolution 3:300–314.

CARMODY, G., A. DIAZ COLLAZO, T. DOBZHANSKY, L. EHRMAN, I. S. JAFFREY, S. KIMBALL, S. OBREBSKI, S. SILAGI, T. TIDWELL, AND R. ULRICH. 1962. Mating preferences and sexual isolation within and between the incipient species of *Drosophila paulistorum*. Amer. Midl. Natur. 68:67–82.

CARSON, H. L. 1968. The population flush and its genetic consequences, p. 123–137. *In* R. C. Lewontin (ed.), Population biology and evolution. Syracuse Univ. Press.

———. 1971. Speciation and the founder principle. Stadler Symp. 3:51–70.

DA CUNHA, A. B., D. BRNCIC, AND F. M. SALZANO. 1953. A comparative study of chromosomal polymorphism in certain South American species of *Drosophila*. Heredity 7:193–202.

DA CUNHA, A. B., T. DOBZHANSKY, O. PAVLOVSKY, AND B. SPASSKY. 1959. Genetics of natural populations. XXVIII. Supplementary data on the chromosomal polymorphism in *Drosophila willistoni* in relation to its environment. Evolution 13:389–404.

DOBZHANSKY, T. 1950. The chromosomes of *Drosophila willistoni*. J. Heredity 41:156–158.

———. 1956. What is an adaptive trait? Amer. Natur. 90:337–347.

DOBZHANSKY, T., L. EHRMAN, AND O. PAVLOVSKY. 1957. *Drosophila insularis*, a new sibling species of the *willistoni* group. Univ. Texas Publ. 5721:39–47.

———. 1969. Transitional populations of *Drosophila paulistorum*. Evolution 23:482–492.

DOBZHANSKY, T., AND E. MAYR. 1944. Experiments on sexual isolation in *Drosophila*. I. Geographic strains of *Drosophila willistoni*. Proc. Nat. Acad. Sci. 30:238–244.

DOBZHANSKY, T., AND B. SPASSKY. 1959. *Drosophila paulistorum*, a cluster of species in *statu nascendi*. Proc. Nat. Acad. Sci. 45:419–428.

EHRMAN, L. 1965. Direct observation of sexual isolation between allopatric and between sympatric strains of different *Drosophila paulistorum* races. Evolution 19:459–464.

FARRIS, J. S. 1972. Estimating phylogenetic trees from distance matrices. Amer. Natur. 106:645–668.

HALL, W. P., AND R. K. SELANDER. 1973. Hybridization of karyotypically differentiated populations of the *Sceloporus grammicus* complex (Iguanidae). Evolution 27:226–242.

HEDGECOCK, D., AND F. J. AYALA. 1974. Evolutionary divergence in the genus *Taricha* (Salamandridae). Copeia (*in press*).

HUBBY, J. L., AND L. THROCKMORTON. 1965. Protein differences in *Drosophila*. II. Comparative species genetics and evolutionary problems. Genetics 52:203–215.

———. 1968. Protein differences in *Drosophila*. IV. A study of sibling species. Amer. Natur. 102:193–205.

JOHNSON, W. E., AND R. K. SELANDER. 1971. Protein variation and systematics in kangaroo rats (genus *Dipodomys*). Syst. Zool. 20:377–405.

JOHNSON, W. E., R. K. SELANDER, M. H. SMITH, AND Y. J. KIM. 1972. Biochemical genetics of sibling species of the cotton rat (*Sigmodon*). Univ. Texas Publ. 7213:297–305.

KASTRITSIS, C. D. 1969. A cytological study on some recently collected strains of *Drosophila paulistorum*. Evolution 23:663–675.

KASTRITSIS, C., AND T. DOBZHANSKY. 1966. *Drosophila pavlovskiana*, a race or a species? Amer. Midl. Natur. 78:244–248.

KIMURA, M., AND T. OHTA. 1972. Population genetics, molecular biometry, and evolution. Proc. Sixth Berkeley Symp. Math. Stat. Prob. V:43–68.

KING, J. L., AND T. H. JUKES. 1969. Non-Darwinian evolution: random fixation of selectively neutral mutations. Science 164:788–798.

LAKOVAARA, S., A. SAURA, AND C. T. FALK. 1972. Genetic distance and evolutionary relationships in the *Drosophila obscura* group. Evolution 26:177–184.

LEWONTIN, R. C., AND J. L. HUBBY. 1966. A molecular approach to the study of genic heterozygosity in natural populations. II. Amounts of variation and degree of heterozygosity in natural populations of *Drosophila pseudoobscura*. Genetics 54:595–609.

MAYR, E. 1963. *Animal Species and Evolution*. Belknap Press, Cambridge.

NAIR, P. S., D. BRNCIC, AND K. KOJIMA. 1971. Isozyme variations and evolutionary relationships in the *mesophragmatica* species group of *Drosophila*. Univ. Texas Publ. 7103:17–28.

NEI, M. 1972. Genetic distance between populations. Amer. Natur. 106:283–292.

PASTEUR, G. 1970. A biometrical study on the semispecies of the *Drosophila paulistorum* complex. Evolution 24:156–168.

PATTON, J. L., R. K. SELANDER, AND M. H. SMITH. 1972. Genic variation in hybridizing populations of gophers (genus *Thomomys*). Syst. Zool. 21:263–270.

PETIT, C., AND L. EHRMAN. 1969. Sexual selection in *Drosophila*. Evol. Biol. 3:177–223.

RENSCH, B. 1940. Evolution above the species level. Columbia Univ. Press, New York.

RICHMOND, R. C. 1972. Enzyme variability in the *Drosophila willistoni* group. III. Amounts of variability in the superspecies, *D. paulistorum*. Genetics 70:87–112.

———. 1973. Genetic similarities and evolutionary relationships among the semispecies of *Drosophila paulistorum*. Evolution 26:536–544.

ROGERS, J. S. 1972. Measures of genetic similarity and genetic distance. Univ. Texas Publ. 7213:145–153.

SELANDER, R. K., W. S. HUNT, AND S. Y. YANG. 1969. Protein polymorphisms and genic heterozygosity in two European subspecies of the house mouse. Evolution 23:379–390.

SPASSKY, B., R. C. RICHMOND, S. PÉREZ-SALAS, O. PAVLOVSKY, C. A. MOURÃO, A. S. HUNTER, H. HOENIGSBERG, T. DOBZHANSKY, AND F. J. AYALA. 1971. Geography of the sibling species related to *Drosophila willistoni*, and of the semispecies of the *Drosophila paulistorum* complex. Evolution 25:129–143.

WEBSTER, T. P., R. K. SELANDER, AND S. Y. YANG. 1972. Genetic variability and similarity in the *Anolis* lizards of Bimini. Evolution 26:523–535.

YANG, S. Y., L. L. WHEELER, AND I. R. BOCK. 1972. Isozyme variations and phylogenetic relationships in the *Drosophila bipectinata* species complex. Univ. Texas Publ. 7213:213–227.

Part II

GENETIC BASIS
OF ISOLATION

Editor's Comments
on Papers 8 Through 11

An understanding of the genetic basis of isolation requires considerably more than a mere enumeration of the number and proportions of genes that are different in, for example, populations, races, species, and genera. We need to know the mechanisms of action of these genes. One of the clearest leads to understanding the nature of these mechanisms in the early genetic literature is one of Haldane's first contributions to genetics (Paper 8). He noted that "when in the F_1 offspring of two different animal races one sex is absent, rare, or sterile, that sex is the heterozygous sex." Dobzhansky (Paper 9) and Muller (1940) suggested that there was a balance between the genes in the X chromosome and those in the autosomes. Since this balance is different for each species, the hybrids would have a more or less shifted balance resulting in various amounts of inviability, sterility, etc.

Dobzhansky (Paper 9) reviewed the various mechanisms which provided for the isolation between the closely related species of the *Drosophila pseudoobscura* group. He identified several categories of "isolating mechanisms" and noted that each species pair used different sets of the mechanisms to assure the species integrity. Many authors have added to the categories and a number have provided assorted classifications. The most useful contribution appears to be Mecham's (1961) identification of the importance of the difference between those mechanisms which prevent mating (premating) and those which prevent gene flow even when mating has occurred (postmating).

Patterson and Dobzhansky (Paper 10) studied the amount of reproductive isolation between two subspecies of *Drosophila pallidipennis*, one from Brazil, the other from Mexico. There was no significant reduction in the fertility, but backcrosses to the female parent type were sterile. The fecundity of hybrid crosses was less than that of the backcrosses and was much less than the controls. There also appeared to be some reduction in mating success of the heterogametic crosses. The forms differ by the presence of a single inversion on one of the chromosomes; additional inversions and identifiable genic differences were not discernable. The study showed that reproductive isolating mechanisms could develop in geographically separate populations of the same species.

In *Drosophila*, reproductively isolated species usually differ by significant chromosomal rearrangements, as demonstrated by Dobzhansky (1944) in the *Drosophila pseudoobscura* complex. Two studies, which space forced us to omit, provided considerable understanding of the relation between isolation and chromosomes.

Sturtevant and Novitski (1941) examined known mutants and linkage maps and the parts or "elements" of the salivary gland chromosomes to determine the homologies within and between a number of species groups. Except for closely related species they found little correspondence of loci sequence even though the homologies of the mutants between the forms was considerable. The arms of the chromosomes "retain their essential identity" among the species of *Drosophila* so far studied." They suggest that inversions are common while translocations were relatively rare or even improbable. This study suggests that we should be able to identify a genetic basis for isolation and to determine where in the chromosome complement are the loci which determine the isolating mechanisms.

C. C. Tan (1946) analyzed the genetic basis of the reproductive isolation between *Drosophila pseudoobscura* and *Drosophila persimilis*. His crosses involved stocks with markers on each of the four large chromosomes. Five males of one species were placed with ten to twenty females equally divided between the two species and kept together long enough that more than 50 percent of the females could be expected to be inseminated. He was able to localize the main factors which distinguish the mating behavior of *D. persimilis* from *D. pseudoobscura* on the X and second chromosomes.

H. T. Spieth (1947; Paper 11) studied the sexual behavior of several species of the *Drosophila willistoni* group by direct observation of intraspecific and interspecific pairings. A series of stimulus-response activities results in insemination of the intraspecific crosses but seldom fail to provide for specific integrity in interspecific pairings. Spieth concluded that in these species sexual differences (premating isolating mechanisms) have accumulated at parallel rates with the morphological divergences.

The most significant measures of differences between species which may be related to isolating mechanisms are those found in flowering plants. In some situations the chromosome numbers change by a variety of demonstrable methods which parallel the differences between closely related species. Additionally many closely related species have chromosome numbers which are multiples of one form. Stebbins (1950) and Grant (1963) suggest that polyploidy is very widespread in plants. They note that almost all pteridophytes appear to have formed this way and that one-third to one-half of all angiosperms fit this mode of origin. Gymnosperms and animals appear to arise by polyploidy only rarely (see Stebbins, 1970, and Jackson, 1971, for recent reviews). Thus, were this volume to properly represent the variety of speciation among living forms it should emphasize polyploid plants rather than *Drosophila* and similar creatures. However, polyploidy is considered in a separate Benchmark volume *Polyploidy* edited by G. L. Stebbins, Jr. Even so, we must emphasize that considerable reorganization of chromosome rearrangements and of chromosome numbers does appear to characterize different species. Species differ in isozymes, in loci sequence arrangements, in visible chromosome structures, and in external morphological and behavioral characteristics, many of which contribute to the isolation process. Stone (1955) pointed out that the acquisition of chromosomal fusions was common in *Drosophila* phylogeny. More than fifty were found and each species is monomorphic. Clearly chromosomal fusions are related to species differences and probably to the process of speciation.

8

Reprinted from *J. Genetics* **12**:101–109 (1922)

SEX RATIO AND UNISEXUAL STERILITY IN HYBRID ANIMALS.

By J. B. S. HALDANE, M.A.
Fellow of New College, Oxford.

Many observers have noted that the crossing of different animal species produces an offspring one sex of which is rare or absent, or if present sterile, whilst occasionally the missing sex is represented by intermediate forms. Doncaster(1) concluded that the missing sex was generally the female, but, as will be shown later, this is by no means always the case. I believe, however, that the following rule applies to all cases so far observed, with one certain, and a few doubtful exceptions:—

When in the F_1 offspring of two different animal races one sex is absent, rare, or sterile, that sex is the heterozygous sex.

By the heterozygous sex is meant that sex which is known to be heterozygous for sex factors and sex-linked factors, to contain an odd pair or an odd number of chromosomes, and to produce two different classes of gametes, which normally determine the sex of the offspring. The heterozygous or digametic sex is in most groups the male, but in birds and Lepidoptera the female. Groups in which the male sex is haploid are only extreme cases of the normal type, in that all the chromosomes here behave like the sex-chromosomes of other groups.

Disturbances of sex-ratio and unisexual sterility have been observed as the result of crosses in Lepidoptera, Aves, Diptera, Mammalia, Anoplura, and Cladocera. I have here recorded all cases known to me in which (*a*) the animals were bred in captivity; (*b*) more than 10 offspring were raised, and (*c*) one sex was absent or sterile, or the sex-ratio was more than 2 : 1. In the tables F denotes fertility, S sterility established by testing several individuals. Of course the fertility is often subnormal.

Table I summarizes the data for Lepidoptera. Goldschmidt's results were each obtained with several different races. In the other crosses there were 24 cases where females were absent or rare, 10 where males were fertile and females sterile, and a number where there was an

121

unstated excess of males; or else the males, though not known to have been fertile, were anatomically normal, whilst the females were clearly sterile.

Of exceptions to the rule there is first the case described by Goldschmidt(20) where crosses between two races of *Lymantria* gave

TABLE I.

Lepidoptera.

Mother	Father	Offspring	Offspring of reciprocal cross	Reference
Cerura erminea	... Cerura vinula	9♂, 1 S♀	—	Guillemot (2)
Clostera curtula	... Clostera anachoreta	21 F♂, 3⚥, 2 S♀	Excess F♂'s, S♀'s	Tutt (3)
Deilephila galii	... Chaerocampa elpenor ...	>20♂, 8♀ [1]	—	Castek (4)
				Grosse (5)
Smerinthus ocellata	... Mimas tiliae	20♂, no ♀	—	Standfuss (6)
,, ,,	... Calasymbolus astylus ...	25♂, no ♀[2]	—	Neumögen (7)
Amorpha populi	... Smerinthus ocellata	490♂, 10♀ and ⚥[3]	2♂, no ♀	Tutt(8)
				Standfuss (6, 9)
,, ,,	... ,, atlanticus ...	9♂ : 1♀	>20♂, no ♀	,, (9)
				Dannenberg (10)
,, austauti	... ,, ocellata ...	93♂ : 7♀		,, (10)
,, ,,	... ,, atlanticus ...	45♂, 5♀	Excess ♂'s	Standfuss (9)
				Austaut (11)
				Dannenberg (10)
Saturnia spini ...	... Saturnia pavonia	113 F♂ : 100 S♀	Excess ♂'s, S♀'s	Standfuss (6, 12)
,, pyri ...	... ,, ,,	106 F♂ : 100 S♀	No ♂, 2♀	,, (6, 12)
Malacosoma franconica .	... Malacosoma neustria ...	12♂, no ♀[4]	No ♂, 1♀	,, (13)
Nyssia graecaria	... Lycia hirtaria ...	65 S♂, no ♀	—	Harrison (14)
,, zonaria	... ,, ,, ...	208 S♂, no ♀	181 F♂, 279 S♀[5]	,, (16)
,, ,,	... Poecilopsis isabellae ...	32♂, no ♀	—	,, (16)
,, ,,	,, pomonaria ...	90♂, no ♀	44♂, 102♀	,, (16)
,, ,,	,, ,, (inbred)	71♂, 7♀	—	,, (16)
,, ,,	,, lapponaria ...	93♂, no ♀	Excess ♀'s	,, (16)
,, ,,	,, ,, (inbred)	62♂, 3♀	—	,, (16)
Lycia hirtaria (English)	,, pomonaria ...	86 F♂, 75 S♀	98 F♂, 92 F♀	,, (14)
,, (Scottish)	,, ,, ...	190 F♂, 14 S♀	—	,, (14)
Poecilopsis isabellae	... Lycia hirtaria ...	38 F♂, 32 S♀	—	,, (14)
,, lapponaria...	Poecilopsis pomonaria ...	38 F♂, 1⚥, 39 S♀	—	,, (15)
Oporabia dilutata	... Oporabia autumnata ...	6♂, no ♀[6]	52 F♂, 47 S♀	,, (17)
Tephrosia bistortata	... Tephrosia crepuscularia	378 F♂, 12 F♀	313 F♂, 327 F♀	,, (18)
				Tutt (19)
Lymantria dispar	... Lymantria dispar	F♂'s, S♀'s	1 F♂ : 1 F♀	Goldschmidt(20)
,, ,,	... ,, ,, ...	F♂'s, ⚥'s	,,	,,
,, ,,	... ,, ,, ...	F♂'s, no ♀	,,	,,
Fumea affinis ...	... Fumea nitidella	♂'s, no ♀[7]	♂'s, no ♀[7]	Standfuss (12)
Basilarchia archippus ...	Basilarchia arthemis ...	>9♂, no ♀[8]	—	Field (21)

[1] Grosse obtained 20♂, 8♀, Castek a number of ♂'s and no ♀'s.

[2] 20 chrysalides wintered over. Their sex was not recorded owing to the author's death, so they may have been the missing ♀'s.

[3] Out of about 500 imagines 98% were ♂'s, the remainder ♀ s, never normally developed, often with ♂ appendages.

[4] " Ein reichliches Dutzend."

[5] I have described the male as fertile, though several males between them only fathered one egg which hatched.

[6] 6 out of 400 pupae, all ♂, survived.

[7] "Eine Anzahl."

[8] These 9 were bred in captivity. All the wild examples were also ♂.

intersexual males, and an excess of males. This took place in two broods only. Goldschmidt's other intersexual males occurred either sporadically or in generations later than F_1, and are therefore not exceptions. It seems just possible that the intersexuality of the two aberrant broods may have been due to disease or other external conditions, or to unsuspected heterozygosis of one parent. His theoretical explanation of them is not convincing, since he ascribes to the race "Fukuoka" on p. 103 (*loc. cit.*) a formula which, according to the analysis on p. 66, is entirely inconsistent with its being a "weak" race as stated on p. 12 and borne out by its behaviour in other crosses.

In two of Harrison's reciprocal crosses noted in the table there was a moderate excess of females, though in one of them these females were sterile. Standfuss(6, 12) mentions five cases where a species-cross gave only females. In three of these the numbers of females recorded were two, one, and one, which are insignificant; one (*Drepana falcataria* ♀ × *D. curvatula* ♂) was subsequently shown by him to give both sexes in equal numbers. In the last (*Malacosoma castrensis* ♀ × *neustria* ♂) Bacot(22) found that the males emerged a year after the females, but in only slightly smaller numbers.

Finally Fletcher(23) obtained a brood of 33 females and no males from a *Cymatophora or* ♀, supposed to have been fertilized by a *C. ocularis* ♂, but he was himself dubious of their paternity. There are thus no undoubted exceptions outside *Lymantria*.

The data for Aves are summarized in Table II.

TABLE II.

Aves.

Mother	Father	Offspring	Reference
Turtur orientalis ...	*Columba livia* ...	13 S ♂, 1 ♀	Whitman and Riddle (24)
Streptopelia risoria ...	,, ...	38 F ♂, no ♀ [1]	,, ,, ,,
,, *alba-risoria* [2]	,, ...	11 ♂, no ♀	,, ,, ,,
,, *risoria* ...	*Zenaidura carolinensis*	16 S ♂, no ♀	,, ,, ,,
,, *alba-risoria*	{ *Stigmatopelia senega-* lensis }	17 F ♂, 1 ♂ or ⚥, 9 F ♀	,, ,, ,,
,, *alba* and 'hybrids' [2]	*Ectopistes migratorius*	10 S ♂, no ♀	,, ,, ,,
Gallus domesticus ...	*Phasianus colchicus* ...	>100 S ♂, 1 ? ♂	Lewis Jones (in litt.)
Phasianus reevesi ...	{ ,, *torquatus* ,, *versicolor* }	161 S ♂, 6 S ♀	{ Smith and Haig-Thomas (25) }
Tetrao urogallus ...	*Tetrao tetrix*	40 ♂, 8 ♀	Suchetet, cit. Guyer (26)

Besides these crosses many have been made, giving smaller numbers, or less aberrant sex-ratios. They are described by the authorities cited

---

[1] One male begot a few living young, most were sterile.

[2] *Alba* and *risoria* yield fertile hybrids with normal sex-ratio. It therefore seems legitimate to include crosses of such hybrids along with crosses of pure species.

above, and Phillips(27). With regard to unisexual sterility the evidence is not clear. Whitman and Riddle(24) report one case (*Columba livia* ♀ × *Turtur orientalis* ♂) which gave two fertile males and one sterile female with rudimentary ovaries, and four cases where the males were fertile, and the females not known to be so, though not apparently proved sterile. The only possible exception is the cross of *Turtur orientalis* ♀ × *T. turtur* ♂, which gave 7 males and 14 females, all fertile. This may be compared with some of Harrison's cases which gave a moderate excess of females.

In Diptera the male is heterozygous. The data for the only recorded cross are given below, from Sturtevant(28).

Drosophila melanogaster ♀ × *D. simulans* ♂ gave 2 ♂, 3552 ♀, the reciprocal 588 ♂, 171 ♀.

Drosophila melanogaster XXY ♀ × *D. simulans* ♂ gave 59 ♂, 128 ♀.

All these hybrids were sterile. The males produced from *XXY* ♀'s were shown genetically to contain a *simulans* X like those of the reciprocal cross. These latter all die in some families, but all or almost all survive in others, the difference perhaps depending on the *simulans* parent. Thus, though one cross often gives an excess of males, there is a far greater excess of females in the reciprocal, the two recorded males being perhaps non-disjunctional exceptions.

The data with regard to mammals, where again the male is heterozygous, are given in Table III.

TABLE III.

Mammalia.

Mother		Father		Offspring	Reference
Cavia porcellus	...	*Cavia rufescens*	...	14 S ♂, 23 F ♀	Detlefsen (29)
Bos indicus	...	*Bibos frontalis*	...	19 S ♂, F ♀'s	Kuhn[1]
,, ,,	...	,, *sondaicus*	...	1 S ♂, F ♀'s	,,
,, *taurus*	...	,, *grunniens*	...	S ♂'s, F ♀'s	,,
,, ,,	...	*Bison americanus*	...	6 S ♂, 39 F ♀	Boyd (30)
,, ,,	...	,, *bonasus*	...	1 S ♂, 3 F ♀	Iwanow (31)

Here the males are always sterile, and sometimes rare. This sterility and paucity may persist after one or more generations of back-crossing. Thus in the guinea-pig cross the F_1 females with *porcellus* males gave 31S ♂, 52F ♀, and it was only in the next generation that a few of the males proved fertile. Similarly 19 yak-cow male hybrids containing $\frac{1}{8}$, $\frac{1}{4}$, $\frac{1}{2}$, $\frac{3}{4}$, and $\frac{7}{8}$ cow "blood" were all sterile, and three out of four males containing $\frac{1}{4}$ bison blood were sterile. Mammalian crosses sometimes give small excesses of males, not exceeding 30 %. Buffon (33)

---

[1] Quoted by Detlefsen (29) and Ackermann (32).

states that he obtained 7 males and 2 females from *Ovis aries* ♀ × *Capra hircus* ♂, but this has never been confirmed.

In Anoplura the method of sex-determination is unknown. Keilin and Nuttall(34) found that *Pediculus corporis* ♀ × *P. capitis* ♂ gave 310 ♂, 12 ⚥, 107 ♀, whilst the reciprocal cross gave 242 ♂, 187 ♀. The normal sex rates for *P. corporis* is 144 ♂ : 100 ♀. The increased excess of males suggests that sex-determination is here perhaps on avian and lepidopteran lines, the female being heterozygous.

In Cladocera there seems to be no obvious cytological difference between the sexes. *Daphnia obtusa* ♀ × *D. pulex* ♂ was found by Agar(35) to give a great excess of sexual broods and males (all sterile) among the descendants by parthenogenesis of the single original female hybrid. As these disturbances did not occur in the first generation they are not really comparable with the other cases cited.

Thus, with the exception of Goldschmidt's intersexual male families the rule always holds as regards sterility, while in the rare cases where an excess of the heterozygous sex is produced the reciprocal cross always gives a greater excess of the homozygotes.

As pointed out by Sturtevant(28) the excess of homozygotes may be due to two distinct processes, a killing-off of the heterozygotes, or their transformation into members of the normally homozygous sex. In *Drosophila* the missing males die as larvae, on the other hand both Goldschmidt and Harrison have shown that in certain moth hybrids partial or complete transformation occurs. If the generalization of this paper is more than a mere coincidence it must be shown how these two effects, and also sterility, may be explained as due to the same cause.

Goldschmidt and Harrison have shown that many of their results can be explained by difference of intensity of the sex factors carried by the Z or X chromosomes in the two parental species. In *Drosophila* at least the other chromosomes play a part as well. In the pure races these factors are balanced by the cytoplasm or W chromosome, but in the hybrids there is a lack of balance. This will be most serious in the heterozygous sex, since in the homozygotes the effect of the two Z or X chromosomes will be the average of the parental values. The heterozygotes will tend to be pushed either towards the homozygous sex or towards an exaggeration of their own sex. Either of these effects in moderation may be expected to cause sterility, as pointed out by Harrison. The former may cause gynandromorphism, sex-reversal, or death when pushed further, the latter only death. Thus where both reciprocal crosses yield males only, as in *Fumea*, we may suppose that in one case some of the males are transformed females as in *Lymantria*, whilst in the other the zygotes with an exaggerated tendency to maleness have died. This hypothesis may be compared with the demonstration by Bridges(36) that in *Drosophila melanogaster* both supermales with one X chromosome and 3 sets of autosomes and superfemales with 3 X's and 2 sets of autosomes are sterile and not very viable.

But since in some cases the heterozygotes are transformed, in others killed off, alteration of sex-potential must have different effects in different animals. That this should be so is intelligible when we consider the great difference between the effects of castration or parabiosis in different groups. In Lepidoptera these conditions have little or no effect on somatic development, in mammals a great deal. The case here is by no means parallel, since the somatic cells are affected directly and not through an internal secretion, but the analogy shows that we need not expect the same effect from the same cause in different groups.

Although the explanation in terms of sex factors is attractive we have no satisfactory evidence of their existence. If sex is due simply to a double dose of a factor in the X chromosome (or sex-linked factor group) we should expect this factor occasionally to mutate like its neighbours. This would lead, if the factor were lost in mammals or Diptera, to the production of males with two X chromosomes and two sets of sex-linked factors, which would now exhibit partial and not complete sex-linkage. But such a condition has never been observed.

Moreover, upsets of the sex-ratio similar to those found in species crosses have been recorded in which factors which are certainly not sex factors are involved. Examples from Drosophila are given in Table IV.

The missing males are not transformed, but die as embryos. The characters concerned are all sex-linked recessives to the normal, "glazed" and "rugose" being multiple allelomorphs. They appear in the normal

TABLE IV.

Mother			Father		Offspring	Offspring of reciprocal cross	Observer
Fused *melanogaster*	...	...	Normal *melanogaster*		No ♂, 823 F♀	1♂ : 1♀	Lynch (37)
Fused *XXY melanogaster*		...	,,	,,	9♂, 744 F♀	—	,,
Rudimentary	,,	...	,,	,,	10♂, 923 F ♀	1♂ : 1♀	Lynch (37) and Bridges (38)
Rudimentary *XXY melanogaster*			,,	,,	93♂, 647 F♀	—	Lynch (37)
Rugose *virilis*	...	...	Glazed *virilis*	...	No♂, S♀'s	Nil	Metz and Bridges (39)

sex-ratio when the mother is a wild type heterozygote, but in each case the recessive female is almost wholly sterile. However "rudimentary" females have given 7 ♀ and 13 ♂ offspring with rudimentary males, so the upset of the sex-ratio is conditioned by crossing. The analogy with species crosses is striking, and may throw light on them. Two autosomal recessives in *melanogaster*, "morula" and "dwarf," behave similarly, except that with morula and dwarf males the recessive females have given 2 ♀ and 7 ♀ respectively, with no males. Finally according to Doncaster(40) colour-blind men have an excess of daughters by normal women. Although the data here are not so satisfactory, there is no sterility in the recessives.

Entia non sunt multiplicanda praeter necessitatem, and if ordinary factors, either sex-linked, like "rudimentary," or autosomal like "morula," can cause the disappearance of the heterozygous sex in crosses, we have no right to postulate sex factors for this purpose. A possible explanation of the phenomena under discussion is then as follows. In the course of the evolution of a species factorial differences arise between it and its parent species. They are perpetuated, probably by natural selection. Some of these factors, like "rudimentary," cause the death (or transformation) of the heterozygous sex when the new form is crossed with the ancestral. How this happens is quite obscure, but such factors do exist, whereas sex factors, though an attractive hypothesis, are nothing more. Moreover Bridges' (36) work on triploidy shows that sex may be determined by other groups of factors than those which normally determine it. It seems possible then, that sex is normally determined, not by a specific factor, but by the simultaneous activity of a fairly large group of factors, each of which has, or may have, other effects. The loss of any one member of this group will not cause a change of sex, though it may cause partial sterility. If sex were determined by a single factor it is very difficult to see what advantage there could be in its being linked with other factors. If on the other hand a number of factors determine it, it is essential that they should be linked. If in any animals sex is determined by one factor, there is probably no sex-linkage or chromosome difference between the sexes. As soon as another factor becomes necessary, complete linkage between the two must appear in the heterozygous sex, and the same mechanism which prevents them from crossing over may be expected to hinder or prevent crossing over of all factors in that sex.

I shall not attempt here to discuss the phenomena observed in the F_2 of the crosses considered. Their variability is partly explained by the fact that the fertile F_1 may either be all homozygotes, or in part transformed heterozygotes, partly by failures in reduction.

It is worth noticing that other disturbing influences do not affect the heterozygous sex more than the homozygous. Thus late fertilization turns XX frog zygotes into males, and the blood of their brothers converts XX mammalian embryos into freemartins. On the other hand the distinction between homozygous and heterozygous sex is more fundamental than that between male and female in determining the intensity of partial linkage between factors. Obviously sex-linked factors must be completely linked in the heterozygous sex, but linkage between autosomal factors is also always stronger in that sex. In *Drosophila melanogaster, simulans* and *virilis* linkage is always complete in the heterozygous male, in Bombyx, as shown by Tanaka(41), in the heterozygous female. Nabours(42) in *Apotettix* and Haldane(43) in *Paratettix* found linkage much stronger in the heterozygous male. And Dunn(44) showed that in the rat and mouse linkage is slightly stronger in the heterozygous male. If these facts are anything more than a coincidence they may be due to a greater difficulty of fusion of chromosome pairs in the heterozygous sex, and this in turn may be a contributory cause of its sterility. A possible evolutionary explanation of this stronger linkage has been suggested above.

I wish to record my thanks to the Rev. E. Lewis Jones for his information concerning pheasant-poultry hybrids.

Summary.

When in the F_1 offspring of a cross between two animal species or races one sex is absent, rare, or sterile, that sex is always the heterozygous sex.

REFERENCES.

1. Doncaster. *The Determination of Sex*, p. 87.
2. Guillemot. *Ann. Soc. Entom.* France, 1856, p. 29.
3. Tutt. *British Lepidoptera*, Vol. iv. pp. 1—38.
4. Castek. *Int. Ent. Zeit.* Vol. iv. p. 181, 1910.
5. Grosse. *Int. Ent. Zeit.* Vol. v. p. 327, 1912.
6. Standfuss. *Proc. vii. Int. Zool. Congress*, pp. 113—115, 1907.
7. Neumögen. *Entom. News*, Vol. v. p. 326, 1894.
8. Tutt. *British Lepidoptera*, Vol. iii. pp. 395, 448—459, 495.
9. Standfuss. *Bull. Soc. Entom.* France, 1901, pp. 87—89.
10. Dannenberg. *Zeit. Wiss. Insektenbiol.* Vol. viii. p. 27, 1912, Vol. ix. p. 294, 1913.

11. AUSTAUT. *Le Naturaliste*. Vol. XIV. p. 236.
12. STANDFUSS. *Handbuch der Palaearktische Grossschmetterlinge*, pp. 54—117.
13. ——. *Stett. Ent. Zeit.* Vol. XLV. p. 193, 1895.
14. HARRISON. *Journal of Genetics*, Vol. VI. p. 95, 1916.
15. ——. *Journal of Genetics*, Vol. VI. p. 269, 1917.
16. ——. *Journal of Genetics*, Vol. IX. p. 1, 1919.
17. ——. *Journal of Genetics*, Vol. IX. p. 195, 1920.
18. ——. *Journal of Genetics*, Vol. X. p. 61, 1920.
19. TUTT. *British Lepidoptera*, Vol. V. p. 31.
20. GOLDSCHMIDT. *Zeitsch. Ind. Abst. u. Ver.* Vol. XXIII. p. 1, 1920.
21. FIELD. *Psyche*, Vol. 21, p. 115, 1914.
22. BACOT. *Ent. Record*, Vol. XIV. p. 106, 1902, Vol. XV. p. 134, 1903.
23. FLETCHER. *Ent. Record*, Vol. IV. p. 304, 1893.
24. WHITMAN and RIDDLE. *Carn. Inst. Wash. Pub.* 257, Vol. II. 1919.
25. SMITH and HAIG-THOMAS. *Journal of Genetics*, Vol. III. p. 39, 1913.
26. GUYER. *Biol. Bull.* Vol. XVI. p. 193, 1909.
27. PHILLIPS. *Journ. Exp. Zool.* Vol. XVI. p. 143, 1914.
28. STURTEVANT. *Genetics*, Vol. V. p. 488, 1920, Vol. VI. p. 179, 1921.
29. DETLEFSEN. *Carn. Inst. Wash. Pub.* 205, 1914.
30. BOYD. *Journal of Heredity*, Vol. V. p. 189, 1914.
31. IWANOW and PHILIPTCHENKO. *Zeit. Ind. Abst. u. Ver.* Vol. XVI. p. 1, 1916.
32. ACKERMANN. *Thierbastarde.*
33. BUFFON. *Histoire Naturelle*, Oeuvres Complètes. Quadrupèdes, VI. 1787, p. 378.
34. KEILIN and NUTTALL, *Parasitology*, Vol. II. p. 279.
35. AGAR. *Journal of Genetics*, Vol. X. p. 303, 1920.
36. BRIDGES. *Am. Nat.* Vol. LVI. p. 51, 1922.
37. LYNCH. *Genetics*, Vol. IV. p. 501, 1919.
38. BRIDGES and MORGAN. *Carn. Inst. Wash. Publ.* 278, p. 231, 1919.
39. METZ and BRIDGES. *Proc. Nat. Ac. Sci.* Vol. III. p. 673, 1917 ; Vol. VI. p. 421, 1920.
40. DONCASTER. *The Determination of Sex*, p. 48.
41. TANAKA. *Trans. Sapporo Nat. Hist. Soc.* Vol. V. 1914.
42. NABOURS. *Am. Nat.* Vol. LIII. p. 131, 1919.
43. HALDANE. *Journal of Genetics*, Vol. X. p. 47, 1920.
44. DUNN. *Genetics*, Vol. V. p. 325, 1919.

9

GENETIC NATURE OF SPECIES DIFFERENCES[1]

DR. TH. DOBZHANSKY

W. G. KERCKHOFF LABORATORIES, CALIFORNIA INSTITUTE OF TECHNOLOGY

INTRODUCTION

THE boundless diversity of organic forms is impressive even to a casual observer. Reducing this seemingly chaotic multiformity to some sort of rational system was a prerequisite for a scientific study of living things; hence taxonomy and morphology were in the past the most active branches, description and generalizing induction the main methods of biology. Later the main trend of thought has turned from morphology to physiology, from description to experiment, and from peculiarities of single species to properties common to large groups or to all of them. The problem of organic diversity must now be studied in a new aspect, namely, as a general property of living matter, for such it truly is.

The difference between any two individuals or species may be attributed to the differences between their gene complexes, and in a few cases between their cytoplasms. Assuming this statement to be correct (and it is not universally accepted), one must nevertheless admit that it does not represent an adequate solution of the problem of organic diversity, for it disregards the fundamental fact that the living world is subdivided into discrete groups of forms which we call species. The living world is not an array of individuals embodying all the possible combinations of the existing genes; it is certain that only an infinitesimal fraction of the possible gene combinations has been ever realized. Organisms are more or less adapted to their environment, and the gene patterns each of them carries must represent at least a tolerably harmonious whole. With the sexual process being the predominating mode of reproduction, an unlimited inter-

[1] Lecture delivered before the Genetics Society of America and Marine Biological Laboratory at Woods Hole on September 3, 1936.

breeding of all organisms would result, due to the properties of the Mendelian mechanism of inheritance, in a
breakdown of the existing gene patterns and emergence
of an almost infinite mass of recombinations.   Among
these recombinations some would be as harmonious as the
existing ones, some might be even more so, but it is at
least a fair guess that a vast majority would be discordant.   Hence maintenance of life is possible only if
the gene patterns whose coherence is tested by natural
selection are prevented from disintegration due to unlimited hybridization.   It follows that there must exist
discrete groups of forms, species, which consist of individuals breeding *inter se,* but prevented from interbreeding with individuals belonging to other groups of similar
nature.

On the other hand, evolutionary progress is possible
only if new gene patterns are constantly being formed,
since only by a process of trial and error can the always
precarious balance between an organism and its environment be maintained.   Mutation and sexual reproduction
are the mechanisms that supply a store of new genic patterns.   The process of evolution may then be described
in a most general way as a result of the interplay of forces
tending toward fixation of the already tested gene patterns, and forces producing new gene patterns some of
which may become the forerunners of the world to come.
One of the tasks of genetics is to secure an understanding
of these forces and their interactions (*cf.* Wright, 1931).

It is a remarkable fact that in different organisms
causes preventing free interbreeding of species are frequently different; isolation of species from each other is
accomplished in nature by different means.   Moreover,
taking a given pair of species it is not uncommon to find
that their interbreeding is averted not by a single but by
several causes reinforcing each other's action.   The expression "isolating mechanisms" seems to be a convenient general name for all the mechanisms hindering or
preventing the interbreeding of racial complexes or spe-

cies. The present article gives an account of the isolating mechanisms found in three species of Drosophila, namely, *D. pseudoobscura* "race" A, *D. pseudoobscura* "race" B and *D. miranda.* The two "races" of *D. pseudoobscura* are very closely related; they seem to be morphologically identical, but can be distinguished because when crossed they produce sterile hybrids, and because they differ in a number of cytological and physiological characteristics (Lancefield, 1929, Dobzhansky, 1935, and others).[2] *D. miranda* differs from either "race" of *D. pseudoobscura* in a set of slight morphological characters, and also by its cytological and physiological properties (Dobzhansky, 1935). The discrimination of these species must be made through laboratory studies on living materials.

GEOGRAPHICAL ISOLATION

The geographical distribution of the three species under consideration is now known with a fair degree of accuracy (see map in Sturtevant and Dobzhansky, 1936). *Drosophila pseudoobscura* race B inhabits the country from British Columbia to California, and from the Pacific to the eastern slopes of the Sierra Nevada-Cascades mountain range. The distribution of *D. pseudoobscura* race A is much wider: from British Columbia to southern Mexico, and from the Coast Ranges (in the North) and the Pacific (in the South) to the Rocky Mountains and the western edge of the prairies. The coast of British Columbia, Washington, Oregon and northern California is inhabited by race B alone (race A reaches the coast only at Puget Sound, southern California, and possibly at the mouth of Columbia River). East of the Sierra Nevada-Cascades and southward from California race A only is found. The two races occur together in the southern Coast Ranges, in Sierra Nevada, and between the northern

---

[2] It is solely because of the lack of externally visible distinctions that these two forms are described as races of the same species. By any other criterion they should be considered distinct species, as the reader can see for himself on the basis of the data presented below

Coast Ranges and the Cascades.   It follows that although
the areas inhabited by the two races are clearly different,
the geographical isolation is far from complete; they
occur together in so broad a zone that if their interbreeding were not prevented by other isolating mechanisms
(see below) a large hybrid population would result.

The area inhabited by *Drosophila miranda* is compara-
tively very small, comprising only the region around
Puget Sound.   Since both races of *D. pseudoobscura* are
found in parts of this region, no geographical isolation
between *miranda* and *pseudoobscura* may be said to exist.

ECOLOGICAL ISOLATION

Ecological isolation is a condition in which species or
races are restricted to different habitats within the same
geographical area.   Since occupation of different geographic regions by two species may be due to preferences
exhibited by each of them to habitats found only in its
own region, there may exist situations which may be
classed either as a geographical or as an ecological isolation.

D. pseudoobscura as well as *D. miranda* lives in forests,
and is not usually found in treeless or desert localities
(although a row of trees along a dry streambed may be
sufficient to maintain a small population).   In the south
the distribution of *D. pseudoobscura* is sharply discontinuous, being restricted mostly to islands of forest growing on sufficiently high mountain ranges.   The combined
distribution of race A and race B of *D. pseudoobscura*
is rather similar to, but wider than, that of the western
yellow pine, *Pinus ponderosa*.   Yet these flies are not
bound to that tree only, and flourishing populations of
either race were found in other coniferous (*e.g., Pseudo-
tsuga*) or deciduous (*e.g.,* oak, aspen) forests.

Race A has a higher temperature optimum than race B
(Dobzhansky, 1935), and the optimum for *D. miranda*
is even lower than for race B.   In view of this fact it is
not surprising that in mountainous regions where both

races occur together race A occupies predominantly the lower and race B the higher elevations. Thus, a locality in the Kern River valley (California) lying at about 3,500 feet is inhabited by race A only, while on the tops of the surrounding mountains (Greenhorn Mountains, about 7,000 feet) a mixture of race A and race B with a predominance of the latter is found. This suggests a weak ecological isolation between race A and race B. *D. miranda* has been found thus far only in company with *D. pseudoobscura,* and the ecological preferences of the former are unknown.

Sexual Isolation

Lancefield (1929) observed that males of either race of *D. pseudoobscura* copulate with females of their own race sooner than with those of the opposite race. His results were corroborated by Mr. R. D. Boche working in our laboratory (unpublished). In Mr. Boche's experiments males were offered a choice of females of both races; several freshly hatched males of a given race were placed together with the same number of freshly hatched females of the same race and of females of the other race. At stated intervals of time some females were dissected, and the presence of sperm in their seminal receptacles was determined by microscopic examination. Boche found that at first males pair predominantly with females of their own race, but after the supply of the unfertilized females becomes small some interracial matings also take place. Thus, in one experiment race A males (Texas strain) were kept with race A (Texas) and race B (Seattle–4) females for 72 hours at 25° C.; 93 per cent. of the former and 19 per cent. of the latter females were fertilized. A pronounced sexual isolation between race A and race B is therefore established. On the other hand, no indication of even slight isolation was observed by Boche between strains of the same race coming from different geographic localities.

An aversion to mating with individuals of another species is clearly apparent also in crosses between *D. miranda* and either race of *D. pseudoobscura*. In a series of experiments conducted by the present writer batches of five females and five males from the same strain of *D. pseudoobscura* and five females of *D. miranda* were kept together in the same vial for approximately 96 hours (at 21–23°). The presence of sperm in the seminal receptacles of these females was subsequently determined by dissection and microscopic examination. Among 376 *D. pseudoobscura* females 351, or 93.4 per cent., were found fertilized, while among 377 miranda females only 83, or 22.0 per cent., were fertilized. In another series of experiments five females and five males of *D. miranda* and five females of *D. pseudoobscura* were kept together in vials for 96 hours. The examination showed that 40.0 per cent. of miranda and only 13.75 per cent. of pseudoobscura females contained sperm (the totals of the flies dissected are 235 miranda and 240 pseudoobscura). In a third series of experiments *D. pseudoobscura* females were kept for nine days with *D. miranda* males, or *vice versa*. Although in this case the possibility of mating with representatives of their own species was excluded, a large percentage of females remained unfertilized. An interesting detail is that different strains of *D. pseudoobscura* exhibit different degrees of aversion to mating with *D. miranda*. Thus, the Oaxaca–5 strain (from southern Mexico) mates with *D. miranda* rather easily, while the Seattle–4 strain (Washington) refuses to cross in almost 90 per cent. of cases. This result indicates that within the species *D. pseudoobscura* hereditary factors are present which affect the crossability of this species with *D. miranda*. The potential evolutionary importance of such factors is obvious; it is fair to guess that the sexual isolation between two incipient species may be built up as a result of summation of a number of genetic factors of this kind.

MECHANICAL ISOLATION

Discrepancies between the structure of the male genitalia of one species and the female genitalia of another may render copulation of representatives of these species difficult or impossible. Since in insects the external genitalia are made of inflexible chitin, and since species very similar in appearance are sometimes clearly distinct in genitalic structures, entomologists are prone to ascribe a great significance to the mechanical isolation of species (Jordan, 1905). There is no doubt that the structure of the genitalia may make interspecific crosses difficult; for instance, copulation of *D. melanogaster* male with *D. pseudoobscura* female may result in failure of separation and death of both participants. There is, however, no experimental evidence to show that small differences in the genitalia frequently prevent crossing, and Kerkis (1931) has proved statistically that at least in some Hemiptera the genitalia are as variable within a species as are the external structures. The claims that genitalic differences are of paramount importance in isolating species are greatly exaggerated.

Races A and B of *D. pseudoobscura* have identical genitalia, hence mechanical isolation is out of the question in this case. The genitalia of *D. miranda* are identical in structure with those of *D. pseudoobscura,* but since the former species is generally larger than the latter, the absolute size of the genitalia is correspondingly different. Nevertheless, observations on the copulation of *D. miranda* and *D. pseudoobscura* seem to show that no mechanical difficulty is encountered. Any one having experience with Drosophila breeding knows how greatly the dimensions of these flies vary under the influence of culture conditions, but offspring can be obtained from matings in which parents are very different in size.

VIABILITY OF THE F_1 HYBRIDS

The isolating mechanisms reviewed above have the common property of tending to prevent the appearance of hybrid zygotes. The mechanisms that remain to be considered concern the hybrids already produced, and tend to handicap or to eliminate these hybrids from the breeding populations of the parental species. The simplest mechanism of this class is lowering of the viability of the F_1 hybrids, which in extreme cases results in death of the latter before they reach the stage of sexual maturity (*e.g.,* the fish hybrids described by Moenkhaus, 1910, Newman, 1914, and others).

The F_1 offspring from the race $A \times$ race B crosses in *D. pseudoobscura* seem to be about as vigorous somatically as the non-hybrid individuals of either race, although some observations indicate that the male progeny of the $A♀ \times B♂$ cross consists of individuals that tend to be small in size. The male offspring from the cross *D. pseudoobscura*♀ $\times$ *D. miranda*♂ are almost completely inviable, the sex-ratio being about $1♂ : 200♀$. The reciprocal cross produces males that are abnormal in appearance, sluggish and rather short lived. The viability of the hybrid females from either cross is higher than that of their brothers but lower than that of the parental species.

HYBRID STERILITY

When crossed, race A and race B of *D. pseudoobscura* produce in F_1 fertile females and sterile males. The female hybrids can be back-crossed to males of either parental race; their daughters are all more or less fertile, while some of the sons are fertile and others are sterile (Lancefield, 1929). The cytological basis of the sterility of the F_1 males is a disturbance of the spermatogenesis: chromosome pairing is incomplete or absent, the first meiotic division abortive, the second division absent, degenerate polyploid cells are formed instead of spermatozoa. Although these disturbances are greater in crosses between some strains than between others, and although in any given cross the abnormalities are greater at high than at low temperatures, the derangement of the spermatogenesis is under all conditions so profound that the sterility of the F_1 males is complete (Dobzhansky, 1934). Preliminary studies on the spermatogenesis in back-cross males show a whole gamut of conditions, ranging from

normal to even greater disturbance than that observed in
F, males. The hybrids between *D. miranda* and either
race of *D. pseudoobscura* are sterile in both sexes. In the
males testes are vestigial, while females deposit eggs
which produce no larvae. Several studies of the causes
of the sterility of the above hybrids have been made; only
a summary of the results obtained may be presented here.

In general, hybrid sterility may be due to several
causes. Perhaps the most thoroughly studied case of
sterility, that of the hybrids between the European and
the Japanese races of *Lymantria dispar* (Goldschmidt,
1934), is due to a lack of balance between the sex-deter-
mining factors coming from the parental races. The
sterile hybrids are here intersexes. That the *D. pseudoobscura* A × B, and the *D. pseudoobscura* × *D. miranda*
hybrids are not intersexes follows from the fact that their
secondary sexual characters, as well as their reproductive
systems except the gonads, are normal (Dobzhansky and
Boche, 1933). The writer has recently found several individuals of race A *D. pseudoobscura* which were probably (and one of them certainly) triploid intersexes.
Their reproductive organs were quite different from those
of the sterile hybrids.

Another possible cause of hybrid sterility is dissimilar-
ity of the gene arrangement in the chromosomes of the
parental forms (chromosomal sterility). In a number of
cases, especially among plants, it is now established that
races and species may differ in gene arrangement. The
first case in which a difference of this sort has been found
is that of *D. melanogaster* and *D. simulans* (Sturtevant
and Plunkett, 1926, an inverted section in one of the chromosomes). Tan (1935) and Koller (1935) have shown
that race A and race B of *D. pseudoobscura* differ in four
inverted sections (two in the X-chromosome, one in the
second and one in the third chromosomes). The chromosomes of *D. miranda* are built very differently from those
of *D. pseudoobscura* (Dobzhansky and Tan, 1936, and a
paper in press). In all the chromosomes many genes have

changed their relative locations due to inversions. Some genes located in the same chromosome in one of these two species are located in different chromosomes in the other, indicating that translocations have taken place in the phylogeny. Each species has chromosome sections that can not be identified with certainty in the other; these sections may be accounted for either on the supposition that losses of genic materials have taken place in the phylogeny, or on the supposition that certain parts of the chromosomes were subject to so many reorganizations of the inversion or translocation types that they are no longer identifiable with the aid of the salivary gland chromosome method which was employed in these studies. Dobzhansky and Tan estimate that in order to derive the gene arrangement observed in *D. miranda* from that present in *D. pseudoobscura*, or *vice versa*, at least forty-eight, and probably many more, chromosome breakages and reattachments must take place.

Granting that some, and possibly all, species differ from each other in gene arrangement, one nevertheless must be circumspect in attributing the hybrid sterility to this cause. Cumulative effects of rearrangements of genic materials within the chromosomes may lead to a situation where meiotic pairing between the original and the altered chromosomes will be mechanically difficult or impossible; this, in turn, may result in disturbances at disjunction, and in production of gones containing unbalanced chromosomes complements. In plants such gones are frequently inviable, and thus sterility of a hybrid may result. It is, however, not obvious how such a mechanism can produce complete sterility, since even if chromosomes disjoin at meiosis entirely at random a few gones containing balanced chromosome complements should be produced. Hence, accessory hypotheses are needed to explain the complete absence of functional gones in many sterile hybrids. An additional, and even more serious, difficulty is met with if the sterile hybrids in animals are considered. For it is known that, at least in Drosophila, gametes carrying even grossly unbalanced chromosome complements remain functional in fertilization. Translocation heterozygotes and triploids in animals produce functional gametes, some of which may give rise to inviable zygotes. Yet, sterile hybrids in animals, just as in plants, are characterized by non-production of functional gametes rather than by production of inviable zygotes. The writer believes that thus far no case of sterility either in plants or in animals has been conclusively proved to be chromosomal in nature. The main argument that chromosomal sterility exists at all is the occurrence of fertile allopolyploids derived from sterile diploid hybrids, but this argument is not necessarily decisive.

The sterility of the hybrids between race A and race B of *D. pseudoobscura* is certainly not chromosomal, as shown by the following evidence. (1) The inverted sections found in the chromosomes of these hybrids are too few to produce sterility; fertile individuals heterozygous for a larger number of inversions can be obtained artificially in *D. melanogaster*. (2) The hybrids between some strains of *D. pseudoobscura* show complete chromosome pairing at meiosis and yet they are sterile. (3) In the hybrids abnormalities in spermatogenesis are observed at stages preceding as well as following meiosis. (4) Reduplication of the chromosome complement (allotetraploidy) in a section of the testis in the F_1 males does not alter the course of the spermatogenesis (Dobzhansky, 1933, 1934). On the other hand, it has been shown that the sterility of the hybrids under consideration is genic in nature, that is dependent upon interactions of complementary genes contributed by both parents (Dobzhansky, 1936). Such "sterility genes" are present in all the chromosomes of each race studied, and in the parts of the chromosomes having different gene arrangement in the two races, as well as in the parts in which the gene arrangement is similar. The back-cross males are sterile or fertile, depending upon which combination of the chromosomes of the ancestral races they carry. The precise mechanism through

which the sterility genes exert their action leading to the
disturbance of the spermatogenesis in the hybrids is unknown, but this mechanism is probably intracellular in nature. This is suggested by the experiments of Dobzhansky
and Beadle (in press), who transplanted testes of the
hybrid males into males of the pure races and *vice versa*,
observing that in all cases the development of the implants
as well as of the host's testes proceeds autonomously, *i.e.*,
in accordance with their own genetic constitution.

The cause of the sterility of the *D. miranda* × *D. pseudoobscura* hybrids is unknown at present. The profound
differences in gene arrangement observed between these
species warrant a suspicion that in these hybrids chromosomal sterility, or a combination of chromosomal and
genic sterility, may be involved, but further studies are
needed to elucidate this point (*cf.* Dobzhansky and Tan,
1936).

Viability in the F_2 and in Further Generations of Hybrids

As stated above, the F_1 hybrids from the cross *D.
miranda* × *D. pseudoobscura* are completely sterile, and
no F_2 generation can be obtained. The F_1 hybrid females
from A × B crosses in *D. pseudoobscura* are, however,
fertile, and back-cross progenies can be produced. Lancefield (1929) has noticed that in these back-cross progenies
the sex-ratio is distorted in favor of females. Dobzhansky
and Sturtevant (1935) have confirmed this observation,
and pointed out that the general viability of the back-cross
products is very low in comparison both with the pure
races and with the F_1 hybrids. Some flies of either sex
are visibly weak and show various somatic abnormalities,
many of the females are either completely sterile or produce very few offspring, the longevity of the flies is generally low. This weakness is more pronounced among
males than among females, which fact accounts for the
modification of the sex-ratio.

Some of the individuals obtained from the back-crosses
must have all the chromosomes, and hence all the genes,

of the race to which the father of the back-cross belongs; other individuals are identical in chromosomal constitution with the F_1 hybrids; but the majority of individuals carry various combinations of the chromosomes of race A and race B. It was tempting to suppose that the low viability of the back-cross products is due to unfavorable effects of mixtures of chromosomes of the two races, that is to say, that individuals carrying some chromosomes of one race and other chromosomes of the other race have an inferior viability. A closer study has shown, however, that this guess is not true, or at any rate not adequate to account for the whole complex of facts (Dobzhansky and Sturtevant, 1935, and unpublished data).

Experiments were so arranged that it was possible to determine the racial origin of all the chromosomes (except the very small fifth chromosome) present in a given back-cross individual by inspection of its phenotype. For this purpose strains of race A and race B having the chromosomes marked by appropriate mutant genes were intercrossed, and the resulting F_1 females were back-crossed to males of both parental races. The startling result of these experiments was the fact that those individuals in the back-cross progenies that are identical in their chromosomal constitution with individuals of pure races or with the F_1 hybrids proved to have a low viability, just as low as the individuals carrying various mixtures of the chromosomes of both races. In other words, the low viability observed in the back-crosses between race A and race B is general, and not restricted to some classes carrying particular combinations of chromosomes. The only way to account for this situation is to suppose that the low viability of the back-cross products is due to a maternal effect, that is, to an influence exerted by the chromosomal constitution of the mother on the development of her eggs. The F_1 females from the interracial crosses carry half of the chromosomes of race A and another half of race B; it appears that the presence of this hybrid chromosome complement in the developing oocyte (or in the surrounding tissues) influences the constitution of the resulting egg in such a way that the viability of a zygote coming from this egg is decreased. Furthermore, this decrease of viability is independent of the chromosomal constitution which the eggs possess after reduction and fertilization, in the sense that individuals having the same chromosomal constitution are less viable if they come from eggs deposited by an F_1 female than if they develop from eggs of a pure race mother. Thus, an individual carrying all race A chromosomes obtained in a back-cross of an F_1 hybrid female to a race A male is greatly inferior in viability to an individual of pure race A parentage.

On the other hand, the offspring of a given F_1 hybrid female may be more or less viable, depending upon the male to which she is mated. Thus, in one experiment made by the present writer race A females carrying the genes beaded, yellow, vermilion, singed and short were crossed to race B males carrying the genes scutellar and prune. The resulting F_1 females were back-crossed to race A beaded yellow vermilion singed short males. About one hundred culture bottles of this back-cross have produced not a single adult offspring; an inspection of the bottles has shown, however, that many eggs were deposited in them, but that the larvae coming from these eggs have died in very early stages. The decrease of the viability observed here is, consequently, so great that all the back-cross zygotes die before reaching maturity. Nevertheless, the same F_1 females proved capable of producing relatively more viable offspring. They were separated from their mates and re-crossed to wild-type race A males (the Texas strain); larvae soon appeared in the cultures, and at least some of them grew to maturity and produced adults. This experiment has been repeated twice with identical results, and moreover some other experiments involving different strains of A and B races have behaved similarly.

The phenomena of maternal effects have considerable interest intrinsically, and further experiments in this field are in progress. At present we are interested in this subject only in so far as it has a bearing on the problem of isolating mechanisms. The good viability of the F_1 generation of the interracial hybrids stands in sharp contrast to the low viability of the offspring of the F_1 hybrid females. It is safe to assume that under the conditions of competition in nature this deterioration of viability will tend to eliminate the interracial hybrids from the breeding populations of the ancestral races.

Summary and Conclusions

The interbreeding of race A and race B of *Drosophila pseudoobscura* is impeded by (1) a pronounced, though incomplete, geographical isolation, (2) a weak ecological isolation, (3) a marked sexual isolation, (4) a complete sterility of the F_1 hybrid males and of a part of the back-cross males, and (5) a low viability of the offspring of the back-crosses of the F_1 hybrid females to males of the parental races. None of these isolating mechanisms is in itself sufficient to achieve a complete separation of the breeding populations of the two ''races,'' but taken together they probably accomplish this task with a margin of safety.

The interbreeding of *D. miranda* with either race of *D. pseudoobscura* is precluded by (1) a strong sexual isolation, (2) a decrease of the viability and (3) complete sterility of the F_1 hybrids of both sexes. The last of these isolating mechanisms is sufficient for a total separation of the two species, the others increasing the margin of safety.

The great variety and the apparent high efficiency of the mechanisms isolating the two ''races'' of *D. pseudoobscura* from each other is rather surprising, since these ''races'' seem to be, at least judging by their external similarity, very closely related. No indication that interracial hybrids occur in nature has been found. In other groups of organisms, notably in some families of plants, the isolation of species is by no means so secure, and hybridization of species in nature is frequently reported in literature. The significance of such differences in the behavior of different groups of organisms is unknown at present, but it seems certain that they must exert a profound influence on the evolutionary pattern of a given group.

The mechanisms isolating species from each other must be considered the only true specific characters, if the expression "specific character" is to have any real meaning. The genetics of species differences is therefore a study of the hereditary nature of the isolating mechanisms, and of their rôle in the dynamics of Mendelian populations.

It has been contended by many authors that the grouping of individuals into species is merely a matter of convenience, since species have no existence apart from the mind of investigator. As a proof of this contention, it has been pointed out that such criteria of species distinction as the production of sterile hybrids sometimes break down because some forms which are classed as species can be crossed experimentally and can produce semi-fertile or fertile hybrids. This point of view is fallacious, and is based on a failure to understand that the fact that some species can be crossed and can produce fertile hybrids does not prove that these species cross regularly in nature. Species is a dynamic rather than a static entity, and the essential feature of the process of species differentiation is the formation of discrete groups of individuals which are prevented from interbreeding with other similar groups by one or more isolating mechanisms. Isolating mechanisms seem to be a rather haphazard collection of phenomena, and yet their genetic effects are alike in kind, namely, the formation and maintenance of discrete groups of organisms. The degree of isolation of these groups from each other is of necessity variable, presumably increasing with time, but in some cases perhaps also receding and disappearing. A thorough understanding of the nature and the functioning of isolating mechanisms is essential, because without it no trustworthy picture of the mechanism of evolution can be drawn.

LITERATURE CITED

Dobzhansky, Th.
 1933. *Proc. Nat. Acad. Sci.,* 19: 397–403.
 1934. *Zeits. Zellf. mikr. Anat.,* 21: 169–223.
 1935. *Genetics,* 20: 377–391.
 1935. *Jour. Exp. Zool.,* 71: 449–464.
 1936. *Genetics,* 21: 113–135.

Dobzhansky, Th., and G. W. Beadle
 1936. *Genetics* (in press).

Dobzhansky, Th., and R. D. Boche
 1933. *Biol. Zentralblatt,* 53: 314–330.

Dobzhansky, Th., and A. H. Sturtevant
 1935. *Proc. Nat. Acad. Sci.,* 21: 566–570.

Dobzhansky, Th., and C. C. Tan
 1936. *Zeits. ind. Abst. Vererbungsl.* 72: 88–114.
 1936. Am. Nat., 70: 47–48.

Goldschmidt, R.
 1934. *Bibliogr. Genetica,* 11: 1–186.

Jordan, K.
 1905. *Zeits. wiss. Zool.,* 83.

Kerkis, J.
 1931. *Zool. Anzeiger,* 93: 129–143.

Koller, P. Ch.
 1936. *Jour. Genetics,* 32: 79–103.

Lancefield, D. E.
 1929. *Zeits. ind. Abst. Vererbungsl.,* 52: 287–317.

Moenkhaus, W. J.
 1910. *Proc. Indiana Acad. Sci.,* 353–393.

Newman, H. H.
 1914. *Jour. Exp. Zool.,* 16: 447–499.

Sturtevant, A. H., and Th. Dobzhansky
 1936. In press, Amer. Nat.

Sturtevant, A. H., and C. R. Plunkett
 1926. *Biol. Bull.,* 50: 56–60.

Tan, C. C.
 1935. *Genetics,* 20: 392–402.

Wright, S.
 1931. *Genetics,* 16: 97–159.

10

Reprinted from *Genetics* **30**:429–438 (1945)

INCIPIENT REPRODUCTIVE ISOLATION BETWEEN TWO SUBSPECIES OF DROSOPHILA PALLIDIPENNIS

J. T. PATTERSON AND TH. DOBZHANSKY

INTRODUCTION

THE process of transformation of races into species is in general slow. The only approach to its study is through examination of its successive stages represented on our time level in different species and species groups. Nor is the process uniform in all organisms. Even though the essential feature of speciation in sexual cross-fertilizing forms is the development of reproductive isolation between the diverging races, the isolation is attained by different means in different cases. This necessitates careful study of diverse groups of organisms, as well as of different related species with contrasting reproductive biologies, modes of life, and distributional relationships.

For many years it appeared that species of Drosophila, though they offer some of the best material for investigation of many genetic problems, are not favorable for studies on speciation; it looked as though the intraspecific variation among natural populations is very small, while the reproductive isolation between species of this genus is almost always complete. In other words, the critical stages of speciation, the intermediates between races and species, seemed to be absent, as if species formation has come to a standstill. Facts brought to light during the last decade have, however, shown that the above impressions were erroneous, based on a failure to realize that the speciation in Drosophila is frequently accompanied by very little differentiation in the visible characters. Undoubtedly separate species of this genus may be morphologically similar and even identical, while morphologically distinguishable subspecies are, compared to other organisms, rare. It is now clear that the genus Drosophila, contrary to the old idea, is quite rich in "borderline cases" between race and species. Owing to the inherent advantages of many Drosophila species as laboratory materials, they offer excellent opportunities for studies on the genetics of speciation.

In the present article we wish to report on two subspecies of *D. pallidipennis* which have developed slight morphological differences and partial hybrid sterility, without either differentiation of the gene arrangements in their chromosomes or sexual isolation. We are obligated to MRS. N. P. SIVERTZEV-DOBZHANSKY for her help in making the wing measurements, and to MISS IRENE MARKREICH for technical assistance.

MORPHOLOGICAL DIFFERENCES

Our material consisted of a strain of *D. pallidipennis pallidipennis* from Iporanga, State of São Paulo, Brazil (collected by DR. C. PAVAN), and a strain of *D. pallidipennis centralis* from Jalapa, State of Vera Cruz, Mexico (collected by G. B. MAINLAND). After the work was almost completed we obtained another strain of *D. pallidipennis pallidipennis* collected in the city of São Paulo by Dr. C. Pavan.

The published descriptions of the two subspecies (Dobzhansky and Pavan 1943; Patterson and Mainland 1944) indicate that they are very close in external appearance, as well as in anatomical and cytological features. To obtain material for detailed comparison, flies of the Iporanga *pallidipennis* and the Jalapa *centralis* strians were transferred daily to fresh culture bottles, the number of parents being adjusted to prevent overpopulation. The cultures developed in a room at 20°–22°C. When the flies hatched, they were placed to harden for a day or two in fresh bottles with food, whereupon the body length was measured in 100 freshly etherized females and as many males of each of

TABLE 1

Body and wing lengths (in mm) and the wing indices of D. pallidipennis pallidipennis and D. pallidipennis centralis.

CHARACTER	SEX	PALLIDIPENNIS		CENTRALIS	
		M ± m	σ	M + m	σ
Body length	♀	4.620 ± 0.020	0.199	4.227 ± 0.017	0.172
"	♂	4.245 ± 0.014	0.141	3.982 ± 0.014	0.141
Wing length	♀	3.680 ± 0.017	0.116	3.252 ± 0.017	0.120
"	♂	3.386 ± 0.017	0.121	3.220 ± 0.017	0.122
Wing length/width index	♀	1.970 ± 0.009	0.061	2.103 ± 0.009	0.065
"	♂	1.936 ± 0.009	0.064	2.059 ± 0.010	0.072
Costal index	♀	5.132 ± 0.050	0.347	5.338 ± 0.045	0.311
"	♂	5.108 ± 0.049	0.347	5.242 ± 0.050	0.353
4th vein index	♀	1.160 ± 0.008	0.054	1.159 ± 0.009	0.060
"	♂	1.163 ± 0.010	0.070	1.145 ± 0.012	0.083
5×index	♀	0.997 ± 0.011	0.075	1.101 ± 0.016	0.111
"	♂	1.035 ± 0.012	0.084	1.195 ± 0.016	0.112

the two subspecies. Then the flies were preserved in alcohol, and served later to make the wing measurements of 50 females and 50 males of each subspecies. In making the measurements the conventions indicated in Dobzhansky and Pavan 1943) were observed. In addition to the usual measurements, "maximum wing width" was taken in order to compute the wing length: wing width index; "maximum wing width" is not generally a satisfactory measurement, since it must be taken between two not very well fixed points on the wing margins; it was taken in this work because an inspection of the wings of the two subspecies suggested that they differ in the length : width ratio. A summary of the results of the measurements is given in table 1.

The data in table 1 show that *pallidipennis* is a larger fly, with an absolutely longer but relatively narrower wing, a lower costal index, and a lower 5x index than *centralis*. But none of the distinctions are sharp, and the variation distributions overlap in all cases. The 4th vein indices do not differ significantly.

If *pallidipennis* and *centralis* are raised under identical conditions, it is possible, with practice, to classify mixed lots of etherized living flies with only a few mistakes. Attempts to classify mixed lots of flies raised in mass cultures without special efforts to make the environments uniform were less successful, although still more than half of the flies were classified correctly. No attempt to classify dried flies was made. The principal characters used in the classification are the larger body size and the more rounded (instead of parallel-sided) wing shape in *pallidipennis*. It is also possible that the eye color of young flies is a little brighter, the eyes relatively larger and the cheeks relatively narrower in *centralis*, and the mesonotum darker and suffused with a more silky sheen in *pallidipennis*. Since we studied only a single strain of each subspecies, the objection may be raised that the distinctions cited are characteristic of these strains only and not of the subspecific populations as a whole. All we can say is that an inspection of the São Paulo *pallidipennis* strain showed

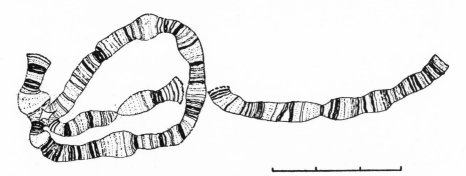

FIGURE 1.—Chromosome D in a salivary gland cell of a *D. pallidipennis pallidipennis*×*D. pallidipennis centralis* hybrid larva. The scale on the right represents 30 micra.

that it resembles the Iporanga *pallidipennis* rather than the Mexican *centralis* and that differences such as here described are seldom found between strains derived from the same population of a species of Drosophila.

CHROMOSOMES

The metaphase chromosomes of the two subspecies are similar. Salivary gland preparations were made of the F_1 hybrid larvae. Their examination disclosed that the pairing of the chromosomes in these hybrids is just as intimate as it is within either subspecies. Neither numerous unpaired sections nor the general lack of tautness, so characteristic of the salivary gland chromosomes in hybrids of species of Drosophila, were found. The only difference between the gene arrangement of *pallidipennis* and *centralis* is a fairly long inversion near the base of chromosome D found in all hybrid larvae. This inversion is shown in figure 1 (*cf.* fig. 15 in DOBZHANSKY 1944). A search for possible small rearrangements gave negative results.

Even if the above inversion should be found characteristic of the whole subspecies, and not simply of the strains at our disposal, the amount of chromosomal differentiation is still very low. Individuals heterozygous for several inversions are frequent in populations of many species of Drosophila; strains of the same species coming from regions as remote as Mexico and southern Brazil would, in general, be expected to differ in more than a single inversion.

TABLE 2

Crossability of D. pallidipennis pallidipennis (abbreviated as P) and D. pallidipennis centralis (abbreviated as C); the female parent is shown first.

	MATING	PERCENTAGE FERTILE		MATING	PERCENTAGE FERTILE
Controls	P×P	58		(PC)P×P	27
				(PC)C×P	26
	C×C	35		(CP)P×P	33
				(CP)C×P	30
P₁ crosses	P×C	76		(PC)P×C	38
				(PC)C×C	50
	C×P	35		(CP)P×C	34
				(CP)C×C	65
First backcrosses	PC×P	37		(PC)P×C×P	31
	PC×C	31		(PC)C×P	20
	CP×P	22		(CP)P×P	22
	CP×C	22		(CP)C×P	24
	P×PC	Sterile		(PC)P×C	20
	P×CP	Sterile	Third backcrosses	(PC)C×C	58
	C×PC	Sterile		(CP)P×C	18
	C×CP	Sterile		(CP)C×C	36
Second backcrosses	(PC)P×P	22		P×(PC)P)P	2
	(PC)C×P	25		P×(PC)C)P	Sterile
	(CP)P×P	21		P×(CP)P)P	5
	(CP)C×P	37		P×(CP)C)P	Sterile
	(PC)P×C	44		C×(PC)P)P	2
	(PC)C×C	35		C×(PC)C)P	1
	(CP)P×C	51		C×(CP)P)P	3
	(CP)C×C	46		C×(CP)C)P	Sterile
	P×(PC)P	Sterile		P×(PC)P)C	8
	P×(PC)C	5		P×(PC)C)C	6
	P×(CP)P	Sterile		P×(CP)P)C	Sterile
	P×(CP)C	1		P×(CP)C)C	10
	C×(PC)P	Sterile		C×(PC)P)C	Sterile
	C×(PC)C	Sterile		C×(PC)C)C	6
	C×(CP)P	Sterile		C×(CP)P)C	Sterile
	C×(CP)C	2		C×(CP)C)C	10

CROSSABILITY

Hybridization of *D. pallidipennis pallidipennis* and *D. pallidipennis centralis* (denoted as P and C respectively in tables 2 and 3) succeeds without difficulty. The following technique has been evolved at the Texas laboratory to obtain quantitative data on the crossability and hybrid sterility in Drosophila crosses. Virgin females and males of the strains to be tested are selected and aged for three to five days in isolation; 132 pair matings are then made and placed in

$3\frac{3}{4} \times 1$ inch vials with food, one pair per vial. The vials are inspected on the fifth day after the mating, and any vials in which either of the prospective parents has died are discarded. On the twelfth day the vials are inspected again to record those in which offspring have and have not been produced. The number of vials among the first 100 examined which contain offspring is referred to as "percentage fertile" in table 2. It can be seen that 58 per cent of the vials contain offspring when *pallidipennis* females are crossed to *pallidipennis* males; when the same females are crossed to *centralis* males the percentage rises to 76 (the difference is probably not significant). With *centralis* females, 35 per cent of the matings produce offspring with either kind of the males.

The fecundity of the inter-racial crosses is lower than that of intra-racial matings. Fecundity is expressed as the average number of adult offspring produced by a single pair of parents under the conditions of our experiments (table 3). Approximately 35 offspring are produced by a pair of either *pallidipennis* or *centralis*. With *centralis* females crossed to *pallidipennis* males, this number falls to 16, and in the reciprocal cross it falls to only 8.

TABLE 3

Fecundity of crosses of D. pallidipennis pallidipennis and D. pallidipennis centralis (the female is shown first).

MATING	FECUNDITY
P×P	34.5
C×C	35.0
P×C	8.0
C×P	16.0
P×(PC)P)C	2.9
P×(CP)C)C	6.9
C×(PC)C)C	4.7
C×(CP)C)C	5.6

The causes of the reduction of fecundity in the inter-racial crosses are obscure. The adult F_1 hybrid flies show no indication of constitutional weakness compared to the representatives of the parental races. It is, therefore, rather improbable that a greater proportion of the hybrid than of the pure larvae succumb before reaching maturity. More likely, the lowered fecundity reflects either a lowered vitality of the sperm of one subspecies in the sperm receptacles of the other (as demonstrated in crosses of species of the *virilis* group by PATTERSON, STONE, and GRIFFEN 1942) or the delivery of fewer spermatozoa in inter-racial compared to intra-racial matings. This last possibility was suggested quite independently from the fecundity data by direct microscopic observations on the amount of sperm in the sperm receptacles of the females inseminated by males of their own or of the foreign subspecies.[1]

[1] The number of fertile eggs deposited by a female is, of course, only a fraction of the number of the spermatozoa transferred during copulation. The insemination mechanism in Drosophila is rather wasteful of spermatozoa (KAUFMANN and DEMEREC 1942). Although we did not attempt to count the spermatozoa, examination under a microscope suggested that the amounts of sperm in the receptacles vary quite considerably from female to female and that females inseminated by foreign males have fewer spermatozoa.

Observations on the amount of sperm in the receptacles were made in the course of experiments designed to test the possibility that an incipient sexual isolation may exist between the subspecies. Ten freshly hatched females of each of the two subspecies were confined with ten males of one of them for four days in $3\frac{1}{4} \times 1$ inch vials. The females were then dissected and their sperm receptacles examined for sperm under a microscope (for details of this technique see STALKER 1942, DOBZHANSKY and MAYR 1944). The results are summarized in table 4.

TABLE 4

Numbers of the females dissected and percentage of them containing sperm in experiments in which males of D. pallidipennis pallidipennis or D. pallidipennis centralis were confined with females of both subspecies.

MALES	pallidipennis ♀ ♀		centralis ♀ ♀	
	NUMBER DISSECTED	PERCENTAGE INSEMINATED	NUMBER DISSECTED	PERCENTAGE INSEMINATED
pallidipennis	106	55.7	106	33.0
centralis	111	42.3	109	42.2

Table 4 shows that equal proportions of females of the two subspecies are inseminated by *centralis* males; with *pallidipennis* males, a slightly but significantly higher proportion of *pallidipennis* than of *centralis* females are inseminated (the χ^2 is equal to 6.12, which, for one degree of freedom, is expected to occur by chance about once in 100 trials). Sexual isolation between the subspecies is, therefore, both weak and confined to only one of the two possible reciprocal crosses.

HYBRID STERILITY

Crosses of *D. pallidipennis pallidipennis* and *D. pallidipennis centralis* produce hybrids of both sexes, which appear to be morphologically normal and at least equal to the parents in vigor. The F_1 hybrid males however, are, completely sterile. This has been established not only in pair matings (table 2) but also in mass cultures involving, in the aggregate, several thousand hybrid males. On the other hand, the F_1 hybrid females are fertile when backcrossed to males of either parental form. The percentage fertility tends to be lower in the F_1 hybrids than in the controls or in the P_1 crosses.

Extensive tests of the fertility of the hybrids obtained in the backcrosses have been made with the aid of the technique described above under the "Crossability" heading. Nearly 6,000 pair matings have been made for this purpose. The results are summarized in table 2. In this table the pedigree of each type of hybrid is indicated as follows. The original cross is given between parentheses, the females being always shown first. Thus (PC) is a hybrid from the cross *pallidipennis* ♀ × *centralis* ♂ and (CP) symbolizes the reciprocal cross. The male parent of the first backcross is shown next; thus, (PC)P is the offspring of an F_1 hybrid female crossed to *pallidipennis* male. The male parent used in the second backcross is shown to the right of another parenthesis—(PC)P)P or (PC)P)C.

Females obtained in the offspring of the first backcross are fertile when backcrossed to males of either subspecies (see "Second backcrosses" in table 2); the same is true for the females obtained in the offspring of the second backcross (see "Third backcrosses" in table 2). The percentage fertility in these females is, on the average, about as high as it is in the F_1 females (see "First backcrosses" in table 2). However, the degree of fertility of the backcross females varies considerably—from 18 per cent in (CP)P)C to 65 percent in (CP)C)P. A part of this variation is doubtless due to chance, but there is a certain amount of evidence that some of the hybrid combinations are not as fertile as others, since the repetition of the crosses usually gives essentially the same results as did the original tests. It looks as though the backcross females tend to be on the average more fertile when crossed to *centralis* than when crossed to *pallidipennis* males, but this may or may not be significant.

In contrast to the complete sterility of the F_1 hybrid males, some of the males obtained in the backcrosses are fertile, although the percentage fertility is 10 or lower (table 2). It is significant that in the offspring of the second backcrosses the males derived from two backcrosses to the same subspecies are more likely to be fertile than those derived from backcrosses to different subspecies. Thus, the (CP)C)C, (CP)P)P, (PC)C)C, and (PC)P)P males are frequently fertile, while (CP)C)P, (CP)P)C, (PC)C)P, and (PC)P)C males are mostly sterile. In other words, males which carry half of the chromosomes of one subspecies and half of the chromosomes of the other are sterile, while the greater the preponderance of the chromosomes of one of the parental forms the greater the chance that a male may be fertile. This fact is compatible with the hypothesis that the sterility of the hybrids is due to interaction of several, possibly of many, genetic factors contributed by the two subspecies. The sterility of the *pallidipennis* × *centralis* hybrid males seems, therefore, to be comparable with that of the male hybrids between *D. pseudoobscura* and *D. persimilis* (DOBZHANSKY 1936).

The fecundity of the fertile males obtained in the offspring of the backcrosses is very low—such a male mated to a single female of either subspecies produces less than ten offspring on the average (table 3).

SPERMATOGENESIS IN THE STERILE MALES

Species of Drosophila having spiral testes are less favorable as material for studies on spermatogenesis than species having ellipsoid testes. *D. pallidipennis* has spiral testes which contain relatively few spermatogonia, spermatocytes, and division figures even in freshly hatched males. No detailed study of spermatogenesis has, therefore, been made either in the pure forms or in the hybrids. Nevertheless, some aceto-orcein smear preparations of the testes have revealed the essentials of the cytological situation with enough clarity.

Both subspecies of *D. pallidipennis* have five pairs of chromosomes, one of these pairs being dot-like autosomes too small to be visible in the meiotic cells. About a dozen clear diakinesis and first metaphase configurations were observed in the spermatocytes of the hybrid males, and all of them showed four bivalents, just as the corresponding cells in the normal males. The first meiotic division is, nevertheless, abortive. All the chromosomes become included into a single restitution nucleus which shows the diploid number of dyads, the equational halves of which flair widely apart; no cell division takes place. The second meiotic division is apparently also abortive; at any rate, one can see many nuclei with approximately the tetraploid number of chromosomes now reduced in size. Groups of very abnormal spermatids finally degenerate to form granular masses which fill the proximal end of the testis in the hybrid males.

Normal meiotic pairing of the chromosomes followed by abortive divisions and degeneration of the spermatids may seem a surprising sequence of events. Yet, this sequence has been observed also in the hybrids between "weak" strains of *D. pseudoobscura* and *D. persimilis* (DOBZHANSKY 1934). The sterility of these latter hybrids is known to be genic rather than chromosomal; the degenerative phenomena in the spermatocytes and spermatids are not causally related to any lack of correspondence between the gene arrangements in the chromosomes of the parental forms. This is certainly true also in the *pallidipennis* × *centralis* hybrids, since in this case the parents differ in only a single inverted section (see above), which assuredly can not be responsible *per se* for the failure of spermatogenesis.

DISCUSSION

Drosophila pallidipennis pallidipennis and *D. pallidipennis centralis* are the products of a process of evolutionary divergence which seems to have reached the stage of speciation in the strict meaning of that word: these forms are on the "borderline" between race and species. They are distinguishable morphologically, at least in living flies raised under standardized conditions; yet, they show no more than a trace of the sexual isolation so characteristic for full species of Drosophila. The gene arrangements in their chromosomes differ in but a single inversion, yet the F_1 hybrid males are completely sterile and the males in the offspring of the backcrosses mostly sterile. Morphological differentiation, divergence of the gene arrangements, and the development of sexual isolation and hybrid sterility are the usual components of speciation in Drosophila. The example of *D. pallidipennis* shows that these components need not progress simultaneously.

Some closely related, though unquestionably distinct, species of Drosophila, such as *D. pseudoobscura* and *D. persimilis*, are scarcely if at all distinguishable morphologically; *pallidipennis* and *centralis* on the other hand are so distinguishable. The question may then be asked: why should the latter forms be regarded subspecies and not full species? Although it must be admitted that we are dealing here with a "borderline case," and that the information at hand is far from complete, the course adopted seems justified if systematic categories are to express the biological value of the populations concerned and not merely the degree of morphological distinctiveness. The distribution areas of *D. pseudoobscura* and *D. persimilis* broadly overlap, and yet no trace of gene exchange has been discovered in the region in which these species are sympatric. This proves that reproductive isolation between these forms is strong enough to make their genotypes closed systems in nature. The distribution areas of *pallidipennis* and *centralis* are, unfortunately, little known. The strains at our disposal came from southern Brazil and from Mexico respectively, and no related forms have been recorded in the vast intervening territory, except perhaps DUDA's (1925) *D. hyalipennis* from Peru which appears, judging from the description, to be a fairly distinct species. Our estimate of the degree of reproductive isolation between *pallidipennis* and *centralis* rests on inference.

Laboratory experiments indicate little if any sexual isolation between *pallidipennis* and *centralis*, and no trace of inviability of their hybrids. Therefore, it is fair to assume that if populations of these forms were living side by side, numerous hybrids between them would be produced. To be sure, the propagation of these hybrids would be handicapped by the sterility of the males and the lowered fecundity of the females. However, the female hybrids are fertile enough so that the backcrosses would constitute a channel for extensive gene exchange. The lack of inversions to prevent crossing over in four out of the five large chromosomes means that gene recombinations will be formed freely. In the absence of evidence to the contrary, we believe that *pallidipennis* and *centralis* have not become reproductively isolated to an extent sufficient to maintain their genetic independence without geographical isolation. In other words, they are subspecies rather than species.

Even though *D. pallidipennis pallidipennis* and *D. pallidipennis centralis* are regarded as subspecies, the great similarity of their gene arrangements makes them the most extreme case known in Drosophila of a failure of chromosomal differentiation to accompany the genetic divergence which apparently leads to speciation. This raises the general problem of the role played by chromosomal differentiation in evolution.

SUMMARY

Drosophila pallidipennis pallidipennis and *D. pallidipennis centralis* are known to occur in southern Brazil and in Mexico respectively. The strains examined show slight morphological differences sufficient to distinguish the subspecies in the living material raised under standardized conditions but probably not in dried specimens raised in different environments.

The gene arrangements in the chromosomes of the two subspecies are identical, except for an inversion in one of the autosomes. The pairing of the homologous chromosomes in the salivary gland cells of the hybrids is as intimate as it is in the parental forms. The subspecies cross readily and produce fully viable hybrids. No sexual isolation is apparent. The F_1 hybrid males are completely sterile, but the females are fertile. Females obtained in the offspring of the backcrosses are fertile. Some of the males obtained in the offspring of the first backcross are fertile, and the proportion of fertile males increases in the offspring of the second backcross. Taken as a whole, the data suggest that the sterility of the hybrids is caused by interaction of several, perhaps of many, genes contributed by the parental forms. Gross disturbances are apparent in spermatogenesis of the sterile hybrid males, although the meiotic chromosome pairing seems to be normal.

The combination of a slight but perceptible morphological differentiation with the near-identity of the gene arrangement, and of the lack of sexual isolation with hybrid sterility suggests that the different components of the process of speciation characteristic for the genus Drosophila are largely independent.

LITERATURE CITED

DOBZHANSKY, TH., 1934   Studies on hybrid sterility. I. Spermatogenesis in pure and hybrid *Drosophila pseudoobscura*. Z. Zellf. mikr. Anat. **21**: 169–223.

1936   Studies on hybrid sterility. II. Localization of sterility factors in *Drosophila pseudoobscura* hydrids. Genetics **21**: 113–135.

1944   Distribution of heterochromatin in the chromosomes of *Drosophila pallidipennis*. Amer. Nat. **78**: 193–213.

DOBZHANSKY, TH., and E. MAYR, 1944   Experiments on sexual isolation in Drosophila. I. Geographic strains of *Drosophila willistoni*. Proc. Nat. Acad. Sci. **30**: 238–244.

DOBZHANSKY, TH., and C. PAVAN, 1943   Studies on Brazilian species of Drosophila. Bol. Facul. Fil. Cien. e Letr. Univ. São Paulo **36** (Biologia Geral No. 4): 7–72.

KAUFMANN, B. P., and M. DEMEREC, 1942   Utilization of sperm by the female *Drosophila melanogaster*. Amer. Nat. **76**: 445–469.

PATTERSON, J. T., and G. B. MAINLAND, 1944   The Drosophilidae of Mexico. Univ. Texas Publ., **4445**: 9–101.

PATTERSON, J. T., W. S. STONE, and A. B. GRIFFEN, 1942   Genetic and cytological analysis of the *virilis* species group. Univ. Texas Publ. **4228**: 162–200.

STALKER, H. D., 1942   Sexual isolation studies in the species complex *Drosophila virilis*. Genetics **27**: 238–257.

11

Reprinted from *Evolution* 3:67–81 (1949)

SEXUAL BEHAVIOR AND ISOLATION IN DROSOPHILA. II. THE INTERSPECIFIC MATING BEHAVIOR OF SPECIES OF THE *WILLISTONI* GROUP.

HERMAN T. SPIETH

The City College of New York and The American Museum of Natural History

Divers mechanisms reproductively isolate animals of a bisexual species from those of all other species. These may operate at various times in the life of the organism. Some are of greater potency than others, but usually complete isolation is dependent upon the sum total of the effects of several mechanisms.

Within the Diptera, sexual isolation seems to be one of the most dynamic and efficient isolating barriers. Because many species of Drosophila can be maintained conveniently for study, they can serve as material for investigations of the manner in which sexual isolation operates and the effectiveness thereof under laboratory conditions.

There are three major methods (Patterson *et al.,* 1947) by which this type of isolation can be studied, i.e., by multiple-choice experiments, by non-choice experiments (pair matings), and by direct observations of the sexual behavior of the specimens. The last method is laborious and ill suited for obtaining sufficient data for statistical analysis; however, it yields qualitative data that are unavailable by the other two methods.

The multiple-choice and non-choice methods have been used extensively (see Patterson *et al.,* 1947). Direct observation of *interspecific* crosses, however, has been infrequent. Stalker (1942) watched the interspecific mating behavior of *D. virilis* and *D. americana;* Mayr (1946) observed that of *D. pseudoobscura* and *D. persimilis;* Wallace and Dobzhansky (1946) watched that of *D. subobscura, D. persimilis,* and *D. pseudoobscura.* Previously the *intraspecific* or "normal" mating behavior of the *willistoni* group had been explored by the same method (Spieth, 1947).

The present paper is concerned with the *interspecific* behavior of the *willistoni* group, and its primary aim has been to identify, if possible, some of the sexual isolating mechanisms that operate within the group. The data were obtained by direct observations. Of the seven species described for this group (*fumipennis* Duda, *nebulosa* Sturt., *sucinea* Patt. and Main., *capricorni* Dobz. and Pavan, *willistoni* Sturt., *equinoxialis* Dobz. and *paulista* Dobz. and Pavan), all were available for study except *paulista.*

TECHNIQUE

The preparatory steps for the present study were similar to those used for obtaining intraspecific crosses: i.e., virgin individuals were collected from laboratory cultures and the two sexes were isolated in small vials which contained food media. The various stocks of flies were all supplied through the courtesy of Dr. Th. Dobzhansky from the Columbia University collection and were originally collected at the following localities: *equinoxialis*—Teffe, Brazil; *willistoni*—Axtla, Mexico; Belem do Para, Bertioga, Campinas and Rio de Janeiro, all in Brazil; *capricorni*—Jacarepagua, Brazil; *sucinea*—Jalapa, Mexico; *nebulosa*—Belem do Para and Rio de Janeiro, Brazil; *fumipennis*—Praia Grande and Cantareira, Brazil. The virgin individuals were then introduced without etherization into an observation cell (glass top and bottom; beeswax walls) and were studied under 10 × magnification. Introduction into the cell always seems to cause some irritation and invariably the insects immediately preen themselves, after which they start moving about in the cell. They prefer to stay on the side walls and normally avoid both

157

the top and bottom of the cell. They do this even when the bottom of the cell is coated with beeswax.

As appears to be typical of most insects, the degree of physical activity tends to be cyclic, i.e., given individuals are active for a time and their activity stimulates the other specimens in the cell to activity. After a while, one by one, they become quiescent or at least partially so. The net result is that physical activity occurs in surges intercalated between periods of relative quiet. With the six species used for this study, at least two and often three surges of activity occur within thirty minutes after the flies have been introduced into the cell. These surges of action insure that the various specimens come into close proximity if not physical contact with each other. Thirty minutes was therefore chosen as the length of the observation period.

For most of the observations, two females of one species and three to six males of another species were placed in the cell for each observation. There is obviously a certain amount of individual variation, and since for various non-apparent reasons some individuals are refractory, it was decided to use several specimens for each individual observation. In a few instances, one male and one female were observed. The activities of these pairs seemed no different from those observed in the type of experiment most frequently employed.

The breeding stocks were reared at a temperature of $21° \pm 2°$. It was observed that the specimens react much more satisfactorily if the temperature of the cell is higher than that of the environment in which they are normally kept. An increase of light intensity also seems to facilitate the experiment.

The specimens used varied in age from three and a half to 43 days. Of the 92 observations, 10 utilized specimens of 3½ to 5 days' age; 64 of 7 to 28 days' age; and 18 of 28 to 43 days' age. Under existing circumstances, it was not feasible to make all observations at such times so that the ages of the individuals would fall in narrow age categories. The specimens of the two species utilized at any given time were, however, of the same approximate chronological age, i.e., they were collected as virgins on the same day.

DISTRIBUTION OF THE SPECIES

Although the limits of the range occupied by each of the six species is not known, nevertheless sufficient data are available to draw some conclusions as to which are sympatric and which are allopatric species. The known distribution (as reported by Sturtevant, 1921; Duda, 1925, 1925a; Patterson and Wagner, 1942; Patterson and Mainland, 1944; Dobzhansky and Pavan, 1943, and Dobzhansky, 1946) is as follows:

D. fumipennis has been reported from Costa Rica and the Brazilian states of Petropolis and São Paulo (southeastern Brazil); *nebulosa* is known from southeastern Brazil (Rio de Janeiro) and northern Brazil (Belem do Para); Panama; Cuba; Haiti; Puerto Rico; St. Vincent's; the Florida Keys, various localities in southern Texas and numerous plateaus and lowland stations in Mexico. *D. willistoni*, like *nebulosa*, has a wide distribution and has been recorded from southeastern Brazil (Federal District and São Paulo), northern Brazil (Belem do Para), Bolivia, the West Indies, Panama, Costa Rica, Guatemala, southern Florida, and various coastal localities in Mexico. Unlike *nebulosa*, it is not found in Texas. *D. equinoxialis* is known from only a single upper Amazon locality (Teffe, Amazonas, Brazil). Sturtevant has reported *willistoni* from Manaos in the same state but since this record was made before *equinoxialis* was described and since the two species can not be separated on the basis of external morphology, it is impossible at this time definitely to say which of the two species he might have had. *D. sucinea* is known only from several localities in Mexico, and *capricorni* only from southeastern Brazil.

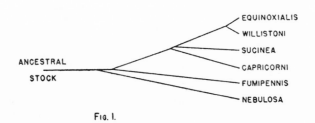

Fig. 1.

FIG. 1. Probable relationships of the species of
the *willistoni* group.

Inspection of these records shows that *nebulosa* and *willistoni* are the most widely spread of the six species and have sympatric ranges over most of their distribution. It is possible, but not probable, that both of these species have had their ranges extended by the activities of man. Dobzhansky reports that *willistoni* is the commonest wild species both in cultivated and jungle localities in the vicinity of São Paulo and Rio de Janeiro, but it is not a scavenger like *D. ananassae* and *D. simulans* which exceed it in frequency in the cultivated zones.

D. sucinea and *capricorni* are probably allopatric. *D. fumipennis* is sympatric with *capricorni* but probably not with *sucinea*. These last three all are found within ranges of *willistoni* and *nebulosa,* and have been collected at the same localities as have *willistoni* and *nebulosa.*

RELATIONSHIPS

On the basis of external morphology, *fumipennis* and *nebulosa* (Fig. 1) are widely separated from each other and from the other four species. *D. willistoni* and *equinoxialis* are indistinguishable (Dobzhansky, 1946) in their external morphology, although *equinoxialis* averages slightly smaller in size. The females of the two species can be separated by means of the structure of the distal end of the dorsal spermathecal duct. This part of the duct is invaginated within the spermatheca, and is differentiated from the remainder of the duct. In *equinoxialis,* it is vase-shaped (Fig. 3) with flowing lines and tapering to the diameter of

the external part of the duct. In *willistoni* (Fig. 2) it is of different shape, with a short cylindrical terminal part, a median sharply constricted section which is followed by an expanded region of approximately the same diameter as that of the external portion of the duct (external to the spermatheca). If virgin specimens are dissected and the reproductive system placed in saline on a slide and examined with a microscope, then these differences can be seen through the walls of the

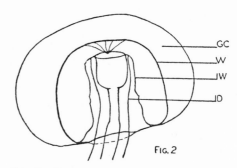

FIG. 2

FIG. 2. Dorsal spermatheca of *D. willistoni.*

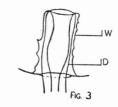

FIG. 3

FIG. 3. Inner part of dorsal spermatheca of *D. equinoxialis.* Parts not shown identical with those found in *D. willistoni.*

GC—Gel like outer coating.
W—Wall of spermatheca.
IW—Invaginated section of wall of spermatheca.
ID—Invaginated duct.

spermatheca. Fecundation, however, fills the spermatheca with sperm and renders them opaque. It is then necessary to compress the spermatheca by means of pressure applied to the coverslip, so as to cause the invaginated part of the duct to be extruded from the body of the spermatheca. For all ages of the adults and for all strains of *willistoni*, this seems to be a positive method of identifying the two species.

D. sucinea and *capricorni* seem more closely related to each other than to any of the other four. They are, however, especially *sucinea,* closer to *willistoni* and *equinoxialis* than to *fumipennis* and *nebulosa.*

The intraspecific mating behavior (Spieth, 1947) supports inferences of relationships derived from the external morphology. Certain other features of the reproductive biology are somewhat at variance with the mating behaviors, although in general the species show the same sequence of relationships. When the females are reared at a temperature of $22° \pm 2°$ and mated with males of their own species, *willistoni* females copulate first; *equinoxialis* next; then *sucinea* and *nebulosa* at approximately the same time; while *capricorni* and *fumipennis* copulate later than any of the other species. The start of egg laying after emergence occurs at about 48 hours in the case of *willistoni* and quickly reaches a high rate of production. *Equinoxialis* is next at 60 hours, but does not reach a high rate of production until 110 hours. *Sucinea* and *nebulosa* both start oviposition at about 72 hours after emergence, but while *nebulosa* soon reaches a high rate of production *sucinea* is much slower (120 hours). *Capricorni* and *fumipennis* are still slower in starting oviposition and *capricorni* is much slower in reaching a high rate of egg production. Thus *willistoni* and *nebulosa* reach a high egg production rate *earlier* than do any of the other four species even though some factors in their reproductive biology are quite different. It is interesting that these two species have

the widest geographical distribution of any of the six species.

It was also observed that *willistoni, equinoxialis,* and *sucinea* females would engage in copulation before any yolk was deposited in any one of the oöcytes. *Fumipennis* females would not copulate before at least one oöcyte contained approximately one-third of the total yolk mass. Females of *capricorni* and *nebulosa* would not copulate until at least one ovum was practically ready to be shed.

TERMINOLOGY

The terms used to identify specific courting activities, e.g., circling, vibrating, tapping, etc., are the same as have been used by other workers and were described in a previous paper (Spieth, 1947). One additional activity, however, seems common to the males of all the species and because of its significance needs to be here specifically named and described. The term *counter-signalling* is proposed for this activity which is as follows:

A male will approach another male of the same species and tap in normal fashion. The *courted* individual immediately spreads his wings very slightly and vibrates both of them rapidly up and down. Usually the wings are elevated only a fraction of a millimeter but sometimes the upper wing of some species (*willistoni* and *equinoxialis*) is raised to the vertical position. Having counter-signalled, the courted individual then usually, but by no means always, spins about and taps the suitor. This reverses the roles and now the former suitor counter-signals. Normally this causes the contact to break and the two individuals move apart. The intensity of counter-signalling varies between species. It is least obvious in *capricorni, fumipennis* and *sucinea,* and most apparent in *equinoxialis, willistoni* and *nebulosa.* Males of the latter two species often engage in violent activity which includes elements in addition to those described above. In the case of *willistoni,* the courted male will often spin about, rear up and then strike down with his entire force at the suitor. In doing so, he usually strikes the posterior half of the suitor's body and often catches the suitor's wings between the folded femur and tibia of the fore leg. *D. nebulosa* is still more spectacular in that the courted individual, having given the typical counter-signal, then extends his wings and raises them to about 45°, bends his abdomen laterally toward the suitor and spins about with a sharp slashing movement, driving his abdomen against the side of the suitor. Sometimes the suitor is literally knocked off his feet. Usually the suitor replies in kind and then the two individuals separate.

If the males of two different species approach each other then the pattern is modified, e.g., if a *sucinea* male approaches and taps a *nebulosa* male, the latter merely counter-signals but does not spin and slash. Nevertheless the two immediately break contact. Likewise if a *nebulosa* male taps a *sucinea* male, the latter does not spin but merely counter-signals and contact is broken.

SEXUAL DRIVE

Those organic tensions which are relieved by courtship and copulatory activities can be denoted as the sexual drive. Assuming the amount and intensity of the courtship and copulatory activities to be accurate indicators of this sexual drive, it is possible then to estimate the relative strength of drive which is found in the various species. *D. fumipennis* and *D. capricorni* have a weak sexual drive, e.g., the individuals are not sexually aggressive; in the case of *fumipennis* the males will not court immediately after they have finished a copulation. *D. willistoni* and *D. nebulosa* have a strong sexual drive. In all six species, copulation temporarily satisfies the sexual drive of the females. In all males, except those of *fumipennis,* more than one copulation is necessary to stay temporarily the sexual drive. One specimen of *D. nebulosa* was observed to be satisfied after four copulations within one hour.

In the case of interspecific crosses, the sexual drive definitely shows up as strong in the case of both the males and females of *willistoni* and *nebulosa*.

EXCITATION THRESHOLD

The observable activities resulting from the sexual drive are greatly modified by a related phenomenon. This can be called the excitation threshold, and is best conceived as a variable barrier that exists between the insect and its environment. When the threshold is low, a small stimulus will elicit a reaction, while at other times the threshold may be high and then the same stimulus will cause no response. For example, if a number of virgin males of *fumipennis* are observed in a vial or observation cell, it can be seen that when two individuals come into close proximity of each other they occasionally tap with their fore legs. The courted individual responds by counter-signalling and the contact breaks off. Within a relatively narrow range, probably due to individual variation, all the specimens display about the same degree of activity, i.e., the threshold is stable and relatively high. If females are now introduced, there is no change in behavior until a male taps a female. The stimulus received by the male immediately lowers his threshold; he becomes visibly excited and proceeds to court vigorously. Soon all the males have tapped females and all are excitedly courting.

Once the threshold is lowered, males will often court each other whereas before the females were introduced they merely tapped each other. As far as can be determined, the stimulus received by a male *when he taps another male* must be the same regardless of whether females are present or not, and therefore the differences in behavior must be caused by some other factor which is related to but not part of the sexual drive.

If the *fumipennis* females have copulated just previous to their introduction to the males, they constantly repel the males since their sexual drive is satisfied. The males, however, court vigorously and persistently for a period of time, but finally their activity becomes reduced as the threshold rises, and the individuals break off contact with the females, i.e., the stimuli received are now not sufficient to call forth the next action in the courting pattern and the individual becomes quiescent. Yet the sexual drive remains unsatisfied and after resting for a short period, the individual will approach another fly and tap. If the tapped fly is a female, the courting sequence starts again. Thus there can be a periodic rise and fall of threshold.

Interspecific crosses still further elucidate the relationship between the excitation threshold and the sexual drive. If virgin, sexually mature *willistoni* males are introduced to virgin, sexually mature *sucinea* females, the males with their large sexual drive will quickly start courting the females in typical fashion. At this point they become excited, the threshold lowers, and they not only court the females but will court each other. After ten or fifteen minutes, they cease courting the females who constantly fail to respond to the courtship, and finally the males return to the same level of activity as when only males are together, i.e., they merely tap an individual if it comes within close proximity. In fact they often show less response to the females than they do to other males. Thus, even though the sexual drive is unsatisfied, the threshold is so high that tapping no longer elicits the next step in courtship. If now *willistoni* females are introduced, the male threshold drops and they furiously court the *willistoni* females.

STIMULUS-REACTION PATTERN

Basic to an interpretation of the mating behavior of these insects is the principle propounded by many workers that higher functions should not be invoked in describing behavior in a particular case, if lower functions are consistent with all the observations. Since there is no evidence that individual Drosophila possess consciousness and the ability to form judgments, it must be assumed that when certain stimuli, either external or internal, are received by the individual these elicit definite responses. Such responses result in further stimuli being received which in turn cause further responses. The sexual drive represents the responses to internal stimuli which are as yet unidentifiable. If these responses bring the male fly within close proximity of another fly, the male is stimulated and responds by tapping the other fly. (It should be noted that females will sometimes tap males and do so in exactly the same manner as do the males.) If a female has been tapped, the male receives a stimulus which elicits the next courting response. The female also is stimulated and her response depends on the height of the excitation threshold and the status of her sexual drive. She may ignore the male; she may respond with a repelling response, or she may respond with an action that stimulates the male to continue further with courtship. Thus there is a series in which stimulus-response succeeds stimulus-response, finally culminating in a completed copulation, the effect of which is to cause the cessation of those internal stimuli responsible for the sexual drive. Once these internal stimuli cease, the individual becomes quiet.

REACTIONS OF MALES

Three hundred and ninety-nine males were utilized for 92 observations. The exact number of males and observations per species is listed under the separate discussions. Males of each species were observed separately with the females of all other species. Except for *capricorni* males, 3 to 4 observations were made with each of the possible combinations. Since *capricorni* males reacted so uniformly with females of all other species, it is felt that the thirteen observations (2 to 3 per possible combinations) are adequate.

In order to understand better the results of these observations, the basic mating behavior of the *willistoni* group is reviewed first. There are sundry differences between the patterns followed by the six species, but nevertheless they all conform to a general basic plan which is as follows:

The male, perceiving an individual close by, approaches and taps with his fore legs; if the individual tapped is a female of his own species, the male becomes excited, taps vigorously and then proceeds to the posturing position. *Nebulosa* and *fumipennis* posture in front of the female and the others at the rear or side of the female. Posturing always involves movements of the wings. Posturing movements are intermittent in nature and those species that posture at the rear or side may intercalate tapping and licking with posturing movements. *Nebulosa* and *fumipennis* always circle from the posturing position to the rear and then lick and perhaps tap. If not accepted by the female, they return to the posturing position. Refractory females are restimulated by circling. The females may respond to these activities either by repulsing actions (ignoring, decamping, or extruding) or by the acceptance response. The acceptance response consists of spreading the wings and the genitalia. The male then licks, mounts, and inserts the phallus all in one movement. Copulation is of variable length, but is never terminated until the male turns 180° and dismounts.

The results of the reactions of the males are set forth below and are summarized in Table 1.

TABLE 1

♀ / ♂	fumipennis	nebulosa	sucinea	capricorni	willistoni	equinoxialis	
fumipennis		0–1*	0	0	0	4†	75/15**
nebulosa	3†		0–1*	0–2–3*	0	1–4	62/16
sucinea	0	0–5		0*	0–1–2	0–2	72/16
capricorni	0	0*	0		0	0	56/13
willistoni	0–1–3	0–1*	2–3	2–3		0–2	71/16
equinoxialis	4	0–1–2	0–2	0	0–1		63/16

399/92

0—Males tapped and then quit.
1—One male postured once and then quit.
2—Males postured several times and then quit.
3—Males postured regularly but infrequently.
4—Males postured typically.
5—Male postured and female accepted.
† Male attempted to mount female.
* Female approached male and tapped.
** The first number in the right hand margin represents the number of males observed. The second number represents the number of observations per species.

D. nebulosa males

Sixty-two specimens were utilized for 16 observations. When introduced to *fumipennis* females, they postured typically and steadily but not as frequently as with their own females. Toward the end of each of the observation periods, they began to treat the *fumipennis* females as if they were other *nebulosa* males. One male was observed once trying to mount although no female ever gave the acceptance response. With *sucinea* females, they tapped at first but soon reached a state where they merely gave a single or at most a double tap to passing females. One male postured once before a female but scissored his wing twice only before desisting. The males tapped and counter-signalled each other vigorously. When placed with *capricorni* females, twenty-one day old males reacted as with *fumipennis* females; fourteen day old males merely tapped, while four day old males postured at first but then quit except for tapping. Apparently there is great variation in the response of the males to the females. With *equinoxialis* females, twenty-five and forty-three day old males postured typically, persistently and frequently, but four and fourteen day old males postured at first and then quit, reducing their activities with the females to tapping. This is the only case where *nebulosa* males showed a difference in threshold that possibly is attributable to age effect. *Willistoni* females elicited only the tapping response from the males, at first of moderate intensity but soon of a perfunctory nature.

During the observations with all females, the males tapped and counter-signalled and slashed at each other vigorously but the four day old males seemed much less aggressive than did the still older ones. Both male and female *nebulosa* have the characteristic habit of constantly and repeatedly raising, extending and lowering their wings. This movement, especially when combined with a high degree of boisterousness, apparently startles the in-dividuals of other species. Often the females moved away from the close proximity of the *nebulosa* males in a manner that can best be described as fleeing.

D. fumipennis males

Seventy-five males were utilized for 15 observations. *D. fumipennis* males when placed with *sucinea*, *willistoni* and *capricorni* never proceeded further than tapping the females. With *willistoni* when first introduced, they tapped vigorously but soon reached a state where they merely tapped once if they happened to be close to the females. *Sucinea* females never elicited more than perfunctory tapping while the males showed a definite aversion (expressed by turning away sharply) to the *capricorni* females. With *nebulosa* females, one male out of 17 tested postured once before a female. Otherwise they treated *nebulosa* females as they did *willistoni* females. With *equinoxialis* females, the picture was entirely different since the males postured typically and persistently. The *equinoxialis* females never accepted, i.e., never spread their wings and genitalia, and no male was observed attempting to mount.

D. sucinea males

Seventy-two males of *sucinea* were utilized for 16 observations. When placed with *fumipennis* and *capricorni*, tapping of moderate to weak intensity was the only reaction observed in these *sucinea* males. The males actually turned away from the *capricorni* females as if repelled. At the same time, they did not turn away from their own males when tapping them. Of 13 males observed with *equinoxialis* females, one male postured several times but all others merely tapped. Thirteen males were placed with *willistoni* females and one postured briefly and then quit; one postured several times, the posturings being scattered throughout the observation period; two postured several times during the first part of an observation period but later restricted themselves to tapping. Fifteen *sucinea* males were placed with *nebulosa* females. All of these males restricted their activities with the females to tapping except for one individual. This specimen was 15 days old. Shortly after being placed in the observation cell with *nebulosa* females of similar age, he approached a female, tapped, and postured. Immediately the female responded with the acceptance reaction. He licked, mounted and inserted the phallus in typical fashion, grasping her outstretched wings with his fore tarsal claws. She folded her wings in the characteristic manner of a *nebulosa* female. Immediately she seemed irritated and attempted to kick off the male. He maintained his position and continued with the copulation. For the next 21 minutes, except for two periods of less than one minute each (at 7 and 13 minutes after copulation started), she tried constantly to kick off the male but although he lost his grasp he did not dismount. During this time the union of the genitalia seemed normal and the sclerotized portion of the male's phallus could be seen moving back and forth in what appeared to be a normal manner. At the end of 21 minutes, the male turned to dismount, but was unable to withdraw his phallus. For the next 12 minutes the two individuals struggled to disengage the genitalia and finally succeeded. Immediately they were *lightly* etherized. The male genitalia seemed normal, but those of the female seemed swollen slightly more than normal. The specimens were returned to their isolation vials and the male recovered almost immediately, but the female never regained c o n s c i o u s n e s s . Forty-nine minutes after the termination of the copulation, the female was still alive but moribund. One hour and 45 minutes still later, she was obviously dead and upon dissection at that time no sperm could be observed in the dorsal spermatheca or ventral receptacle. The vagina was filled with a gummy mass but there were no signs of living sperm. It is possible that whatever spermatozoa may have been present became immobilized when the female died or even before.

D. capricorni males

Fifty-six *capricorni* males were utilized for 13 observations and no one of them ever did more than tap the females with which it was placed. Age semed to make no difference. In every case the males tapped and counter-signalled each other, but their tapping of the females was desultory. With *willistoni* they actually appeared to be repelled merely by approaching the female, for often they would perceive the individual, rush toward her in typical fashion and then turn sharply away just before getting close enough to start tapping. However, if the individual perceived was another *capricorni* male, then invariably the courting male would not show any repelling response until he had tapped and the other male had counter-signalled.

D. willistoni males

Seventy-one males were utilized for 16 observations. Seventeen males were used for three observations with *fumipennis* females. In one observation the males merely tapped; in the next they tapped and postured during the first part of the period but during the last part they merely tapped. In the next experiment sexual activity with the females was restricted to tapping except for one male who postured once. With *nebulosa* females, one male postured twice and another one once; the other 11 specimens merely tapped the females. The wing lifting habit of the females seemed definitely to repel the males. *Capricorni* females elicited posturing from the *willistoni* males in all experiments, but of low frequency. Thus the males would posture occasionally but not aggressively. It should be remembered in this connection that *willistoni* males when placed with females of their own species are ardent suitors. With *sucinea* females, the *willistoni* males postured readily when first introduced but within 15 to 20 minutes the threshold of most of the males rose to such a point that they restricted themselves to tapping. The males responded to *equinoxialis* females in somewhat the same manner as with *fumipennis*, i.e., some observations resulted only in tapping on the part of the male but others elicited posturing. Invariably the posturing took place during the early part of the period and during the latter half activity was restricted to tapping. During all of the observations, the males tapped and counter-signalled each other vigorously. Sometimes they postured before each other but usually the vigorous counter-signalling and the accompanying kneeing resulted in termination of the contact. None of the females showed any indication of giving the acceptance reaction.

D. equinoxialis males

Sixty-three males were utilized for 16 observations. With *fumipennis* females, the males reacted as if they were courting their own females. They tapped, postured, licked and restimulated vigorously and persistently. The females became quickly sensitized and extruded violently, but this did not repel the males. Thus the males of *equinoxialis* and *fumipennis* both court the females of the other species as if they were females of their own species. Eleven males were used for three observations with *nebulosa* females. During one observation, two posturings were observed; during another observation one posturing was observed but this contact broke as soon as the male licked the female. The males did tap vigorously and sometimes licked without posturing. With *sucinea* females, *equinoxialis* males postured during the first part of one observation period but two other experiments showed only tapping. The males tapped fairly vigorously and somehow this seemed to lower the threshold and males were observed during two separate observations to tap, posture and lick other males. *Capricorni* females were tapped briefly but that was all. Both the males and females seemed lethargic as if they exerted a depressing effect on each other. With *willistoni* females, contacts were mostly restricted to tapping but during one ob-

servation one male postured very briefly once and another experiment resulted in two separate posturings by a male.

REACTIONS OF FEMALES

The reactions of the females are much more difficult to evaluate than are those of the males. There are three typical methods by which the females of this species can refuse males, i.e., by decamping, by ignoring, and by extruding the genitalia. Even with males of their own species, *virgin* females are often non-receptive. When non-receptive virgin females are placed with males of their own species, usually they ignore or decamp when first courted but after several courtships or even as a response to a single persistent courting, they commence to extrude. Soon, however, they reach a stage where they extrude whenever tapped and some become so "sensitized" that they extrude whenever a specimen, either male or female, comes within close proximity. There are, however, individual differences, for if two females are placed in the cell one may start extruding upon the first contact with a male while the other may merely ignore the male. Further, there is variation between the species. Females of *fumipennis* and *nebulosa* are much more regularly and quickly "sensitized" than are the females of the other four species.

The behavior of the females in the interspecific crosses roughly parallels that of the intraspecific crosses as can be seen from the following observations.

D. fumipennis females

The *fumipennis* females extruded and decamped regularly when courted by *nebulosa* males, but *sucinea* males elicited decamping and extrusion in two observations and merely the ignoring reaction in a third. *Capricorni* males likewise elicited extrusion sometimes and the ignoring reactions other times. With *willistoni* and *equinoxialis*, they ignored the males at first but quickly reached the extruding state.

D. nebulosa females

Nebulosa females extruded and decamped when placed with *fumipennis, capricorni,* and *willistoni* males. One observation with *equinoxialis* gave only the ignoring reaction but in two other observations, the females extruded and decamped. They consistently decamped from *sucinea* males but never extruded or ignored them. The wing raising proclivities of this species startled the males of other species, and in some cases seemed to intimidate the males. Often a male would tap, the female would raise her wings, and he would immediately break contact.

D. sucinea females

Sucinea females never extruded in response to *fumipennis* males, but did decamp or ignore them. They ignored *nebulosa* and *equinoxialis* males consistently. With *capricorni* males, the reactions varied from ignoring to extruding. They both decamped and extruded in response to *willistoni* males.

D. capricorni females

Two observations with *fumipennis* males yielded only the ignoring reaction on the part of *capricorni* females, while a third experiment gave all the refusal responses. The females usually decamped when placed with *nebulosa* males, but also ignored and extruded sometimes. With *sucinea* males, the females sometimes extruded weakly but usually they ignored the males. Extruding and decamping occurred in two observations with *willistoni* males, but in a third observation the females gave the ignoring response. With *equinoxialis* males, they either decamped or ignored but never extruded.

D. willistoni females

Willistoni females ignored and decamped usually, but sometimes extruded when observed with *fumipennis*. *Nebulosa* males elicited nothing more than the ignoring response except in the case of one female who extruded during the lat-

ter part of an observation period. The ignoring response only was given to *capricorni* and *equinoxialis* males but *sucinea* males caused them to extrude.

D. equinoxialis females

Fumipennis males caused *equinoxialis* females to ignore or decamp regularly, even though the males courted persistently. Only once was a female observed extruding. With *nebulosa* they extruded and decamped. They merely ignored *capricorni* males and responded similarly to *sucinea* and *willistoni* except for an occasional extrusion during a single observation with each species.

DISCUSSION

The males of each species tapped the females of all five other species. In the case of *capricorni* the sexual drive was low as shown by the fact that tapping was infrequent and perfunctory. At the other extreme were the very aggressive males of *nebulosa* and *willistoni* which showed a great sexual drive. The other species fell somewhere between these two extremes.

With most species, changing excitation thresholds could be observed during interspecific encounters. When first introduced into the observation cell, the individuals preened and then started moving about the cells. As soon as the "foreign" females were contacted and tapped, the males would become excited and there would be a flurry of activity. Not only did they tap the females with greater vigor and intensity but also they tapped and countersignalled each other vigorously. If the sexual activity was of Grade 1 or 2 (Table 1) then almost invariably such posturing as occurred would take place during this first flurry of activity. Even with Grade 0 the intensity of tapping would be highest at this time. Shortly thereafter the threshold would rise and then the males would merely tap once or twice those females which came within close proximity. Toward the end of the observation period, the males would practically ignore the females although they would continue tapping and counter-signalling each other at an intensity level equal to that when only males were present. *D. capricorni* was the only species in which this rise and fall of the threshold was not observed. With *capricorni* the threshold seemed to remain level despite age of the males or species of the females introduced into the cell with them.

With the Grade 4 crosses (both *equinoxialis-fumipennis* crosses and two observations of *nebulosa* males with *equinoxialis* females), the threshold was maintained at approximately the same level as when males are introduced with females of their own species, i.e., intraspecific crosses. In these instances the males courted persistently and vigorously, interspersed, of course, with the customary periods of quiescence.

The Grade 3 crosses also showed lowered thresholds but not as much as with the Grade 4. In these cases the males courted but not with the persistence or intensity of the Grade 4 activity. When a male encountered a female, often he would break off contact after tapping but in a number of instances, always scattered throughout the entire observation period, after tapping he would posture. Regardless of what the reaction of the male was to the female, only once during all the observations did a female accept a courting male. This does not mean that the females were responsible for breaking contact. It should be remembered that usually in the normal *intraspecific* cross, once the male has tapped he then proceeds to posture regardless of the response of the female to his tapping. Thus in all those crosses of 0 Grade in which contact between the male and female ceased at the tapping level, the break was due to the reaction of the male and not to that of the female. Obviously the male receives a stimulus when he taps another individual. If the other individual is a female of his own species (intraspecific crosses), then the threshold immediately drops and the male proceeds with the posturing response. If a foreign female (another species) has been tapped, then the male re-ceives a different type of stimulus. In all those cases which are listed as 0 (Table 1), the stimulus received was such that it did not elicit the posturing response. In the Grade 4 crosses, however, even though foreign females were tapped, the stimulus-reaction pattern was such that the males proceeded to posture. But here, too, we can see variations in the pattern. With the *equinoxialis-fumipennis* crosses, regardless of age or condition, the males re-sponded as if the females belonged to their own species. With *nebulosa* males and *equinoxialis* females, if the males were young, then the response was Grade 0, but if the males were older they responded by posturing. This can be attributed to the age effect but it does not tell us what actually happens. Since these older males do not seem any more aggressive than are the younger ones, probably there has been no change in their sexual drive. There are two other possible explanations, e.g., either the stimulus received is quantitatively different or else the threshold is lowered so that a stimulus which with a higher threshold would not be sufficient to call forth the posturing response is now adequate and results in posturing.

If a male taps another male, then he apparently receives a response from the tapping that is similar to that which he receives when he taps a female of his own species. However, the male that has been tapped responds with a counter-signalling response and the suitor then is also stimulated by this as well as by his tapping. This causes a quite different reaction, namely, cessation of the courtship. If the male that has been tapped does not counter-signal, then the tapping male may posture before the male. Occasionally, especially when the tapped male is decrepit, such a condition was observed. Further, if the wings are removed from males, they tap each other vigorously but can not counter-signal in typical fashion. Then the suitor will often assume the posturing pose and, by means of the wing stubs, it can be ascertained that he is going through the posturing movements.

The question arises as to how the males

are specifically stimulated by the tapping action. Is a chemical produced by the female responsible, or is it merely that stimuli are received mechanically from the surface of the female's body? At present it is unknown, but perhaps both of these or other possibilities are involved. Indirect evidence indicates that the stimuli can be received via chemoreceptors. If *capricorni* males are placed with *willistoni* females, it can be observed that often the males will approach an individual as if to tap, but if it is a *willistoni* female, just before they come close enough to tap, they turn very sharply away. If, however, the approached specimen is another *capricorni* male, invariably the suitor goes on to tap. In the case of the females, the males definitely are repelled without ever having made physical contact. Such stimuli probably are received by the receptors located in parts of the body other than the fore tarsi, i.e., antennae or mouthparts. Often males when tapping foreign females may touch their antennae accidentally against some part of the female's body, especially the edges of the wings, and then immediately cease tapping. Further, males of *sucinea, willistoni,* and *equinoxialis* often tap when situated directly behind the females and occasionally they lick a foreign female. Such actions almost always cause the males to turn away sharply. Barrows (1907) shows that *Drosophila melanogaster* is able to taste food substances by means of its legs, and various investigators have shown that other dipteran adults are able to taste food material with their pedal appendages.

It is impossible to evaluate completely the responses of the females. As shown in Table 1 and in the descriptions of the observations, only one female ever accepted a male. The others all ignored, decamped or extruded. Inspection of the female reactions clearly shows that they reacted differently to various species of males. Females of this group, however, are unpredictable in their responses even to the males of their own species, for often virgin individuals consistently refuse courting males. Just why this happens is unknown but it is possible that some of these recalcitrant females may be carrying a fully developed egg in the vagina. That females may carry an egg in the vagina for some time is indicated by the fact that a fecundated female when etherized sometimes deposits an egg that is ready to hatch. Sometimes the act of oviposition causes the embryo to rupture the shell, whereupon the larva can be seen crawling out of the egg. Probably such an egg had been carried for some time in the vagina and there is no evidence that fertilization takes place until the egg leaves the common oviduct and passes into the vagina. If the fecundated females can carry eggs for some time in the vagina, there seems no reason why the virginal individuals should not do likewise. Considering the size of the egg and the size of the vagina, it seems improbable that an individual in such a state would accept a male. That this is not the sole factor is abundantly shown by the fact that often with intraspecific crosses a female consistently refuses the male's overtures for a considerable length of time and then suddenly, without any visible or apparent difference in conditions, accepts with alacrity.

In the interspecific crosses, some females (Table 1), especially those of *nebulosa* or *capricorni,* showed great sexual drive. They actually approached the males and tapped in typical fashion. The male would then spin and tap and the female would give a repelling reaction. Thus, although the drive was great, nevertheless the stimulus-response pattern was such that the females responded by giving the repelling reaction. In some observations, the *nebulosa* females actually gave the accepting reaction if another individual passed close by or if their abdomens struck against a small elevation in the uneven wax of the observation cell. No male ever tried to copulate with one of these females, but perhaps this was due to chance. If, however, the foreign males tapped such females, even when they had their wings spread, the females immediately closed their wings and gave the refusal response.

169

Finally it should be noted that in 17 crosses, the females refused males that actually postured, and 8 of these were of Grade 3 or 4. Thus it is safe to say that the breakdown of the stimulus-response pattern can be caused either by the male or by the female, and can occur at any time between initiation by the tapping on the part of the male and the acceptance reaction on the part of the female.

The single acceptance response is of interest since the actual courtship was extremely brief, the response of the female was typical, and all other females in this and the other observations of this cross (*sucinea* ♂ × *nebulosa* ♀) consistently failed to respond to the males. Further this was the only *sucinea* male that proceeded further than the tapping action when observed with *nebulosa* females. These two species are sympatric and there is no reason to doubt that they come into physical contact in nature. Unfortunately since the female died, we do not know whether other factors would have reproductively isolated the species even though sexual isolation had broken down. It does give a clue as to how those specimens which appear to be hybrids and are occasionally collected in nature may have originated. It also indicates that perhaps in this group once copulation has been started it proceeds to termination; that the female cannot dislodge the male, and that the male determines exclusively the termination of copulation. The male in this case attempted to dismount after twenty-one minutes, and the average time for *sucinea* copulations is 20′ 33″, while for *nebulosa* it is 1′ 37″ (Spieth, 1947).

Under the conditions in which the experiments were conducted, sexual isolation between the six species is almost complete, not because the various species do not attempt to court and copulate, but because at some stage in the courtship the stimuli received are such that the response causes a breakdown in the courtship pattern. In nature specimens of Drosophila are attracted to decaying fruits, etc., and usually a number of species will be present in such a restricted area. Having arrived at these places, their exploratory actions bring them into close proximity to other flies. The males and probably in a few instances the females then "investigate" these individuals. The male counter-signalling response then seems to be of adaptive value since the contact is quickly broken and these flies proceed to move about and encounter other individuals. Eventually the males usually encounter a female of their own species, the threshold drops, and the male courts vigorously. If the female has been very recently inseminated or if she is non-receptive for some other reason, she gives a repulsing response and at the same time continues with her activities of feeding, cleaning, ovipositing, etc., or she may accept and then copulation ensues. If the males encounter females of other species, the courtship usually quickly breaks down even though in rare instances "accidental" copulations might occur.

Finally, it should be noted that the sexual behavior and reproductive biology of this group of species, so far as is now known, offers no evidence that the evolution of the group has been by large saltations but rather that it has proceeded primarily by the accumulation of minor differences that have occurred independently throughout the group. The qualitative differences that exist are such that they could quite conceivably have arisen by modification of a pre-existing pattern.

SUMMARY

Data on the interspecific sexual behavior of six species of the *Drosophila willistoni* group were accumulated by the direct observation method.

Assuming that the intensity and quantity of the mating activities are an accurate index of the sexual drive of the species, it is shown that (1) there is considerable interspecific variation in the sexual drive, *capricorni* having the lowest drive, *willistoni* and *nebulosa* the highest sexual drive, while *fumipennis, sucinea,* and *equinoxialis* are in ascending order intermediate to the two extremes; (2) the two species with the highest sexual drive have the widest geographic ranges.

The sexual activities of the two sexes can best be explained as a series of stimulus-response activities which normally culminate with insemination in the case of the *intraspecific* crosses.

The stimulus-response pattern is quantitatively modified by the excitation threshold level. The level of the excitation threshold fluctuates in accordance to the inherent constitution and the previous history of the specimens involved in any particular encounter.

For studying the possible 30 interspecific crosses, 399 males were employed for 92 observations. Only *one* copulation resulted (*sucinea* ♂ × *nebulosa* ♀). In all other cases the courtship broke down somewhere between the tapping action of the male and the acceptance response of the female. In 12 of the 30 possible combinations, the males were invariably responsible for the breakdown of the courtship sequence. In two crosses (*fumipennis* ♂ × *equinoxialis* ♀ and *equinoxialis* ♂ × *fumipennis* ♀) the females were always responsible for the breakdown. In the other 16 crosses sometimes the males and sometimes the females were responsible for the cessation of the courtship.

In only one cross (*nebulosa* ♂ × *equinoxialis* ♀) did older males pursue courtship more vigorously than younger males. This age effect posibly is due to the lowering of the excitation threshold.

The single copulation observed indicates that "accidental" copulations between species may occur in nature.

Conspecific males displayed a counter-signalling reaction that normally prevented them from courting each other.

This counter-signalling reaction and the usual breakdown in the early stages of courtship of the interspecific bisexual crosses would serve an adaptive function in nature where several species of Drosophila collect in a limited feeding-breeding area.

The species differences in sexual biology of this group can best be accounted for by assuming that evolutionary divergence has occurred by accumulation of minor differences that have arisen independently throughout the group. In general the degree of differences of the sexual biology parallels the morphological divergences, i.e., the evolution of the morphological differences and that of the sexual differences have proceeded at about the same rate.

SELECTED BIBLIOGRAPHY

BARROWS, W. M. 1907. The reactions of the pomace fly, Drosophila, to odorous substances. J. Exp. Zool., 4: 515–537.

DOBZHANSKY, TH. 1946. Complete reproductive isolation between two morphologically similar species of Drosophila. Ecology, 27: 205–211.

DOBZHANSKY, TH., AND C. PAVAN. 1943. Studies on Brazilian species of Drosophila. Bol. Facul. Fil. Cien. Letr. Univer. São Paulo, No. 36, Biol. Geral., 4: 7–42.

DUDA, O. 1925. Die Costaricanischen Drosophiliden des Ungarischen National-Museums zu Budapest. Ann. Hist.-Natur. Musei Nat. Hungarici, 22: 149–229.

——. 1925a. Die südamerikanischen Drosophiliden Dipteren unter Berücksichtigung auch der anderen neotropischen sowie nearktischen Arten. Arch. Naturgesch., 91 (11): 1–228.

MAYR, E. 1946. Experiments on sexual isolation in Drosophila. VII. The nature of the isolating mechanisms between *Drosophila pseudoobscura* and *Drosophila persimilis*. Proc. Nat. Acad. Sci., 32: 128–137.

PATTERSON, J. T. *et al.* 1947. Studies in the genetics of Drosophila. V. Isolating mechanisms. Univ. Texas Publ., 4720: 7–184.

PATTERSON, J. T., AND G. B. MAINLAND. 1944. The Drosophilidae of Mexico. Univ. of Texas Publ., 4445: 9–101.

PATTERSON, J. T., AND R. P. WAGNER. 1942. Geographical distribution of species of the genus Drosophila in the United States and Mexico. Univ. of Texas Publ., 4313: 217–281.

SPIETH, H. T. 1947. Sexual behavior and isolation in Drosophila. I. The mating behavior of species of the *willistoni* group. Evolution, 1: 17–31.

STALKER, H. D. 1942. Sexual isolation studies in the species complex *Drosophila virilis*. Genetics, 27: 238–257.

STURTEVANT, A. H. 1921. The North American species of Drosophila. Carnegie Inst. Washington Publ., 301: 1–150.

WALLACE, B., AND TH. DOBZHANSKY. 1946. Experiments on sexual isolation in Drosophila. VIII. Influence of light on the mating behavior of Drosophila subobscura, Drosophila persimilis, and Drosophila pseudoobscura. Proc. Nat. Acad. Sci., 32: 226–234.

Part III

ORIGIN OF ISOLATION– THEORETICAL

Editor's Comments
on Papers 12 Through 15

Most workers agree that geographic separation in different environmental regimes for a sufficient number of generations will result in evolution in different directions and through the accumulation of genetic differences the development of reproductive isolation between the two lineages. Probably most workers agree that most animal and many plant species owe their origin to this process. How much geographic isolation is required and for how long? How different must the environments be? Is geographical isolation a necessary component? Theoretical studies of the origin of isolation between populations have centered on this, the most controversial component of speciation.

Darwin and Wallace in 1859 did not indicate the necessity for isolation to precede the divergence of species. Both Wagner (1868) and Gulick (1873) indicated the significance of isolation in the formation and distribution of species. Yet many workers of the time perceived the formation of species by divergence to involve some form of discontinuous variation. Galton (1894), Bateson (1894), Huxley (1887), de Vries (1889), and others felt some saltation was involved in the process and were not as concerned by the need for isolation or the role of continuous change in continuous characters.

D. S. Jordan (1905), in his presidential address to the annual meeting of AAAS, pointed out that naturalists had long recognized that "geographic isolation was a factor or condition in the formation of every species, race or tribe of animal or plant we know on the face of the earth." He clearly delineated the position of the naturalists quoting widely from solicited examples provided by leading naturalists of the day.

Haldane (1930) considered the problem of the relation between isolation and selection. He considered the situation where a new form is very slightly favored in a limited area and each generation the area is invaded by some very small number of the original form. Haldane assumed selection and emigration rates were small and positive and considered ten cases representing a spectrum of one and two locus conditions (dominance, recessive, sex-linked) and determined the conditions necessary to prevent swamping by immigration. He noted that the initial type in the selected population must be large and the ratio of immigration to selection must be above a critical value which differs with the genetic situation and, more important, varies widely in nature because of environmental factors.

Fisher (1922) modeled variable loci and determined that one way of getting polymorphic stability is for selection to favor the heterozygote. Levene (Paper 13) noted that this heterozygotic advantage was sufficient to maintain polymorphism in a single environment. He examined the possibility of maintenance of polymorphism in a single environment. He then examined the possibility of maintenance of polymorphism when several ecological niches were present even though there was random mating over the entire population. He noted that stable equilibria can exist and that preferential habitat selection, and nonrandomness of mating are conditions more favorable for equilibrium.

Haldane and Jayakar (Paper 14) listed causes of stable polymorphism and examined the conditions necessary to maintain polymorphism when selection was in different directions. They note that a series of changes through time, in the direction of selection, will maintain polymorphism. Bazykin (1969) suggested a model to describe speciation when isolation is spatial and selection is variable in direction. His model might apply to sibling species of *Drosophila* or other forms which differ by a single chromosome inversion.

Maynard-Smith (Paper 15) examined a model which describes how polymorphism can be maintained in two niches with overall random mating and differential selection of the homozygotic genotypes in the two niches. He described the necessity for density regulation to be different in the two populations, and for selective advantages to be large. If the conditions are met, reproductive isolation should evolve.

We have examined the theoretical conditions necessary for differentiation to occur when the systems are simple and the assumptions are restrictive. Given differentiation, reproductive isolation is expected. We can turn now to a consideration of genetic analyses of the origin of reproductive isolating mechanisms.

12

Reprinted from *Proc. Cambridge Phil. Soc.* **26**:220-230 (1930)

A MATHEMATICAL THEORY OF NATURAL AND ARTIFICIAL SELECTION. PART VI. ISOLATION

J. B. S. Haldane

It is generally believed that isolation has played an important part in evolution. If an organism is to evolve so as to adapt itself to a special type of environment, e.g. a cave or a desert, it must not be swamped in each generation by migrants from the original habitat.

We consider a series of cases, in each of which a new form is favoured in a limited area, the coefficient of selection being k. In each generation a number of migrants of the original type, equal to the whole population of the limited area multiplied by a constant l, migrate into it. k and l are taken to be small and of course positive. It is required to find the relationship between k and l if selection is to take place, and what equilibrium is reached, if any. We shall consider ten different cases.

1. *No amphimixis.* This is analogous to the cases considered on p. 21 of Part I of this series*, where several reasons are discussed which may lead to a failure of amphimixis. We may consider two types, A and B, which do not interbreed, A being the normal type, B that favoured in the area considered. Let u_n be the ratio of $A : B$ in the nth generation. The proportion of A is transformed in one generation, as the result of selection and immigration, from $\dfrac{u_n}{u_n+1}$ to $\dfrac{u_n(1-k)}{u_n+1}+l$. Hence

$$u_{n+1} = (1-k)\,u_n + l\,(u_n+1), \quad \text{and} \quad \Delta u_n = l\,(u_n+1) - ku_n.$$

Hence equilibrium is possible when $u_\infty = \dfrac{l}{k-l}$, a number which is positive only if $k > l$. If $k < l$, Δu_n is always positive, and the type B disappears. If $k > l$, $\Delta u_n = (k-l)(u_\infty - u_n)$. Hence the equilibrium is stable, and whatever be the value of u_0, that is to say the initial state of the population, the final state is $lA : (k-l)\,B$. Hence if A is to disappear nearly completely, k must greatly exceed l.

2. *Dominants favoured, recessives immigrate.* Let the nth generation produce gametes in the ratio $uA : 1a$, where aa is the immigrant recessive type. Then the composition of the population after selection and immigration is

$$\frac{u_n^2}{(u_n+1)^2}\,AA : \frac{2u_n}{(u_n+1)^2}\,Aa : \left[\frac{1-k}{(u_n+1)^2}+l\right]aa.$$

---

* *Trans. Camb. Phil. Soc.* **23** (1924), 19–41.

Thus

$$u_{n+1} = \frac{u_n(u_n+1)}{u_n+1-k+l(u_n+1)^2} \text{ and } \Delta u_n = \frac{u_n}{u_n+1}[k-l(u_n+1)^2],$$

approximately.

Hence $u_\infty = \sqrt{\dfrac{k}{l}} - 1$, which is positive if $k > l$.

If $k < l$, Δu_n is always negative, so that dominants disappear, and selection is ineffective. If $k > l$ the equilibrium is stable, the final ratio being $k - l$ dominants to l recessives.

3. *Recessives favoured, dominants immigrate.* With the same convention as above, except that AA is the immigrant type, the transformed population is

$$\left[\frac{u_n^2}{(u_n+1)^2}+l\right]AA : \frac{2u_n}{(u_n+1)^2}Aa : \frac{1+k}{(u_n+1)^2}aa.$$

Thus

$$u_{n+1} = \frac{u_n^2 + u_n + l(u_n+1)^2}{u_n+1+k}, \text{ and } \Delta u_n = \frac{l(u_n+1)^2 - ku_n}{u_n+1},$$

approximately.

Hence $\qquad u_\infty^2 + (2-k/l)u_\infty + 1 = 0,$

i.e. $\qquad u_\infty = \{k - 2l \pm \sqrt{k(k-4l)}\}/2l.$

If $k < 4l$, these roots are complex, Δu_n is always positive, and recessives disappear. If $k > 4l$, Δu_n is negative when u_n lies between the two values of u_∞, otherwise it is positive. Hence the larger root represents an unstable equilibrium. If

$$u_0 > \{k - 2l + \sqrt{k(k-4l)}\}/2l,$$

i.e. if initially there are too few recessives, recessives ultimately disappear in the face of natural selection. If u_0 be less than this value, the final state is given by the stable equilibrium

$$u_\infty = \{k - 2l - \sqrt{k(k-4l)}\}/2l,$$

and the final proportion of recessives is

$$\{k - 2l + \sqrt{k(k-4l)}\}/2k,$$

a number lying between unity and $\frac{1}{4}$. When we compare this case with the last, it is clear that selection is much less effective. Not only must it be relatively four times more intense to produce any permanent result, but, if k is not much greater than $4l$, a chance fluctuation may push the population past the point of unstable equilibrium, and the recessives be finally eliminated.

4. *No dominance.* Consider a population as above, where, after selection and immigration, the proportions are

$$\frac{u_n^2}{(u_n+1)^2} AA : \frac{2(1-K)u_n}{(u_n+1)^2} Aa : \left[\frac{1-k}{(u_n+1)^2}+l\right] aa,$$

K, as well as k, being small and positive. If K were negative, the population would come into equilibrium in the absence of immigration. The most important case is that in which $K < k$. We have

$$u_{n+1} = \frac{u_n^2 + (1-K)u_n}{(1-K)u_n + 1 - k + l(u_n+1)^2},$$

so that

$$\Delta u_n = \frac{Ku_n(u_n-1) + ku_n - lu_n(u_n+1)^2}{u_n+1}, \text{ approximately.}$$

Hence

$$K(u_\infty - 1) + k - l(u_\infty + 1)^2 = 0, \text{ or } u_\infty^2 + \left(2 - \frac{K}{l}\right)u_\infty + 1 + \frac{K-k}{l} = 0,$$

i.e.

$$u_\infty = \{K - 2l \pm \sqrt{4kl - 8Kl + K^2}\}/2l.$$

The roots are real if $4kl + K^2 > 8Kl$. This condition is obviously fulfilled if $k > 2K$. But both are negative, i.e. no equilibrium is possible, if $2l > K$, and $l + 4K > 4k$. Hence for an equilibrium to be possible $K > 2l$, or $4k > 4K + l$. If only the former is true one root is positive, and one negative. The positive root represents a stable equilibrium, and this is reached whatever the initial composition. If $K > 2l$, and $4k > 4K + l$, both roots are positive, the smaller representing an unstable equilibrium, so that u_0 must exceed the smaller root for selection to be effective.

In any case, when equilibrium is reached, the proportion of recessives is

$$\frac{K^2 + 2kl - 4Kl - K\sqrt{4kl + K^2 - 8Kl}}{2(k-2K)^2}.$$

If $k = 2K$, i.e. the heterozygotes are exactly intermediate, this expression is equal to l^2/K^2.

5. *Sex-linked dominants favoured, recessives immigrate.* Let the nth generation produce eggs in the ratio $u_n A : 1a$, spermatozoa in the ratio $v_n A : 1a$. After selection and migration, the population is in the proportions

$$\frac{u_n v_n}{(u_n+1)(v_n+1)} AA\,♀ : \frac{u_n + v_n}{(u_n+1)(v_n+1)} Aa\,♀$$

$$: \left[\frac{1-k}{(u_n+1)(v_n+1)}+l\right] aa\,♀,$$

and

$$\frac{u_n}{u_n+1} A\,♂ : \left[\frac{1-k}{u_n+1}\right] a\,♂.$$

Thus
$$u_{n+1} = \frac{2u_n v_n + u_n + v_n}{u_n + v_n + 2 - 2k + 2l\,(u_n + 1)\,(v_n + 1)},$$

$$v_{n+1} = \frac{u_n}{1 - k + l\,(u_n + 1)}.$$

Hence, since $u_n - v_n$ is a small quantity,

$$\Delta u_n = \frac{v_n - u_n}{2} + \frac{k u_n}{u_n + 1} - l u_n\,(u_n + 1), \text{ approximately,}$$

and
$$\Delta v_n = u_n - v_n + k u_n - l u_n\,(u_n + 1), \text{ approximately.}$$

Thus
$$\Delta u_n = \frac{k u_n\,(u_n + 3)}{3\,(u_n + 1)} - l u_n\,(u_n + 1), \text{ approximately,}$$

and $3l\,(u_\infty + 1)^2 = k\,(u_\infty + 3)$, i.e. $u_\infty = \{k - 6l \pm \sqrt{k\,(k + 24l)}\} / 6l$.

The roots are always real, but neither is positive unless $k > l$, and one is always negative. Hence, if $k < l$, selection is ineffective, whilst, if $k > l$, the population, whatever its initial composition, reaches a stable equilibrium in which the proportion of recessive males is $\frac{1}{4}(\sqrt{1 + 24l/k} - 1)$, that of recessive females being the square of this quantity. Clearly they may assume any value between 0 and 1.

6. *Sex-linked recessives favoured, dominants immigrate.* Adopting the same convention as above, we find

$$u_{n+1} = \frac{2u_n v_n + u_n + v_n + 2l\,(u_n + 1)\,(v_n + 1)}{u_n + v_n + 2 + 2k}, \quad v_{n+1} = \frac{u_n + l\,(u_n + 1)}{1 + k}.$$

Thus
$$\Delta u_n = \frac{v_n - u_n}{2} - \frac{k u_n}{u_n + 1} + l\,(u_n + 1), \text{ approximately,}$$

$$\Delta v_n = u_n - v_n - k u_n + l\,(u_n + 1), \text{ approximately,}$$

and
$$\Delta u_n = l\,(u_n + 1) - \frac{k u_n\,(u_n + 3)}{3\,(u_n + 1)}, \text{ approximately.}$$

Thus
$$3l\,(u_\infty + 1)^2 = k u_\infty\,(u_\infty + 3),$$

i.e.
$$u_\infty = \{3k - 6l \pm \sqrt{3k\,(3k - 8l)}\} / (6l - 2k).$$

The roots are real if $k > 8l/3$. If $k < 8l/3$ selection is ineffective. If $3l > k > 8l/3$ the larger root represents an unstable equilibrium, the smaller a stable. So selection is ineffective if the original population contains too many dominants. If however $k > 3l$, one root is negative, the positive root represents a stable equilibrium, and selection is effective whatever the original composition. When stable equilibrium is reached the proportion of recessive males is $\frac{1}{4}\{1+\sqrt{9-24l/k}\}$. The proportion may thus have any value between $\frac{1}{4}$ and 1. The proportion of females is the square of this number.

In the remaining four cases we first consider a character determined by two genes, and then generalize the result to apply to one determined by m. In the former case we can clearly represent any population by a point in a plane. If our coordinates are u and v, the ratios of the genes $A:a$ and $B:b$, we require one quadrant of an infinite plane. If we plot $\dfrac{1}{u+1}$ and $\dfrac{1}{v+1}$, or $\dfrac{1}{(u+1)^2}$ and $\dfrac{1}{(v+1)^2}$, which correspond to the actual proportions of genotypes, all populations can be represented within a finite square. Under the influence of natural selection the representative point takes up a series of positions, which, if selection is slow, are very close together, and lie on a definite trajectory passing to a point of stable equilibrium. In the case of m genes, the populations are represented by points in m-dimensional space, through each of which, in general, passes one and only one trajectory.

7. *Double or single dominants (i.e. all genotypes save aa bb) favoured, double recessives immigrate.* Consider a population whose nth generation produces gametes in the ratios $u_n A : 1a$, $v_n B : 1b$. The proportion $(u_n+1)^{-2}(v_n+1)^{-2}$ of double recessives is reduced by $k(u_n+1)^{-2}(v_n+1)^{-2}$ as the result of selection. Hence the proportion $(u_n+1)^{-2}$ of the genotype aa is reduced by

$$[1-k(v_n+1)^{-2}].$$

At the same time it is increased by l as the result of immigration.

Thus
$$u_{n+1}=\frac{u_n{}^2+u_n}{u_n+1-\dfrac{k}{(v_n+1)^2}+l(u_n+1)^2},$$

whence

$$\Delta u_n=\frac{ku_n}{(u_n+1)(v_n+1)^2}-lu_n(u_n+1),\text{ approximately,}$$

$$\Delta v_n=\frac{kv_n}{(u_n+1)^2(v_n+1)}-lv_n(v_n+1),\text{ approximately.}$$

Thus
$$(u_\infty+1)^2(v_\infty+1)^2=k/l.$$

Any of the singly infinite number of populations in which the proportion of double recessives is l/k is therefore in equilibrium, provided that $k>l$, and the equilibrium is stable.

We have
$$\frac{du_n}{dv_n} = \frac{\Delta u_n}{\Delta v_n}, \text{ approximately}$$

$$= \frac{u_n (u_n + 1)}{v_n (v_n + 1)},$$

so that
$$\frac{u_n}{u_n + 1} \cdot \frac{u_0 + 1}{u_0} = \frac{v_n}{v_n + 1} \cdot \frac{v_0 + 1}{v_0}.$$

If therefore we put $x_n = 1/(u_n + 1)$, $y_n = 1/(v_n + 1)$, x_n and y_n are the proportions of the genes a and b respectively, lying between 0 and 1, and $\dfrac{1 - x_n}{1 - x_0} = \dfrac{1 - y_n}{1 - y_0}$. The trajectories are thus all straight lines passing through the point $(1, 1)$ and all end on the segment of the hyperbola $xy = (l/k)^{\frac{1}{2}}$ included within the square containing the representative points.

In the case of m genes, let z_n be the proportion $\Pi (_r u_n + 1)^{-2}$ of multiple recessives, where $_r u_n$ is the ratio of $A_r : a_r$.

Thus
$$_r u_{n+1} = \frac{_r u_n}{1 + (_r u_n + 1)(l - kz_n)},$$

$$\Delta_r u_n = {}_r u_n (_r u_n + 1)(kz_n - l).$$

Hence the trajectories are straight lines passing through

$$(1, 1, 1, \ldots, 1)$$

and ending on the $(m - 1)$-dimensional manifold

$$x_1 x_2 x_3 \ldots x_m = (l/k)^{\frac{1}{2}},$$

where x_1, x_2, etc. are the proportions of the gene a_1, a_2, etc. in the population. The final proportion of recessives is again k/l.

8. *Double recessives favoured, double dominants immigrate.* With a population constituted as in the last case,

$$u_{n+1} = \frac{u_n^2 + u_n + l (u_n + 1)^2}{u_n + 1 + \dfrac{k}{(v_n + 1)^2}},$$

so that

$$\Delta u_n = l (u_n + 1) - \frac{k u_n}{(u_n + 1)(v_n + 1)^2}, \text{ approximately,}$$

$$\Delta v_n = l (v_n + 1) - \frac{k v_n}{(u_n + 1)^2 (v_n + 1)}, \text{ approximately}$$

Thus
$$l (u_\infty + 1)^2 (v_\infty + 1)^2 = k u_\infty = k v_\infty,$$
or, putting
$$u_\infty + 1 = v_\infty + 1 = p,$$
$$l p^4 - k p + k = 0.$$

This has two real positive roots if $k > 256l/27$. Otherwise the roots are complex and selection is ineffective. When the roots are real the larger represents an unstable equilibrium, the smaller a stable. Plotting v against u, each representative point lies on a trajectory leading either to the point of stable equilibrium or to $u = v = \infty$. The two families of trajectories are separated by a curve passing through the point of unstable equilibrium, symmetrical about the line $u = v$, and having $u = 0$, $v = 0$ for asymptotes. At equilibrium the proportion of double recessives is necessarily greater than $\frac{81}{256}$.

In the case of m genes,

$$_r u_{n+1} = \frac{_r u_n + l \left(_r u_n + 1 \right)}{1 + k \left(_r u_n + 1 \right) y_n},$$

so that
$$\Delta_r u_n = \left(_r u_n + 1 \right) \left(l - k \,_r u_n y_n \right).$$

Putting $_r u_\infty + 1 = p$, we have

$$l p^{2m} - k p + k = 0.$$

This equation has two real positive roots if, and only if,

$$\frac{k}{l} > \frac{2m^{2m}}{(2m - 1)^{2m-1}}.$$

Again the larger represents an unstable, the smaller a stable equilibrium. The families of trajectories either pass to the latter or to infinity, being separated by a $(m-1)$-dimensional manifold passing through the point of unstable equilibrium. At equilibrium the proportion of double recessives necessarily exceeds $\dfrac{(2m-1)^{2m}}{2m^{2m}}$.

We now pass from these cases, characteristic of allopolyploids such as wheat, where a character may be determined by any one of a number of genes, to cases where, as in many diploids, all of several dominants are needed to determine it.

9. *Double, but not single, dominants selected, double recessives immigrate.*

In a population composed as above the favoured individuals possess at least one A and one B. Now a proportion $[1 - (v_n + 1)^{-2}]$ of the AA and Aa zygotes are BB or Bb. Hence the effect of selection is to increase the numbers of AA and Aa by the factor $[1 + k - k (v_n + 1)^{-2}]$. Thus

$$u_{n+1} = \frac{u_n (u_n + 1) \left[1 + k (v_n^2 + 2v_n)(v_n + 1)^{-2} \right]}{u_n \left[1 + k (v_n^2 + 2v_n)(v_n + 1)^{-2} \right] + 1 + l (u_n + 1)^2},$$

so that

$$\Delta u_n = \frac{k u_n (v_n^2 + 2v_n)}{(u_n + 1)(v_n + 1)^2} - l u_n (u_n + 1), \text{ approximately,}$$

$$\Delta v_n = \frac{k v_n (u_n^2 + 2u_n)}{(v_n + 1)(u_n + 1)^2} - l v_n (v_n + 1), \text{ approximately.}$$

Thus

$$u_\infty = v_\infty = 0, \text{ or } l(u_\infty + 1)^2(v_\infty + 1)^2 = k(u_\infty{}^2 + 2u_\infty) = k(v_\infty{}^2 + 2v_\infty).$$

Hence $u_\infty = v_\infty$. Putting $(u_\infty + 1)^2 = q$, we have

$$lq^2 - kq + k = 0,$$

$$q = \{k \pm \sqrt{k^2 - 4kl}\}/2l.$$

The roots are real if $k > 4l$. Otherwise selection is ineffective, and dominants disappear. If the roots are real, both exceed unity, and therefore represent equilibria, the larger representing a stable equilibrium, the smaller an unstable. The proportion of double dominants in the population in stable equilibrium is

$$\{k - 2l + \sqrt{k^2 - 4kl}\}/2k,$$

which necessarily exceeds $\frac{1}{4}$.

As before, the trajectories form two families, one passing to the point of stable equilibrium, the other through the point $(0, 0)$ when u and v are plotted. They are separated by a curve passing through the point of unstable equilibrium.

Generalising for the case of m genes A_r, the ratio $A_r : a_r$ in the nth generation being $_r u_n$, the proportion of multiple dominants

$$y_n = \prod_{r=1}^{m} [1 - (_r u_n + 1)^{-2}].$$

Of these $\dfrac{_r u_n}{_r u_n + 2}$ are $A_r A_r$, $\dfrac{2}{_r u_n + 2}$ are $A_r a_r$. Thus

$$_r u_{n+1} = \cfrac{\dfrac{_r u_n{}^2 + _r u_n}{(_r u_n + 1)^2} + \dfrac{k(_r u_n + 1)\, y_n}{_r u_n + 2}}{\dfrac{_r u_n + 1}{(_r u_n + 1)^2} + \dfrac{k y_n}{(_r u_n + 2)} + l},$$

and

$$\Delta\, _r u_n = (_r u_n + 1)\left(\frac{k y_n}{_r u_n + 2} - l\, _r u_n\right),$$

whence

$$k y_\infty = l\, _r u_\infty (_r u_\infty + 2).$$

Hence $_r u_\infty$ is independent of the value of r. Putting

$$1 - (u_\infty + 1)^{-2} = z^{-1},$$

we have $y_\infty = z^{-m}$, where $lz^m - kz + k = 0$.

This has two real positive roots if, and only if,

$$\frac{k}{l} > \frac{m^m}{(m-1)^{m-1}}.$$

The larger root of z corresponds to small values of u_∞ and defines an unstable equilibrium, the smaller a stable equilibrium. At the stable equilibrium $z < m/(m-1)$, so that $y_\infty > \{(m-1)/m\}^m > \frac{1}{4}$. The trajectories in m-dimensional space again form two distinct families.

10. *Double, but not single, dominants selected against, double dominants immigrate.* The effect of selection is as in the last case, the sign of k being changed. Thus

$$u_{n+1} = \frac{u_n(u_n+1)\{1 - k(v_n^2 + 2v_n)(v_n+1)^{-2}\} + l(u_n+1)^2}{u_n\{1 - k(v_n^2 + 2v_n)(v_n+1)^{-2}\} + 1},$$

and $\Delta u_n = l(u_n+1) - \dfrac{ku_n(v_n^2 + 2v_n)}{(u_n+1)(v_n+1)^2}$, approximately,

$$\Delta v_n = l(v_n+1) - \frac{kv_n(u_n^2 + 2u_n)}{(v_n+1)(u_n+1)^2}, \text{ approximately.}$$

Thus $l(u_\infty+1)^2(v_\infty+1)^2 = ku_\infty v_\infty(v_\infty+2) = ku_\infty v_\infty(u_\infty+2).$

Hence $u_\infty = v_\infty$, being a root of

$$u_\infty^4 + (4 - k/l)u_\infty^3 + (6 - 2k/l)u_\infty^2 + 4u + 1 = 0.$$

This equation always has two real negative roots. It has also two real positive roots if and only if $k > 2^{-10} \cdot 7^{-1}(\sqrt{17}+1)^6(\sqrt{17}-3)l$, or about $3.57\,l$. Otherwise selection is ineffective. If k exceeds this value the situation is similar to that of case 8, the larger root representing an unstable equilibrium, the smaller a stable. At stable equilibrium the proportion of double dominants is less than $\left(\dfrac{23 + \sqrt{17}}{32}\right)^2$, or $71.8\,\%$; that of double recessives exceeds $\left(\dfrac{\sqrt{17}-1}{8}\right)^4$, or $2.32\,\%$. As before, the trajectories in the u, v plane fall into two families, one passing to infinity, the other to the point of stable equilibrium.

In the case of m factors,

$$_ru_{n+1} = \frac{\dfrac{_ru_n}{_ru_n+1} - \dfrac{k(_ru_n+1)y_n}{_ru_n+2} + l}{\dfrac{1}{_ru_n+1} - \dfrac{ky_n}{_ru_n+2}},$$

so that $\Delta\,_ru_n = (_ru_n+1)\left(l - \dfrac{ky_n}{_ru_n+2}\right).$

At equilibrium

$$u_\infty + 2 = (k/l)[1 - (u_\infty+1)^{-2}]^m,$$

or, if $u_\infty + 1 = p$,

$$p + 1 = (k/l)(1 - p^{-2})^m.$$

This has two real positive roots if

$$\frac{k}{l} > \frac{\sqrt{8m+1}+3}{2} \left(\frac{4m+1+\sqrt{8m+1}}{4m}\right)^m \left(\frac{4m-1-\sqrt{8m+1}}{4(m-1)}\right)^m.$$

As above, the larger root represents an unstable equilibrium, the smaller a stable, and the trajectories fall into two families. At equilibrium the proportion of double dominants is less than

$$\left(\frac{4m-1+\sqrt{8m+1}}{4m}\right)^m \left(\frac{4m+1-\sqrt{8m+1}}{4m}\right)^m,$$

that of double recessives exceeds

$$\left(\frac{\sqrt{8m+1}-1}{4m}\right)^m.$$

It will be seen that in every case k/l must exceed a certain critical value unless the selected type is to be completely swamped by immigration. When this value is exceeded it is further necessary, in some cases, that the proportion of the selected type in the initial population should exceed a certain fraction. Now in nature the value of k/l must fluctuate widely round an average. Occasionally a flood must sweep large numbers of normal-eyed aquatic animals into a cave where the majority are blind, and so on. And where one of the equilibria is unstable, this may lead to the disappearance of the selected type. It would thus seem that in partially isolated communities selection is most likely to be effective when it favours a dominant or sex-linked character.

The problem can readily be generalized in several ways. Thus the effects of partial inbreeding might be considered. As however the results of complete inbreeding (case 1) are not very different from those of random mating, the general character of the solution will be unaltered.

One group of cases of a practical character will be considered, namely the result of breeding plants which are partially cross-pollinated, but where seed is only gathered from those of a desirable type. For the sake of simplicity it is assumed that rogues (plants of undesirable types) are destroyed before they produce pollen. We also assume complete self-sterility, so that all fertilization is by pollen of other plants. The average proportion of pollen from the wild population surrounding the group under selection is denoted by l, which in this case need not be a small quantity.

If the cultivated plant be recessive to the wild population, whether for one or many factors, it is obvious that the proportion of rogues in each generation is l. If it is dominant to the wild type with respect to a single factor A, suppose that, after the removal of rogues, gametes are formed in the ratio $u_n A : 1 a$. After admixture of foreign pollen, the ratio of pollen grains will be $(1-l) u_n A : (1+lu_n) a$. Hence zygotes are formed in the ratios

$$(1-l) u_n^2 AA : (2-l+lu_n) Aa : (1+lu_n) aa.$$

The AA and Aa zygotes contribute to the next generation, so that

$$u_{n+1} = \frac{2(1-l) u_n^2 + (2-l+lu_n) u_n}{(2-l+lu_n) u_n} = \frac{(2-l)(u_n+1)}{2-l+lu_n},$$

and

$$\Delta u_n = \frac{2-l-lu_n^2}{2-l+lu_n},$$

whence

$$u_\infty = \sqrt{(2/l-1)}.$$

This represents a stable equilibrium, approached fairly rapidly from both sides. At equilibrium the proportion of rogues is

$$\frac{1+lu_\infty}{(u_\infty+1)^2}, \quad \text{or} \quad \frac{l}{2}.$$

The expression in the case when the selected type is dominant to the wild with regard to several factors is more complicated, but such a case is too improbable to be worth considering. Provided that it is recessive for even one factor, all other factors are automatically eliminated in one generation.

13

Reprinted from *Amer. Naturalist* **87**:331-333 (1953)

GENETIC EQUILIBRIUM WHEN MORE THAN ONE ECOLOGICAL NICHE IS AVAILABLE

Howard Levene

In recent years the attention of experimental evolutionists has been increasingly directed toward polymorphism as furnishing desirable plasticity to a species. In particular, attention has been directed toward polymorphism with a known genetic basis. The best studied case is that of two alleles showing balanced polymorphism: that is, the heterozygote has a higher adaptive value in a certain environment or range of environments than either homozygote. Such balanced polymorphism is the only way a pair of alleles can remain in equilibrium within a single environment (or ecological niche), if we ignore mutation pressure and migration from the outside. On the other hand, it would seem that the existence of several ecological niches, with one allele favored in one niche and the other allele favored in another, might increase the possibilities for attainment of equilibrium with both alleles present in substantial proportions. Recently the question arose of whether it was in fact possible to have equilibrium without the heterozygote being superior to both homozygotes in any single niche. It is shown below that under certain assumptions the answer is yes.

The model here proposed is as follows: Let there be alleles A and A' with gene frequencies of q and $1 - q$ respectively, and let mating be at random over the whole population, so that the initial zygotic frequencies are $q^2 AA$, $2q(1 - q)AA'$, and $(1 - q)^2 A'A'$. After fertilization the zygotes settle down at random in large numbers into each of the niches, and are thereafter immobile. There is then differential mortality ending with a fixed number of individuals in each niche. After selection the relative frequencies of AA, AA', and A'A' will be $W_1 q^2 : 2q(1 - q) : V_1(1 - q)^2$ in niche 1, $W_2 q^2 : 2q(1 - q) : V_2(1 - q)^2$ in the second niche, etc., where W_1 and V_1 are the adaptive values of AA and A'A' individuals relative to AA' in the i-th niche. We need consider only intra-niche comparisons and not the absolute viabilities in the different niches. If we disregard drift and consider only the force of selection, the absolute number of survivors in the different niches is also irrelevant and we may work with the numbers c_i, where c_i is the proportion of the total survivors to be found in the i-th niche, and $\Sigma c_i = 1$. To complete the model, we suppose that at the time of reproduction the survivors leave the niches, and that mating is at random in the entire population. If we denote by q' the frequency of A in this mating population, then $q' = \Sigma c_i q_i$, where q_i is the frequency of A in the i-th niche after selection.

It can easily be seen that under this model Δq is the weighted mean of the Δq's for the individual niches, so that

$$1) \qquad \Delta q = q' - q = q(1-q)\Sigma c_i \frac{(1-V_i) + (W_i + V_i - 2)q}{V_i + 2(1-V_i)q + (W_i + V_i - 2)q^2}$$

The factor $q(1-q)$ gives a trivial equilibrium at $q = 0$ and $q = 1$. The function $h(q) = \Delta q/q(1-q)$ will have the same sign as Δq for $0 < q < 1$. Since $h(q)$ is continuous, if $h(0)$ is positive and $h(1)$ is negative, there will be at least one q between 0 and 1 for which $h(q) = 0$ and hence at least one point of stable equilibrium. Setting $q = 0$ we find $h(q) = \Sigma c_i(1-V_i)/V_i$, which is positive if

$$2) \qquad 1 + \Sigma c_i \frac{1-V_i}{V_i} \equiv \Sigma c_i \frac{1}{V_i} > 1.$$

Setting $q = 1$ we find $h(1) = \Sigma c_i(W_i - 1)/W_i$, which is negative if

$$3) \qquad 1 - \Sigma c_i \frac{W_i - 1}{W_i} \equiv \Sigma c_i \frac{1}{W_i} > 1.$$

Conditions 2 and 3 are equivalent to the conditions that the weighted harmonic means of the W_i and of the V_i (the reciprocals of expressions 2 and 3) be less than one. Since the harmonic mean is less than the arithmetic mean except when all the numbers being averaged are equal, there will, *a forteriori*, be a stable equilibrium if the weighted arithmetic means of the W_i and V_i are less than one. For a single niche, this reduces to W_i and V_i both less than one, which is known to be a necessary and sufficient condition for a stable equilibrium. For more than one niche, conditions 2 and 3 are sufficient but not necessary. For example, with two niches and $c_1 = c_2 = \frac{1}{2}$, $W_1 = 2$, $V_1 = 1.1$, $W_2 = 0.5$, $V_2 = 1.1$, if initially $0 < q < 0.6$, equilibrium will be reached with $q = 0.35$, while if $q > 0.6$, A' will be eliminated; in other words 0.35 is a point of stable equilibrium and 0.6 is a point of unstable equilibrium. In this example, the harmonic mean of V is $1.1 > 1$. On the other hand, with $c_1 = c_2 = \frac{1}{2}$, $W_1 = 2$, $V_1 = 1.2$, $W_2 = 0.5$, $V_2 = 1.2$ there is no equilibrium point between zero and one. An example fulfilling conditions 2 and 3 is $c_1 = c_2 = \frac{1}{2}$, $W_1 = \frac{3}{2}$, $V_1 = \frac{2}{3}$, $W_2 = \frac{2}{3}$, $V_2 = \frac{3}{2}$, giving a stable equilibrium at $q = \frac{1}{2}$. Note that in this example the weighted arithmetic means are greater than one, although the weighted harmonic means are less than one. For this last example the location of the equilibrium point at $\frac{1}{2}$ can be found by considerations of symmetry, but in general the actual value of the equilibrium point must be found by trial and error or some other approximate method.

The model here proposed is obviously not realistic; however, if it is modified by supposing that individuals move preferentially to niches they are better fitted for, or that there is a tendency for mating to occur within a niche rather than at random over the whole population, conditions will be more favorable for equilibrium, so that in a sense we are considering the worst possible case. For another rather artificial model with variable population size, which will be discussed elsewhere, equilibrium is attained under similar conditions.

14

Reprinted from *J. Genetics* **58**:237–242 (1963)

POLYMORPHISM DUE TO SELECTION OF VARYING DIRECTION

By J. B. S. HALDANE and S. D. JAYAKAR

Genetics and Biometry Laboratory, Government of Orissa, Bhubaneswar

INTRODUCTION

Geneticists are showing increasing interest in genetically determined polymorphism. This is especially true of human geneticists, since polymorphism is often associated with a loss of fitness, sometimes described as genetic load. In recent discussions the following causes of more or less stable polymorphism have been distinguished.

(1) The conflict between selection and mutation. An equilibrium is reached when in each generation in a population of given number as many "mutant" genes are destroyed by selection as appear by mutation. The conflict between selection and the abnormal Mendelian segregation now called "meiotic drive" is analogous.

(2) The conflict between selection and segregation. The best known example occurs when a heterozygote is fitter than either of the two corresponding homozygotes. But where several allelomorphs are concerned matters are more complicated, and, as we hope to show later in some detail, the heterozygote need not be fitter in order to stabilize polymorphism when selective intensities differ in the two sexes.

(3) The conflict between fitness and abundance. A genotype may become less fit as it becomes more abundant. The most striking case is perhaps genetically determined self-sterility in plants, but Batesian mimicry probably acts in a similar way, mimics being better protected when greatly outnumbered by distasteful models than when mimics are common. So does resistance to infectious disease if the pathogen can adapt itself fairly rapidly so as to attack the commonest genotypes preferentially.

(4) The conflict between selection and migration. If each of two genotypes is fitter in different areas, migration between them may lead to a cline which may be polymorphic.

(5) The conflict between selections in different directions in the diploid generation and the haploid generation (usually pollen tubes) or in the two sexes.

Finally a polymorphism may be transient. A genotype which was formerly common may be disappearing as the result of changed conditions.

These are not, however, the only conditions which may lead to long-lasting genetic polymorphism, nor is the account of the five situations described above very satisfactory. We hope, in a series of papers, of which this is the first, to add some precision to the accounts of polymorphism so far given by Haldane and others. The present paper deals with polymorphism caused by selection which sometimes favours one phenotype and sometimes another, or in the general terminology of this introduction by conflict between selection in two directions.

THE GENERAL THEOREM

Suppose that the population consists of two phenotypes P and Q, and that the fitness of Q relative to P is F_n in the nth generation, but that F_n sometimes exceeds unity, and sometimes falls short of it. If P and Q are clones or pure lines which do not interbreed; or genotypes of a haploid differing in respect of a single gene pair, and if the ratio of P to Q in generation n is u_n, then $u_{n+1} = F_n^{-1} u_n$.

$$\text{So} \quad u_n = \left[\prod_{r=0}^{n-1} F_r \right]^{-1} u_0 \tag{1.1}$$

that is to say u_n is equal to u_0 divided by the product of the values of F_n. It is most improbable that this will be exactly unity. As time goes on it is almost certain that the product of the values of F_n will be much greater or much less than unity, and P or Q, as the case may be, will disappear. We can also think in terms of the geometric mean. If this differs even slightly from unity over sufficiently many generations, one or other of the phenotypes will disappear. In practice of course it is possible that the rarer phenotype will be restricted to a niche where it is at an advantage, leading to an equilibrium of type (4) considered above.

Now consider a large* diploid random mating population, so large that the probability of the extinction of a temporarily rare gene by random fluctuation is negligible. Let a pair of allelomorphs **A** and **a** at an autosomal locus occur in the gametes which form the nth generation in the ratio u_n **A**: 1 **a**. Let **a** be fully recessive as regards fitness, and let the fitness of **aa** in year n relative to **AA** and **Aa** be F_n. That is to say let P be **AA** or **Aa**, and Q be **aa**. Then (Haldane, 1924)

$$u_{n+1} = \frac{u_n (u_n + 1)}{u_n + F_n}. \tag{1.2}$$

First consider the case when all values of u_n are large.

$$u_{r+1} - u_r = \frac{(1 - F_r) u_r}{u_r + F_r}$$

$$= 1 - F_r + \frac{F_r (F_r - 1)}{u_r + F_r}$$

Hence, by summation

$$u_n - u_0 = n - \sum_{r=0}^{n-1} F_r + \sum_{r=0}^{n-1} \frac{F_r (F_r - 1)}{u_r + F_r}. \tag{1.3}$$

If all values of u_r are sufficiently large, then only the first two terms need be considered. For any finite value of n this can be assured by choosing a large enough value of u_0. Hence if $\Sigma F_r > n$, or, what is equivalent, if the mean value of F_r is greater than unity, u_n will be less than u_0 provided u_0 is sufficiently large.

*Mutation gives a simple criterion for "largeness" of a population. If a population is, say, ten times the reciprocal of the frequency with which a gene appears by mutation, the probability that no mutants will appear in it in any given generation is e^{-10}, or 5×10^{-5}. In a population of this size we may base our calculations on selection and mutation rates, neglecting the possibility of random extinction. The size will be of the order of a million for many human mutation rates.

Now let u_r be small. Then from (1.2)

$$\frac{u_{r+1}}{u_r} = \frac{1+u_r}{F_r+u_r}$$

$$\log u_{r+1} - \log u_r = -\log F_r - \log \left[1 + \frac{(1-F_r)\,u_r}{F_r\,(1+u_r)}\right]$$

So by summation

$$\log u_n - \log u_o = -\sum_{r=0}^{n-1} \log F_r - \sum_{r=0}^{n-1} \log \left[1 + \frac{(1-F_r)\,u_r}{F_r\,(1+u_r)}\right] \tag{1.4}$$

As before, if all values of u_r are sufficiently small, the second term is negligible unless some value of F_r is zero. If however a value of F_r is zero the corresponding term in the sum is $\log (u_r^{-1}+1)$. This is not infinite, but can be made as large as we choose by a suitable choice of u_o. We conclude that if u_o is sufficiently small, u_n will exceed u_o provided $\sum \log F_r < 0$, or $\prod_{r=0}^{n-1} F_r < 1$, or the geometric mean of F_r is less than unity.

It follows that, provided the arithmetic mean of the values of F_r is greater than unity, and the geometric mean less, u_n is bounded, that is to say, it must be between certain values. Neither of the genes **A** and **a** can disappear. If the values of F_r form a cycle, so that $F_{n+c} = F_n$, then the various values of u_n in a cycle converge towards fixed values. An example will be given later.

It may be asked whether the condition that the arithmetic mean should exceed unity, and the geometric mean be less, is not highly artificial. It is easy to give an example where it would be fulfilled. Suppose that the recessive **aa** is normally 5% to 10% fitter than the dominants, but that every twenty generations, on an average, an epidemic disease kills off all the recessives; then the arithmetic mean exceeds unity, but the geometric mean is zero. After each epidemic the frequency of recessive genes is half the frequency of heterozygotes in the previous generation, that is to say somewhat less than a half. It then increases until the next epidemic. It is not of course necessary to suppose that all the recessives are killed off. And the killing agent might be a drought or frost. It is sufficient that the recessive should be fitter than the dominant on the whole, but liable to be killed or sterilized in some abnormal but rare circumstances. It is hard to suppose that this condition is never fulfilled in nature.

If both the arithmetical and geometrical means of their fitness are less than unity, recessives will disappear in the course of time (except insofar as they are replaced by mutation). And if both these means are greater than unity, dominants will disappear. Since the arithmetic mean necessarily exceeds the geometric, unless the fitnesses are constant, there is no situation where either gene may disappear according to its initial frequency, as when heterozygotes are less fit than either homozygote.

Finally we may remark that the arithmetic mean of the relative fitnesses of recessives is the reciprocal of the harmonic mean of the relative fitnesses of dominants. For stability this harmonic mean must be less than unity. As the harmonic mean is a less familiar idea than the arithmetic, we have preferred to use the latter.

BIVOLTINE ORGANISMS

Let us suppose that, like some insects, an organism has just two generations per year. In the spring generation the fitness of **aa** relative to **AA** and **Aa** is F, in the autumn generation f. Suppose the spring generation of year n to be formed from gametes with u_n **A** : 1 **a**, the autumn generation from gametes with u'_n **A** : 1 **a**. Then

$$u'_n = \frac{u_n (u_n+1)}{u_n+F} ,$$

$$u_{n+1} = \frac{u'_n(u'_n+1)}{u'_n+f}$$

$$= \frac{u_n(u_n+1) (u_n^2+2u_n+F)}{(u_n+F) [u_n^2+(1+f)u_n+Ff]} . \tag{2.1}$$

$$u_{n+1}- u_n = \frac{-u_n [(F+f-2) u_n^2-2 (1-Ff)u_n-F (1- Ff)]}{(u_n+F) [u_n^2+(1+f)u_n+Ff]} . \tag{2.2}$$

At equilibrium $u_n = U$, where $U=0$, $U=\infty$, or

$$(F+f-2) U^2-2 (1-Ff) U-F (1-Ff) = 0 \tag{2.3}$$

whence $U = \dfrac{1-Ff\pm(1-F) (1-Ff)^{\frac{1}{2}}}{F+f-2} .$ (2.4)

Since the roots are real, $Ff<1$. Since one must be positive, $F+f>2$. The figure shows the area within which the point (F, f) must lie to ensure an equilibrium with both genes present. Hence the right hand side of (2·2) is negative when u_n is large, positive when it is small. Hence the equilibrium is stable. (2·3) has only one positive root. If $F<1$ the ambiguity in (2·4) must have the negative sign. The equilibrium recessive gene frequencies in spring and autumn are:

$$Q=(U+1)^{-1}$$

$$= \frac{(1-f) - (1-Ff)^{\frac{1}{2}}}{f (F-1)} , \tag{2.5}$$

$$Q' = \frac{F-1-(1-Ff)^{\frac{1}{2}}}{F (1-f)} .$$

Thus if $F = \frac{5}{3}$, $f = \frac{1}{2}$, $Q = \cdot2753$, $Q' = \cdot3101$, so the frequencies of recessives in spring and autumn are 7·58% and 9·62%.

The deviations from equilibrium fall off roughly in a geometric progression. Similar calculations could be made for a cycle of three or more generations.

OVER-DOMINANCE

It is well known (Fisher, 1922) that if the relative fitnesses of **AA** : **Aa** : **aa** in each generation are $F : 1 : f$, being the same in each generation, there is a stable

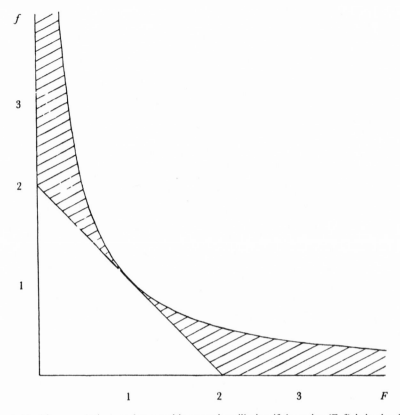

Fig. 1.   A bivoltine population reaches a stable annual oscillation if the point (F, f) is in the shaded area.

equilibrium if and only if F and f are both less than unity.   Let us now consider the case when F and f are variable.

$$u_{n+1} = \frac{F_n u_n{}^2 + u_n}{u_n + f_n} \tag{3.1}$$

$$\text{So } \frac{u_{n+1}}{u_n} = F_n + \frac{1 - F_n f_n}{u_n + f_n} \tag{3.2}$$

$$= f_n{}^{-1} + \frac{(F_n f_n - 1)u_n}{f_n (f_n + u_n)} \tag{3.3}$$

We see that we can choose u_0 so large that $u_{n+1} u_n{}^{-1}$ is as close as we wish to F_n.   Hence $u_o > u_n$ if the geometric mean of F_r is less than unity.   Similarly we can choose u_0 so small that $\frac{u_{n+1}}{u_n}$ is as close as we wish to $f_n{}^{-1}$.   Hence $u_n > u_o$ if the geometric mean of f_r is less than unity.   Thus polymorphism will persist if the geometric mean fitnesses of each homozygote relative to the heterozygotes are each less than unity.   Once again this may occur, even if the mean fitness of homozygotes relative to heterozygotes exceeds unity, provided the relative fitness of homozygotes occasionally falls very low.

It is not sufficient or necessary that the arithmetic mean fitness of the heterozygotes relative to homozygotes (that is to say the harmonic mean of F_r or f_r) should exceed unity.

For example an occasional severe epidemic of *falciparum* malaria might suffice to keep the gene for haemoglobin S from disappearance, even if for generations on end heterozygotes for sickling were at a disadvantage compared with persons homozygous for haemoglobin A.

DISCUSSION

There is no great difficulty in extending the argument to a pair of sex-linked genes when dominance is complete in the homogametic sex. Here however a condition for equilibrium is that the relative fitness of heterogametic "mutants" should exceed unity, that of homogametic mutants being less than unity. It will be best discussed along with other cases where selection is in opposite directions in the two sexes.

We think that we have proved two novel points, first that a mere series of changes in the direction of selection may be enough to secure polymorphism, secondly that one result of Mendelian inheritance is that polymorphism may be permanent, if not exactly stable, when it is not so for a difference inherited clonally, cytoplasmically, or in a haploid. Finally we have shown that a statistical treatment of the intensity of selection can lead to definite results.

The results of this paper can, and doubtless will, be extended. Thus it is clear that inbreeding makes the conditions for polymorphism more stringent, and that the sums in (1·3) and (1·4) can be replaced by integrals when generations overlap.

SUMMARY

In a large random mating population segregating for a pair of allelomorphs with full dominance, the condition that neither allelomorph should disappear is that the arithmetic mean of the fitnesses of recessives in different generations should exceed unity, their geometric mean fall below it.

REFERENCES

HALDANE, J. B. S. (1924). A mathematical theory of natural and artificial selection, Part I. *Trans. Camb. Phil. Soc.*, **23,** 19-41.

FISHER, R. A. (1922). On the dominance ratio. *Proc. Roy. Soc. Edin.*, **42,** 321-341.

15

Reprinted from *Amer. Naturalist* **100**:637-650 (1966)

SYMPATRIC SPECIATION

J. MAYNARD SMITH

Department of Biology, The University of Sussex, Falmer, Brighton, Sussex

"One would think that it should no longer be necessary to devote much time to this topic, but past experience permits one to predict that the issue will be raised again at regular intervals." Mayr (1963)

I. INTRODUCTION

The problem discussed in this paper is whether speciation can occur in a sexually reproducing species without effective geographical isolation. The argument is an old one. It is still alive because it cannot easily be settled by observation; the present distribution of species is equally consistent either with the sympatric or the allopatric theory. The crucial argument against sympatric speciation, admirably summarised by Mayr (1963), is that no mechanism consistent with the known facts of genetics can be suggested.

I have been led to question this argument mainly by the experimental results of Thoday and his colleagues (Thoday and Boam, 1959; Millicent and Thoday, 1960; Thoday and Gibson, 1962). Although I am unable to account for the rapidity with which Thoday and Gibson were able to establish reproductive isolation between two populations of *Drosophila melanogaster*, this series of experiments has shown that disruptive selection (i.e., selection favoring extreme at the expense of average phenotypes) can produce a stable polymorphism.

At first sight this is a puzzling finding. If alleles A and a have additive effects on the phenotype, disruptive selection would make AA and aa fitter than Aa. This is the exact opposite of the situation required for stable polymorphism through heterosis, and would lead to a population consisting wholly of AA or wholly of aa individuals. The explanation lies in the mechanism regulating the population size. If the population forms a single entity whose size is regulated to some number N, regardless of the genotypes of its members, the conclusion that disruptive selection cannot maintain polymorphism is correct. But if the population inhabits two subenvironments or "niches," the population size being separately regulated to numbers N_1 and N_2 in the two niches, and if AA is fitter in one niche and aa in the other, then a stable polymorphism is possible, even if there is random mating between individuals raised in the two niches. The first part of this paper is concerned to establish this point and to determine the conditions which must be satisfied. This part of the paper confirms conclusions reached earlier by Levene (1953), and analyzes the effects of "habitat selection." The condition of separate density-dependent regulation in two niches was in effect satisfied in Thoday's experiments, since constant numbers of "high" and "low" parents were selected in each generation.

Polymorphism however is not speciation. The second part of this paper considers whether reproductive isolation would be likely to evolve between the two morphs. The answer to this question depends on how genes causing reproductive isolation are supposed to act. Four possible mechanisms are distinguished. It is concluded that a stable polymorphism could well provide the starting point of a process of speciation.

The possibility that a stable polymorphism might arise in an environment which is uniform in space, but which varies from generation to generation in such a way that the relative fitnesses of different genotypes changes, has been considered by Haldane and Jayakar (1963) and by Basykin (1965). The latter author considers the conditions which must be satisfied if such a polymorphism in a temporally varying environment is to give rise to speciation. However, this mechanism of sympatric speciation seems less likely to occur than that considered in the present paper.

II. STABLE POLYMORPHISM IN A HETEROGENEOUS ENVIRONMENT

The first point to be investigated is whether a stable polymorphism is possible in a heterogeneous environment. The assumptions which will be made are as follows:

1) The environment is divided into two "niches," 1 and 2, in such a way that the density-dependent factors regulating the population size operate independently in the two niches. The niches can be thought of as different food plants in the case of phytophagous insects, as different host species in the case of parasites, as shore and common or as lake and river in the case of bird species, and so on. The assumption about density-dependence implies that niche 1 will support a population of n_1 adults, and niche 2 of n_2 adults. In much of what follows, it will be assumed that $n_1 = n_2$, but this assumption is not required for the establishment of a stable polymorphism: it has been made to simplify the algebra.

2) Also for simplicity, generations are assumed to be separate.

3) The adults produced in the two niches form a single random-mating population.

4) There may be a degree of "habitat selection" by females.

Allowance for habitat selection is made only in the simple case in which $n_1 = n_2$. It is then assumed that a female herself raised in niche 1 lays a fraction $\frac{1}{2}(1 + H)$ of her eggs in niche 1, and $\frac{1}{2}(1 - H)$ in niche 2, where $0 \leqslant H \leqslant 1$, the proportions being reversed in the case of females raised in niche 2. Thus $H = 0$ implies no habitat selection and $H = 1$ complete habitat selection.

It should be emphasized that the choice by a female of a place to lay her eggs depends not directly on her genotype but on her own upbringing. Evidence for the occurrence of such a process is reviewed by Thorpe (1930).

Equilibrium with dominance, when $n_1 = n_2$

A, a are two alleles, with fitnesses (measured as relative probability of survival from egg to adult) as follows:

	AA	Aa	aa
in niche 1	$1 + K$	$1 + K$	1
in niche 2	1	1	$1 + k$

Thus A is fully dominant in both niches. The case of complete dominance has been chosen for full investigation because there is then no danger that any equilibria discovered will have arisen from a "concealed" overdominance; but similar results can be reached if effects on fitness are additive in both niches.

Let p_1, p_2 be the frequencies of A in adults raised in niches 1 and 2, respectively, in generation 0.

Then in niche 1, a fraction $\frac{1}{2}(1 + H)$ of all eggs laid are laid by females with gene frequencies $p_1 A : (1 - p_1) a$, and $\frac{1}{2}(1 - H)$ by females with gene frequencies $p_2 A : (1 - p_2) a$. All females mate at random with males with gene frequencies $\frac{1}{2}(p_1 + p_2) A : 1 - \frac{1}{2}(p_1 + p_2) a$.

Hence, writing $\frac{1}{2}(p_1 + p_2) = S$, $\frac{1}{2}(p_1 - p_2) = d$, the zygotic frequencies are:

$$AA = \tfrac{1}{2}(1 + H) p_1 S + \tfrac{1}{2}(1 - H) p_2 S$$
$$= S(S + Hd)$$

$$Aa = \tfrac{1}{2}(1 + H)\{p_1(1 - S) + (1 - p_1)S\} + \tfrac{1}{2}(1 - H)\{p_2(1 - S) + (1 - p_2)S\}$$
$$= 2S(1 - S) + Hd(1 - 2S)$$

$$aa = \tfrac{1}{2}(1 + H)(1 - p_1)(1 - S) + \tfrac{1}{2}(1 - H)(1 - p_2)(1 - S)$$
$$= (1 - S)(1 - S - Hd)$$

Now at equilibrium, writing the zygotic frequency of AA as $[AA]$ and so on:

$$p_1 = S + d = \frac{\{2[AA] + [Aa]\}(1 + K)}{\{2[AA] + 2[Aa]\}(1 + K) + 2[aa]}$$

And substituting and simplifying, this reduces to

$$d^2 HK(1 - S) + d\{1 + HKS(1 - S) + KS(2 - S) - \tfrac{1}{2}H(1 + K)\} - KS(1 - S)^2 = 0 \quad (1)$$

The equivalent equation for niche 2 is

$$d^2 Hk(1 - S) + d\{1 - HkS(1 - S) + k(1 - S)^2 - \tfrac{1}{2}H\} - kS(1 - S)^2 = 0 \quad (2)$$

d can be eliminated by multiplying equation (1) by k and equation (2) by K, and subtracting. The resultant equation can then be reduced to the form

$$\frac{k - K}{Kk} = \frac{4S^2 - 8S + 2 + H(1 - 2S)^2}{2 - H} \quad (3)$$

If there is no habitat selection ($H = 0$), females laying eggs in the two niches at random, this becomes

$$\frac{k - K}{Kk} = 2S^2 - 4S + 1 \quad (4)$$

And if there is complete habitat selection ($H = 1$), females always laying eggs in the niche in which they themselves were raised, then

$$\frac{k - K}{Kk} = 8S^2 - 12S + 3 \qquad (5)$$

Equations (3), (4), and (5) give the mean frequency of the dominant allele A in the adult population, S, in terms of the selective advantages k and K.

The stability of these equilibria can be deduced from Fig. 1, in which S is plotted against $(k - K)/Kk$. Considering first the case in which $H = 0$,

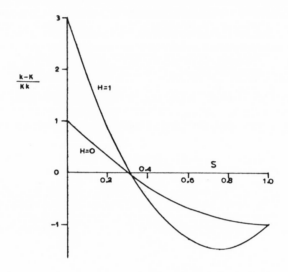

FIG. 1. Relation between $\dfrac{k - K}{Kk}$ and S, the mean frequency of allele A at equilibrium.

the slope of the graph is negative throughout. Suppose then that the values of k and K are such as to maintain an equilibrium with $S = S_0$, and that the actual gene frequency of A is $S_0 + \Delta S$, where ΔS is positive. It follows that $(k - K)/Kk$ is too large, and hence that K is too small compared with k, to maintain the gene frequency at this value. Now since $1 + K$ is the fitness of Aa and AA, and $1 + k$ of aa, in their respective niches, it follows that if K is too small relative to k to maintain the frequency at $S_0 + \Delta S$, then the frequency will fall towards S_0. In other words, the equilibrium is stable provided that the slope in Fig. 1 is negative.

Thus when $H = 0$, if an equilibrium exists it is stable. For an equilibrium to exist, it is sufficient that S should lie between 0 and 1, and hence that

$$1 > \frac{k - K}{Kk} > -1$$

or

$$k(1 - K) < K; \quad k(1 + K) > K \qquad (6)$$

If K is small, this imposes very narrow limits on k. For example, if $K = 0.1$, k must lie between 0.09 and 0.11, a condition most unlikely to be satisfied.

If the selective advantages are large, the range of permissible values is much wider. Thus the first condition is necessarily satisfied if $K \geqslant 1$ and k positive; thus if $K = 1$, a stable equilibrium exists if $k > 0.5$.

When $H = 1$ (complete habitat preference), stable equilibria exist over the range $S = 0$, $\dfrac{k - K}{Kk} = 3$ to $S = 0.75$, $\dfrac{k - K}{Kk} = -1.5$. If $\dfrac{k - K}{Kk}$ lies between -1 and -1.5, a second, unstable equilibrium exists with $S > 0.75$. Thus the conditions for a stable equilibrium are:

$$k(1 - 3K) < K; \qquad k(1 + 1.5 K) > K \tag{7}$$

When K is small, this again imposes narrow limits on k. If $K = 0.1$, k must lie between 0.087 and 0.143.

But if $K \geqslant \frac{1}{3}$, the first condition is necessarily satisfied if k is positive. Thus if $K = \frac{1}{3}$, a stable equilibrium exists if $k > \frac{2}{9}$. The values of k and K for which stable equilibria exist are shown in Fig. 2.

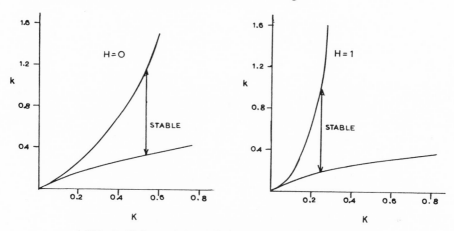

FIG. 2. Values of the selective coefficients k and K for which a stable equilibrium exists.

Equilibrium with dominance, $n_1 \neq n_2$, no habitat preference

The equilibria found in the last section do not depend on there being equal numbers in the two niches. However, when $n_1 \neq n_2$, allowance for habitat selection leads to highly intractable algebra. But in order to see how the equilibrium conditions depend on the relative sizes of the two niches, it will be sufficient to consider the case with no habitat preference ($H = 0$).

Let p be the frequency of allele A in the adult population. Then the relative frequencies of adults in the two niches in the next generation are:

	Niche 1	Niche 2
AA	$p^2(1 + K)$	p^2
Aa	$2pq(1 + K)$	$2pq$
aa	q^2	$q^2(1 + k)$
Total	$1 + K(1 - q^2)$	$1 + kq^2$

201

If the numbers of adults in the two niches are n_1, n_2, respectively, then the frequency of allele A in the new adult population is

$$\frac{n_1}{n_1 + n_2} \cdot \frac{(p^2 + pq)(1 + K)}{1 + K(1 - q^2)} + \frac{n_2}{n_1 + n_2} \cdot \frac{(p^2 + pq)}{1 + kq^2} = p \text{ at equilibrium}$$

and this reduces to

$$q^2 = \frac{n_2 k(1 + K) - n_1 K}{(n_1 + n_2) Kk} \tag{8}$$

An equilibrium exists provided that q lies between 0 and 1, which requires that

$$\left.\begin{array}{c} k\left(1 - K\dfrac{n_1}{n_2}\right) < K\dfrac{n_1}{n_2} \\[3mm] k(1 + K) > K\dfrac{n_1}{n_2} \end{array}\right\} \tag{9}$$

When $n_1 = n_2$, this is equivalent to condition (6).

If the selective advantages are small, they must be nicely adjusted to the relative sizes of the two niches if an equilibrium is to exist; and this is unlikely to occur. But if $K\dfrac{n_1}{n_2} > 1$, the first condition will be satisfied, and an equilibrium will exist if $k > \dfrac{K}{1 + K}\dfrac{n_1}{n_2}$. Suppose, for example, a species were established in a "small" niche, 2, and that a large niche, 1, became available, with $n_1/n_2 = 10$. Then a dominant mutation adapting the species to niche 1 would spread if $K \geqslant 0.1$, i.e., if it gave a 10% selective advantage. But a dominant with $K = 0.1$ would eliminate the recessive allele completely unless $k > \dfrac{0.1}{1.1} \times 10$; i.e., unless the recessive had a twofold advantage in the original niche.

Conditions (9) are subsumed under the more general case considered by Levene (1953), who gives the conditions for a stable equilibrium when there are a number of niches, and when the fitnesses of the three genotypes AA, Aa and aa are different from one another and in different niches. It is implicit in his conditions that, unless there is heterozygous advantage in individual niches, a stable equilibrium requires either that the selective advantages are large, or that they are nicely adjusted to the niche sizes.

III. THE EVOLUTION OF REPRODUCTIVE ISOLATION

It is a characteristic of good species that they rarely interbreed even when occupying the same area. Granted then that a stable polymorphism can exist in a heterogeneous environment, can reproductive isolation evolve between the two morphs?

There are four ways in which this might happen.

1. *Habitat selection*

If in a heterogeneous environment mating takes place within the "niche"—perhaps because individuals tend to return to mate in the habitat in which they were raised (e.g., many bird species)—then the populations from two niches, whether genetically different or not, will be largely isolated. They could, therefore, evolve into separate species exactly as in the case of allopatric speciation. This should perhaps be regarded as a form of allopatric speciation in which isolation is behavioral rather than geographic.

But even if, as must usually be the case, the isolation between niches was only partial, it would favor the establishment of a stable polymorphism of the kind discussed in the last section; i.e., smaller selective coefficients would be required to maintain polymorphism.

Suppose, however, that initially no isolation exists between the two niches, the adults from both forming a single random-mating population. Then, once a stable polymorphism has been established, there will be selection in favor of habitat selection in both sexes, for the following reason. Individuals will tend to be adapted to the niche in which they were raised, because they did in fact survive in that niche. Their offspring will tend to resemble them. Therefore, if they have a genotype causing them to produce offspring in the same niche in which they were themselves raised, this will increase their fitness.

It follows that the establishment of a stable polymorphism may lead to isolation by habitat selection.

2. *Pleiotropism*

The gene pair A, a adapting individuals to different niches may themselves cause assortative mating: i.e., $\overline{A}$ mating with $\overline{A}$ and aa with aa. This seems very unlikely.

3. *Modifier Genes*

It is supposed that the original population, during the establishment of the A, a polymorphism, had a genotype—say bb—such that mating was random. Mating isolation could arise by the replacement of b by B, so that for individuals of genotype $\overline{B}$, there is assortative mating at the A locus. The situation is set out in Table 1, in which + indicates that mating occurs,

TABLE 1

Mating relations between genotypes resulting from the modifier gene B.
+ indicates mating; – indicates no mating.

		♂ genotype			
		$\overline{A}\,bb$	$aa\,bb$	$\overline{A}\,\overline{B}$	$aa\,\overline{B}$
♀ Genotype	$\overline{A}\,bb$	+	+	+	+
	$aa\,bb$	+	+	+	+
	$\overline{A}\,\overline{B}$	+	–	+	–
	$aa\,\overline{B}$	–	+	–	+

– that it does not. In matings between $\bar{B}$ and bb, it has been assumed that the occurrence of mating is determined by the female. The main difficulty is to imagine how a gene B could influence mating in this way; in effect, B is a gene which causes courting individuals to be influenced by the difference between A and a, which bb individuals ignore.

If such genes exist, would they increase in frequency and so cause reproductive isolation? Clearly B will increase in frequency only if individuals selecting mates with the same genotype as themselves at the A locus have more surviving offspring than non-selective individuals. This will be the case if the heterozygote Aa has a lower fitness than AA or aa. For the equilibria considered in the last section, in the absence of habitat selection the three genotypes AA, Aa, and aa are equally fit; and therefore there is no selective advantage in assortative mating. But in the presence of habitat selection by females, the mean fitness of heterozygotes is less than that of homozygotes. This may at first sight seem puzzling, since AA and Aa were assumed to have identical phenotypes; the lower fitness of Aa arises because heterozygotes more often find themselves in the "wrong" niche. Therefore, if there is habitat selection, B will increase in frequency and ultimately lead to reproductive isolation between the two niches.

4. Assortative mating genes

It is perhaps more plausible to consider an allele pair B, b which themselves cause assortative mating, regardless of the genotype at the A locus. The occurrence of mating is then as shown in Table 2.

TABLE 2

Mating relations when alleles B and b determine assortative mating irrespective of the A, a locus

		♂ genotype	
		$\begin{array}{c} A \\ \bar{B} \text{ or} \\ a \end{array}$	$\begin{array}{c} A \\ bb \text{ or} \\ a \end{array}$
♀ genotype	$\begin{array}{c} A \\ \bar{B} \text{ or} \\ a \end{array}$	+	−
	$\begin{array}{c} A \\ bb \text{ or} \\ a \end{array}$	−	+

There are many ways in which genes affecting signals or behavior used in courtship could have this effect. The problem is whether an allele pair of this kind would become associated with the genes A, a responsible for polymorphism, so as to give rise to two isolated populations, one AA BB and the other aa bb (by symmetry, they could equally well be AA bb and aa BB).

In the absence of habitat preference by females, I see no reason why such an association should evolve because, as explained in the last section,

there is no selective advantage in assortative mating. But if there is habitat selection, an association would be expected to evolve because it would
lead to a rise in the mean fitness of the population. I do not find this argument fully convincing, and in any case it says nothing about the rate at
which an association would arise. Unfortunately I have been unable to find
a general solution for the case in which both allele pairs are segregating in
a population. Instead I have investigated numerically a case which I hope
is typical.

The first step is to choose a numerically simple equilibrium for alleles
A, a, as follows:

$$\text{niche sizes equal, } n_1 = n_2$$

$$\text{complete habitat preference, } H = 1$$

$$\text{selective advantages, } K = \tfrac{5}{7}, \quad k = \tfrac{5}{12}$$

It then follows from section II that at equilibrium the genotype frequencies
are as shown in Table 3. It is assumed that assortative mating for the
allele pair B, b is complete, so that BB mates only with BB, and bb with
bb. Heterozygotes Bb will be rare or absent.

TABLE 3

Equilibrium frequencies for a model in which $H = 1$, $K = \tfrac{5}{7}$, $k = \tfrac{5}{12}$, and $n_1 = n_2$.

	Niche 1		Niche 2	
	eggs	adults	eggs	adults
AA	0.3	$\dfrac{3.6}{11}$	0.2	$\dfrac{1.6}{9}$
Aa	0.5	$\dfrac{6}{11}$	0.5	$\dfrac{4}{9}$
aa	0.2	$\dfrac{1.4}{11}$	0.3	$\dfrac{3.4}{9}$

Consider a population in which the frequencies of BB and bb are P and Q,
respectively, but with small departures from these values for different
genotypes at the A locus, as shown in Table 4.

If the values δ_1 to δ_6 correspond to generation 0, we want to find the
corresponding values δ_1' to δ_6' in generation 1.

In the adult male population, among BB males the relative numbers of AA,
Aa and aa are:

$$AA \; BB \qquad \frac{50}{99} P + \frac{3.6}{11} \delta_1 + \frac{1.6}{9} \delta_4$$

$$Aa \; BB \qquad \frac{98}{99} P + \frac{6}{11} \delta_2 + \frac{4}{9} \delta_5$$

$$aa \; BB \qquad \frac{50}{99} P + \frac{1.4}{11} \delta_3 + \frac{3.4}{9} \delta_6$$

TABLE 4

Frequencies of genotypes in two niches expressed as frequencies
P and Q modified by small deviations δ.

Genotype		Niche 1	Niche 2
$AA\begin{cases}BB\\bb\end{cases}$		$P + \delta_1$ $Q - \delta_1$	$P + \delta_4$ $Q - \delta_4$
$Aa\begin{cases}BB\\bb\end{cases}$		$P + \delta_2$ $Q - \delta_2$	$P + \delta_5$ $Q - \delta_5$
$aa\begin{cases}BB\\bb\end{cases}$		$P + \delta_3$ $Q - \delta_3$	$P + \delta_6$ $Q - \delta_6$

and hence among BB males, the frequency of allele A, is

$$p(A \mid BB) = \frac{1}{2}\left(1 + \frac{1}{P}\left[\frac{1.8}{11}\delta_1 - \frac{0.7}{11}\delta_3 + \frac{0.8}{9}\delta_4 - \frac{1.7}{9}\delta_6\right]\right)$$

A table can then be set up showing the numbers of different types of female, and the proportions of different genotypes among their offspring, part of which is shown in Table 5.

TABLE 5

Correspondence between type of female, number in niche, and proportion of different kinds of offspring. Only a part of the complete set of relations is shown.

Type of female	Number in Niche 1	Proportion of offspring		
		AA	Aa	aa
BB AA	$\frac{3.6}{11}(P + \delta_1)$	$p(A \mid BB)$	$p(a \mid BB)$	0
BB Aa	$\frac{6}{11}(P + \delta_2)$	$\frac{1}{2}p(A \mid BB)$	$\frac{1}{2}$	$\frac{1}{2}p(a \mid BB)$
BB aa	$\frac{1.4}{11}(P + \delta_3)$	0	$p(A \mid BB)$	$p(a \mid BB)$

Whence the number of BB AA offspring in niche 1 is:

$$\frac{3.6}{11}(P + \delta_1)\,p(A \mid BB) + \frac{3}{11}(P + \delta_2)p(A \mid BB)$$

Substituting for $p(A \mid BB)$, and remembering that the total number of AA offspring in niche 1 is 0.3, we have in niche 1 in generation 1:

$$\frac{\text{number of } BB\ AA \text{ offspring}}{\text{total number of } AA \text{ offspring}}$$

$$= P + \frac{7.8}{11}\delta_1 + \frac{5}{11}\delta_2 - \frac{0.7}{11}\delta_3 + \frac{0.8}{9}\delta_4 - \frac{1.7}{9}\delta_6 = P + \delta_1'$$

Similar equations can be obtained for δ_2' to δ_6', of which the coefficients are:

	δ_1	δ_2	δ_3	δ_4	δ_5	δ_6
δ_1'	+0.7091	+0.4545	−0.0636	+0.0889	0	−0.1889
δ_2'	+0.2945	+0.5455	+0.1400	−0.0178	0	+0.0378
δ_3'	−0.1636	+0.6818	+0.3818	−0.0889	0	+0.1889
δ_4'	+0.1636	0	−0.0636	+0.5333	+0.5556	−0.1889
δ_5'	+0.0327	0	−0.0127	+0.1956	+0.4444	+0.3400
δ_6'	−0.1636	0	+0.0636	−0.0889	+0.3704	+0.8185

These equations are satisfied when all values of δ are zero; i.e., there is an equilibrium when the frequency of allele B is the same for all genotypes at the A locus. But this equilibrium is unstable, as can be shown by iteration, starting from a small initial disturbance.

Taking, in generation 0, $\delta_1 = 0.01$ and δ_2 to δ_6 as zero, Fig. 3 shows successive values of $P_1(B)$ and $P_2(B)$, the frequencies of allele B in niche 1 and niche 2, respectively.

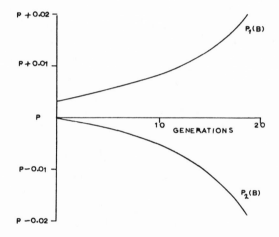

FIG. 3. Frequencies of allele B in niches 1 and 2, after a small disturbance from the initial value P.

Thus, if an initial disturbance raises the frequency of B in niche 1 above that in niche 2, this difference is amplified in subsequent generations. This holds whatever the initial value of P. Hence if allele B were initially rare, but by chance were less rare in niche 1, its frequency would steadily increase in that niche.

Therefore, increasingly individuals raised in niche 1 will tend to mate together, and similarly for those raised in niche 2. This will finally lead to reproductive isolation between the two niches, and, since AA is fitter in niche 1 and aa in niche 2, to the evolution of two isolated populations, $AA\ BB$ and $aa\ bb$.

Although this conclusion has been established only in a particular case, there is no reason why it should not be generally true, provided that females show some degree of habitat selection. But the conditions chosen—complete habitat selection by females, an allele pair giving complete assortative mating, and an allele pair with large selective differences in the two niches—all favor the rapid evolution of isolation. In practice, the establishment of mating isolation between two niches would be very slow, taking hundreds rather than tens of generations.

The preceding discussion has some relevance to the origin of isolating mechanisms in cases of allopatric speciation. If two populations, previously isolated geographically and differing at many loci, come to occupy the same area, there are three possible outcomes:

1) No interbreeding takes place. This could be due either to habitat selection, or to the pleiotropic effects on mating of gene differences, usually polygenic, which evolved in the first place as adaptations to different geographical conditions. In this case, either one population will become extinct, or, if sufficient ecological difference exists between them, both will survive as distinct species in the area of overlap.

2) Mating takes place, but hybrids are inviable or sterile. This is the classic situation in which, as Dobzhansky (1940) pointed out, we could expect to see the evolution of isolating mechanisms, in particular behavioral ones, acting before gametes have been wasted in hybridization. Some experimental evidence (e.g., Koopman, 1950) exists that mating barriers will evolve in these circumstances. But it is not clear whether such barriers will usually be due to modifying genes, or to assortative mating genes.

3) Mating takes place, and hybrids are at least partially viable and fertile. This is likely to lead to a rapid blurring of the genetic difference between the populations, even if the hybrids are initially of low fitness. For example, if two populations of equal numbers mate at random, and if the mean fitness of all hybrids (F_1, F_2, backcross etc.) is 0.25 that of pure-bred individuals, then in five generations the frequency of hybrids will rise to 75%, and in eight generations to 99.9% of the whole population. Thus selection in favor of more viable and fertile hybrid genotypes is likely to have a bigger effect than selection for reproductive isolation.

In practice, the situation will be more complex because the populations will mix only in a zone of overlap into which new pure-bred individuals will continually be migrating. Nevertheless, it seems likely that unless the mean fitness of hybrids is very low, the outcome will be a single interbreeding population rather than reproductive isolation.

However, if the two populations differ by at least one allele pair (or block of closely linked genes) adapting them to different niches, with selective advantages large enough to satisfy equation 6 or 7, this would lead to a stable polymorphism in the zone of overlap, and hence to speciation.

CONCLUSIONS

In a heterogeneous environment, it is possible for there to be a stable polymorphism between alleles adapting individuals to different ecological niches. The conditions which must be satisfied are however severe; they are as follows:

1) The density-dependent factors regulating the population size must operate separately in the two niches; this condition will be satisfied more often than not.

2) The selective advantages must be large. If there is habitat-selection by females, leading them to produce offspring in the niche in which they themselves were raised, this will favor the establishment of a stable polymorphism; but even in this case, selective advantages of 30% or more are required.

If these conditions are satisfied, a polymorphism can exist for allele pairs showing dominant or additive inheritance, even if individuals raised in the two niches form a single random-mating population.

If a stable polymorphism arises, this is likely to be followed by the evolution of reproductive isolation between the populations in the two niches. In particular, if a population is polymorphic for an allele pair A, a, each conferring an advantage in one ecological niche, and if a second allele pair B, b causes assortative mating, BB mating with BB and bb with bb, then, provided that there is some degree of habitat selection by egg-laying females, two reproductively isolated populations, AA BB and aa bb (or AA bb and aa BB) will evolve.

Thus the crucial step in sympatric speciation is the establishment of a stable polymorphism in a heterogeneous environment. Whether this paper is regarded as an argument for or against sympatric speciation will depend on how likely such a polymorphism is thought to be, and this in turn depends on whether a single gene difference can produce selective coefficients large enough to satisfy the necessary conditions (inequalities 6 and 7).

SUMMARY

It is shown that in a heterogeneous environment divided into two "niches," a stable polymorphism can exist between two alleles each conferring a selective advantage in one of the niches, even if adults form a single random-mating population, provided: (1) the population size is separately regulated in the two niches, and (2) the selective advantages are large. The conditions to be satisfied are given; it is difficult to say how often they will be satisfied.

A stable polymorphism is favored if females tend to lay eggs in the niche in which they were themselves raised.

Four genetic mechanisms—habitat selection, pleiotropic genes, modifying genes, and assortative mating genes—which could cause mating isolation are considered. It is concluded that stable polymorphism could be the first stage in sympatric speciation. The relevance of these mechanisms in allopatric speciation is also discussed.

LITERATURE CITED

Basykin, A. D. 1965. On the possibility of sympatric species formation. Bull. Mosc. Soc. Nat. Biol. Div. 70(1):161–165.

Dobzhansky, Th. 1940. Speciation as a stage in evolutionary divergence. Amer. Natur. 74:312–321.

Haldane, J. B. S., and S. D. Jayakar. 1963. Polymorphism due to selection of varying direction. J. Genet. 58:237–242.

Koopman, K. F. 1950. Natural selection for reproductive isolation between *Drosophila pseudoobscura* and *Drosophila persimilis*. *Evolution*. 4:135–148.

Levene, H. 1953. Genetic equilibrium when more than one ecological niche is available. Amer. Natur. 87:331–333.

Mayr, E. 1963. Animal species and evolution. Harvard Univ. Press.

Millicent, E., and J. M. Thoday. 1961. Effects of disruptive selection IV. Gene-flow and divergence. Heredity, 16:199–217.

Thoday, J. M., and T. B. Boam. 1959. Effects of disruptive selection II. Polymorphism and divergence without isolation. Heredity, 13:205–218.

Thoday, J. M., and J. B. Gibson. 1962. Isolation by disruptive selection. Nature, 193:1164–1166.

Thorpe, W. H. 1930. Biological races in insects and allied groups. Biol. Rev. 5:177–212.

Part IV

ORIGIN OF ISOLATION– EXPERIMENTAL

Editor's Comments
on Papers 16 Through 20

Isolating mechanisms appear to arise as the result of one or both of two mechanisms. In one case the two populations are isolated by some extrinsic factor (geography, ecology, topography) and genetic divergence leads to the accumulation of differences, some of which influence reproductive success and prevent free interbreeding between the two populations if they ever again come in contact (Muller, 1940). Another theory, stated by Wallace (1889), developed by Fisher (1930), and advanced by Dobzhansky (1940), suggests that when hybrids are relatively infertile those genes which tend to prevent cross mating will tend to survive and reduce the proportion of heterogametic matings. Whether or not geographic isolation is required for the second mechanism to operate is open to considerable controversy. Some of the attempts to examine this question experimentally are discussed in this section. Sturtevant (Paper 16) pointed out that with reciprocal translocations the heterozygote has a reduced fertility from irregular segregation. He also noted that consecutive inversions can produce heterozygotes with decreased fertility.

Koopman (Paper 17) mixed populations of *D. pseudoobscura* and *D. persimilis* and showed that the amount of reproductive isolation between the two species increased very rapidly as a result of natural selection. He suggested that once the populations had differentiated to the species level the hybrids become "relatively ill-adapted for any available habitat." Kessler (1966) successfully selected for increased and for decreased ethological isolation between these two sibling species.

Blair (1953; Paper 18) studied the populations of the frog *Microhyla* in the southern United States. The two species overlap broadly in Texas, where some ponds have populations which retain their separate identities and in other ponds hybridization is common. He found that morphological differences and behavioral isolation were greater between sympatric populations than between allopatric forms.

The divergence of morphological characteristics in regions of overlap was noted by Darwin and Wallace (1859). Brown and Wilson (1956) called this phenomena "character displacement" and provided a review of past studies and stimulated many later studies. A parallel phenomena is that of species replacement in which the geographical or ecological range of one species is severely restricted by the presence of closely related forms when they are sympatric. For example Miller (1964) found that some species of gophers were able to occupy sandy and rocky soils when not in competition with other gophers, but were restricted to a single soil when competitors were present.

Ehrman (1965) observed behavioral isolation between races of the *Drosophila paulistorum* species complex and found that morphologically distinct sympatric lineages are more strongly isolated than are allopatric populations. Grant (Paper 20) compared crosses between allopatric and sympatric herbs (*Gilia*) and noted that individuals of different species from the sympatric portions of their ranges exhibited strong isolation and fewer hybrid seeds than those from allopatric populations. Levin (1970) reviewed the information on augmentation and concluded that animals appeared to exhibit this phenomena more than plants. He pointed out that animal pollinated plants appear to have the most examples of augmentation.

Thus augmentation of isolating mechanisms appears genetically explainable and exists in diverse plant and animal populations. Presumably these wide ranging populations were geographically isolated, became separate species by the accumulation of genetic differences, and expanded their ranges. Overlapping of the ranges resulted in the loss of the inviable hybrids and the selection for reproductive isolation. A number of workers have asked whether or not it is possible for such reproductive isolation to arise in populations without geographic isolation, e.g., by selection in different directions.

Thoday and Gibson (Paper 19) used disruptive selection of the number of chaetae and noted that the number of "hyrids" was reduced and almost eliminated. Attempts to repeat this experiment have not been successful (Scharloo, 1964; Crenshaw, 1966; Chabora, 1968; Barker and Cummins, 1969). Thoday and Gibson (1970) suggest that this is not surprising because laboratory rather than newly captured stocks were usually used and because selection has usually been for characters not known to be directly relevant to reproductive isolation. For further discussion see Thoday (1972) and Mayr (1974).

Bush (1975) has reviewed the modes of speciation in animals and summarized the evidence for the sympatric origin of new species. He suggests a variety of mechanisms including polyploidy, change in mating phenomes, cytoplasmic incompatibility systems, allochronic divergence in breeding time, and host-parasite shifts. He points out that more than 500,000 phytophagous and zoophagous parasites and parasitoids could have arisen by sympatric speciation. The adherence to the classical geographical speciation model as a universal parsimonious method of speciation may produce tunnel vision to the potentialities of nature.

16

Reprinted from *Quart. Review Biology* 13:333–335 (1938)

ESSAYS ON EVOLUTION

III. ON THE ORIGIN OF INTERSPECIFIC STERILITY

By A. H. STURTEVANT

W. G. Kerckhoff Laboratories of the Biological Sciences, California Institute of Technology, Pasadena, Calif.

THE problem of the origin of interspecific sterility has long presented the greatest difficulty in the way of constructing a complete theory of the evolution of species. This difficulty was felt by Darwin, and has, if anything, become more striking with the development of modern genetical theory. One solution, has, it is true, been developed. It now seems clear that, in certain cases, allopolyploidy may be effective in producing a new fertile form that is cross-sterile with its parents. This solution is, however, certainly a special one, applicable only to hermaphroditic organisms. There is no recognized general scheme, applicable to separate-sexed forms, that can be pictured in detail. It is the purpose of the present note to suggest such a general scheme.

It was pointed out by Fisher (1930) that, if a species is supposed to be broken up into two more or less isolated groups, and the hybrids between these two groups are relatively infertile, then any genes tending to decrease the cross-mating between the two groups will be selected. This is because cross-mating, since it leads to the production of less fertile offspring, will lead to a decrease in the potential ultimate reproductive value of the cross-mated individuals, as compared to those that mate within their own group. In other words, intra-group matings will, if we consider generations later than the first one, produce more descendants than will inter-group matings—and selection will therefore decrease the proportion of the latter.

On this basis, sterility of the F_1 comes first, and leads to an accumulation of genes that prevent cross-mating. The alternative assumption, more often made, is that cross-mating is prevented in some manner, and sterility of the F_1 follows as a more or less incidental consequence. This latter view has always remained rather vague, and presents serious logical difficulties when one attempts to make it more precise. There seems to be no good reason why the hybrid should become sterile, yet sterility of the hybrid is one of the most wide-spread characteristics of distinct species.

There is also a logical difficulty about the view that sterility of the F_1 is primary. For, in this case, there must have been a fertile F_1 present in the beginning. If A and B give a sterile hybrid, how can B be derived from A, unless self-fertilization be assumed? There are two ways of escaping this difficulty: One may suppose the hybrid not to be completely sterile (in which case, as the sterility is decreased, it becomes easier for the condition to become established, but its effectiveness in leading to failure of cross-mating decreases), or one may assume that the sterility arose by two steps. In the latter case, one may assume two pairs of complementary genes, Ss and Tt, such that Ss Tt is sterile, but SS tt, Ss tt, ss TT, ss Tt, and ss tt are fertile. The derivation of the two cross-sterile homozygous types SS tt and ss TT then involves the production, at some stage, of a type (ss tt) that is fertile with both (see elaboration by Dobzhansky, 1937).

Fisher's analysis is based on the assumption that the two diverging groups have become adapted, through selection, to different conditions (usually geographical), and that the hybrids between them are less well adapted to either set of conditions.

There are, however, certain other systems which will lead to the same type of situation, without any difference in the selective agencies acting on the two populations—without any initial differences between them in gene-frequencies. Perhaps the simplest example is that of reciprocal translocations. Here the heterozygote has a reduced fertility, owing to the more or less frequent occurrence of "irregular" segregation. The smaller the pieces of chromosome exchanged, the greater is the frequency of irregular segregation—but also the greater is the chance that some of the products of such irregular segregation may have some degree of viability and fertility (since they will carry duplications or deficiencies for fewer genes). It is presumably for this reason that small, rather than large, translocations appear to have become established in the phylogeny of *Drosophila* species (Sturtevant and Tan, 1937). This system suffers from the disadvantage referred to above—the greater the sterility of the F_1, the greater the difficulty of establishing the translocation in the first instance. It has been shown by Dobzhansky and Tan (1936) that several small translocations have in fact occurred in the course of the differentiation between *Drosophila pseudoobscura* and *D. miranda;* accordingly this method must be considered as a possible one, though the inver-

sion system now to be discussed seems more likely to be of general occurrence.

Another type of chromosome aberration that should have similar effects is furnished by inversions. If two chromosomes differ by a single inversion within an arm, there exists a mechanism such that there is only a negligible effect of crossing over on the fertility of the heterozygote (Sturtevant and Beadle, 1936). If, however, an inversion is followed by a second one not greatly different from it, the situation is otherwise. For example: suppose a chromosome ABCDEFGH is inverted to form AGFED-CBH, and the latter in turn gives rise to AGCDEFBH—it being assumed that the spindle-attachment is at A or H. A heterozygote carrying the first and the third of the above chromosomes may give crossing over in the CDEF region, and the chromatids resulting from such crossing over (one carrying two B's, no G, the other carrying two G's, no B) will pass to the functional egg ,cells at random (Gershenson, 1932; Sturtevant and Beadle, 1936). The result is that such a heterozygote has a definitely decreased fertility. In the limiting case the decrease will amount to 50 per cent.

Such a system is not imaginary. The properties outlined have been experimentally determined; and the existence of inversions in wild populations is now known to be frequent and widespread. It may be concluded that they have in fact often led to the production of relatively infertile combinations. Given these facts, there is present all that is needed for the initiation of the selective process outlined by Fisher. It is possible to postulate such an origin for the two races (A and B) of *Drosophila pseudoobscura* that give sterile F_1 hybrids. These two races do in fact show some degree of sexual isolation; and the most frequent sequence in the third chromosomes of race A

(Arrowhead) is so related to the most frequent one of race B (Klamath) that crossovers of the type described should be relatively frequent (Dobzhansky and Sturtevant, 1938).

This case illustrates a difficulty encountered in such an analysis as is here attempted. The male hybrids between the two races are completely sterile, yet the postulated mechanism does not permit complete sterility at the initial stage. In fact, it is clear that in organisms that cannot self-fertilize, this must usually be so, as pointed out above. There thus arises a difficulty which was recognized by Darwin: the most that can be supposed in the early stages of differentiation is that the hybrid is relatively infertile. This infertility must be supposed to increase up to complete sterility—yet at first sight it seems that a decrease in fertility is precisely what selection cannot accomplish.

I have recently discussed (*Essay II* of this series) a case in which sterile individuals must be supposed to have increased in frequency because of selection. The general method invoked in that case may be so modified as to apply here also—namely, we may suppose that the area between the two incipient forms is occupied by a series of semi-independent small sub-populations, only occasionally interbreeding and ultimately competing with each other.

Within a mixed population, the hybrids themselves, when they do breed, will produce up to half their offspring like themselves. Therefore such fertility as they possess will be a source of new semi-sterile individuals. Selection will operate to increase the fertility of this class; but within a small sub-population, the chance establishment of any genes that decrease still further the fertility of the hybrids will increase the efficiency of the sub-population as a whole, and will give it an advantage over the competing subpopulations. Under these conditions, then, it may be supposed that the fertility of the hybrid may be decreased, while the frequency of crossing of the two races is still decreasing.

It is thus possible to formulate a scheme for the origin of interspecific sterility, starting with Fisher's demonstration that races giving a relatively infertile hybrid will tend to accumulate genes that tend to prevent crossing. Appropriate use of Wright's (1932) idea of competing subpopulations makes it possible to see how the infertility can be increased by selection. Inversions and small translocations furnish ever-present materials for initiating or for increasing such infertility of the hybrids—though it is clear that gene mutations must also be concerned, since not all interspecific sterility can be attributed to chromosome rearrangements (see Dobzhansky, 1937).

LIST OF LITERATURE

DOBZHANSKY, T. 1937. Genetics and the Origin of Species. 364 pp. *New York:* Columbia University Press.

——, and A. H. STURTEVANT. 1938. Inversions in the chromosomes of *Drosophila pseudoobscura*. *Genetics*, 23: 27–64.

——, and C. C. TAN. 1936. Studies on hybrid sterility. III. A comparison of the gene arrangement in two species, *Drosophila pseudoobscura* and *Drosophila miranda*. *Zeitschr. f. ind. Abst. Vererb.*, 72: 88–114.

FISHER, R. A. 1930. The Genetical Theory of Natural Selection. 272 pp. *Oxford:* Clarendon Press.

GERSHENSON, S. M. 1932. Studies on the genetically inert region of the X chromosome of *Drosophila*. I. *Journ. Genet.*, 28: 297–313.

STURTEVANT, A. H., and G. W. BEADLE. 1936. The relations of inversions in the X chromosome of *Drosophila melanogaster* to crossing over and disjunction. *Genetics*, 21: 554–604.

——, and C. C. TAN. 1937. The comparative genetics of *Drosophila pseudoobscura* and D. *melanogaster*. *Journ. Genet.*, 34: 415–432.

WRIGHT, S. 1932. The rôles of mutation, inbreeding, crossbreeding, and selection in evolution. *Proc. VI Internat. Congr. Genetics*, 1: 356–366.

Reprinted from *Evolution* 4:135–148 (1950)

NATURAL SELECTION FOR REPRODUCTIVE ISOLATION BETWEEN *DROSOPHILA PSEUDOOBSCURA* AND *DROSOPHILA PERSIMILIS* [1]

Karl F. Koopman

Department of Zoology, Columbia University [2]

Received December 15, 1949

INTRODUCTION

One of the most important problems in the study of speciation has been that of the origin of reproductive isolating mechanisms, for it is by the building up of intrinsic barriers which prevent gene exchange between populations that we pass from the racial or subspecific to the specific level. Two theories have been proposed to explain how reproductive isolation might arise. The first, favored by Muller (1939, 1942), holds that reproductive isolation is a by-product of genetic divergence. As two subspecies differentiate in geographical isolation, genes which hamper free interbreeding with the other subspecies are incorporated into the genotype in the course of building up adaptive gene complexes. The reproductive isolation may be a pleiotropic effect, or perhaps be a result of change in gene function.

The other theory, advanced by Dobzhansky (1940), holds that provided the two subspecies have diverged from one another far enough so that hybrids between them are less well adapted for any available habitat than either parental type, natural selection will act to build up further reproductive isolation, thus preventing the formation of inadaptive hybrids with consequent wastage of reproductive potential and food resources. These two theories are by no means mutually exclusive, and indeed both mechanisms in all probability play an important part, perhaps being of greatest importance at different stages in the process. Actually, it seems very difficult to conceive of a situation in which the development of isolating mechanisms between two populations could proceed entirely by means of selection, since this would mean that at the outset, when selection is to begin its action, the hybrid and the two parental types would be equally viable and fertile and the former would be at no selective disadvantage. Under these circumstances, however, natural selection against the hybrid would be impossible. On the other hand, it is exceedingly probable that two populations which, during genetic divergence, had developed a considerable amount of reproductive isolation, would upon physical contact complete the process by means of natural selection.

Unfortunately, to date, the evidence, experimental or otherwise, showing either mechanism at work is virtually absent. The experiments herein described were made in order to determine whether, in artificial populations consisting of the two closely related species, *Drosophila pseudoobscura* and *D. persimilis* (the latter formerly known as *D. pseudoobscura*, race B), an increase in the reproductive isolating mechanisms could be detected if in each generation the hybrids between the two species were systematically eliminated. Under these conditions, if any hereditary variability for reproductive isolation was present, natural selection should act to prevent these hybrids from being formed.

MATERIALS AND METHODS

In order that not only representatives of the pure species, *D. pseudoobscura* and *D. persimilis,* but also both male and fe-

---

[1] Submitted in partial fulfillment of the degree of Doctor of Philosophy, Department of Zoology, Columbia University.

[2] Present address: Middletown Collegiate Center, Middletown, New York.

male hybrids could be easily recognized, mutant stocks of both species were used. For the *D. pseudoobscura* stock, males of the second chromosome mutant *glass* were outcrossed to a recently captured strain from Jacksonville, California, and the *glass* mutant reextracted. For the *D. persimilis* stock, males of the third chromosome recessive mutant *orange* were outcrossed to a recently captured strain from Porcupine Flat, California, and the *orange* mutant reextracted. This outcrossing and reextraction was done for two reasons. First, the viability of the strains was improved by heterosis, as well as by introduction of genes which had been under strong natural selection in the wild, as opposed to the relatively weak natural selection experienced by the mutant strains in the laboratory. Secondly, since mass cultures were employed, the store of genetic variability was increased, an important factor in the present experiment. By using these mutant stocks, all *D. pseudoobscura* individuals could be recognized by having *glass* eyes, all *D. persi-*

milis by being *orange*-eyed, while the only wild-type individuals were the hybrids, in which both mutant genes were covered by the wild-type alleles of the other species.

Since sexual isolation was the only isolating mechanism which could be readily measured, preliminary sexual isolation tests were made on the stocks at 16° C., using 10 females of each species and 10 males of either *D. pseudoobscura* or *D. persimilis*. The 30 flies used for each test were virgins and were kept together for a week in an ordinary shell vial with food, after which time the females were dissected and their seminal receptacles examined for sperm. The mating was done at 16° C. because at this temperature sexual isolation between *D. pseudoobscura* and *D. persimilis* is lowest (Mayr and Dobzhansky, 1945). For the population cage experiments, this temperature was desirable in order that changes in the sexual isolation could be most readily detected. For the later sexual isolation tests, the technique was similar, except

TABLE 1. *Main experiments, cage 2*

Generation	Number of parents		Number of offspring			Per cent hybrids
	pseudoobscura	*persimilis*	*pseudoobscura*	*persimilis*	hybrids	
1	320	680	82	313	227	36.5
2	60	60	561	473	322	23.7
3	300	300	246	995	665	34.9
4	120	120	406	336	126	14.5
5	250	250	162	86	292	54.1
6	80	80	273	415	38	5.2
7	180	180	617	478	17	1.5
10	150	150	820	257	72	6.3
11	180	180	653	729	42	2.9
12	440	440	2781	515	40	1.2
13	160	160	568	607	24	2.1
14	400	400	2217	712	259	8.1
15	300	300	2033	593	91	3.3
16	300	300	2613	453	89	2.8
17	300	300	2067	879	85	2.8
18	300	300	1925	1170	64	2.0
19	300	300	2808	1048	155	3.9
20	300	300	3372	1459	357	6.9
21	300	300	2109	1059	37	1.2
22	300	300	2117	1128	88	2.6

Equal numbers of males and females were used in all cases except in generation 6, in which 45 males and only 35 females of both *pseudoobscura* and *persimilis* were used.

TABLE 2. *Main experiments, cage 3*

Generation	Number of parents		Number of offspring			Per cent hybrids
	pseudoobscura	*persimilis*	*pseudoobscura*	*persimilis*	hybrids	
1	450	450	660	1008	464	22.5
2	360	360	544	1050	102	6.0
5	200	200	164	1680	100	5.1
6	130	130	394	1013	644	31.4
7	260	260	512	1569	58	2.7
8	360	360	648	1709	67	2.8
9	300	300	733	2193	60	2.0
10	300	300	1149	657	59	3.2
11	300	300	886	835	106	5.8
12	300	300	473	813	66	4.9
13	290	290	997	1965	159	5.1
14	300	300	1712	1712	182	5.0
15	300	300	1008	2418	79	2.2
16	300	300	1427	1772	180	5.3

TABLE 3. *Main experiments, cage 4*

Generation	Number of parents		Number of offspring			Per cent hybrids
	pseudoobscura	*persimilis*	*pseudoobscura*	*persimilis*	hybrids	
1	220	220	275	133	400	49.5
2	90	90	48	795	180	17.6
3	300	300	600	1006	55	3.3
4	400	400	414	1777	22	1.0
5	340	340	564	1241	25	1.4
6	300	300	1037	964	70	3.4
7	300	300	1214	244	26	1.8
8	150	150	275	1010	32	2.4
9	200	200	1284	1993	554	14.5
10	300	300	1375	3264	29	.6
11	300	300	1356	982	16	.7
12	300	300	2145	2188	74	1.7

that the males and females were aged apart for 10 days at 16° C., then left together for four hours before dissection.

The population cage experiments were done, also at 16° C., using the modified L'Hereditier-Teissier apparatus described by Dobzhansky (1947) and Wright and Dobzhansky (1946). In the present tests, however, the stender jars containing food with larvae were removed from the cages at the end of approximately two weeks and these cups fitted under sections of glass tubing two inches in diameter and approximately five inches in length, the tubes being fastened at the bottom with cellulose tape to the cup and closed at the top with a large cotton plug. The old cage with its adult flies was meanwhile discarded. In this way, all matings took place at 16° C., insuring a maximum number of hybrids, yet, by removing the covered cups to room temperature or to 25°C., more rapid development could take place. In addition, by not having long-continuous occupancy of the cages by the flies, the danger of infection with mites was greatly cut down. Flies were collected from the cups at 24-hour intervals, and counted according to whether they were *D. pseudoobscura, D. persimilis,* or hybrids. Advantage was taken of the fact that the size of the testis in hybrid males is determined by which species was the mother and which the father, since the testis of hybrid males is large in the cross *pseudoobscura* female × *persimilis* male, but small in hybrids from the cross *persimilis* female × *pseudoobscura* male (Lancefield, 1929) (Dobzhansky, 1935). In this way, by observing the testis size, some idea could be gained of the way in which the isolating mechanisms were built up. The *D. pseudoobscura* and *D. persimilis* were then separated, the males separated from the females, the hybrids discarded, and all flies of pure species stored at 16° C., usually up to three weeks. Then equal numbers of males and females of both species were put into a fresh cage and the cycle recommenced. The number of flies put into the cage varied considerably according to the number of individuals of each sex and species that could be collected in three weeks (see Tables 1, 2, and 3), but usually was between 200 and 800 flies. The optimum for obtaining large numbers of all types of flies seemed to be about 600. The only modifications of this procedure were for certain generations of cage 2. When making up this cage for the first generation, more *persimilis* than *peudoobscura* were put in because it was thought at that time that the *pseudoobscura* would be more vigorous than the *persimilis*. When the cage was being made up for generation 6,

only small numbers of *persimilis* were available, especially of *persimilis* females. Hence more males than females were put in, so that the effective population size would be as large as possible, while at the same time the numbers of the two pure species would be kept equal.

Late in the experiments, some mixed-cage tests were made. These were carried out as in the others, except that *D. persimilis* from one cage and *D. pseudoobscura* from another were used. These were run for one generation only.

MAIN POPULATION CAGE EXPERIMENTS

Between ordinary laboratory *D. persimilis* and *D. pseudoobscura,* several isolating mechanisms can be observed in operation (Dobzhansky and Epling, 1944). First of all, there is usually considerable sexual isolation, varying with the stocks used and with the temperature (Mayr and Dobzhansky, 1945). Hybrids seem to have the same viability as the pure species, but hybrid males are completely sterile. Females, when backcrossed to either parental species, lay the usual number of eggs, but the larvae arising from these eggs have such poor viability that in competition with larvae of the pure species, as in population cages, they never reach the adult stage. Hence, in a population cage with both species present, even if the hybrids were not removed each

TABLE 4. *Results of partial correlation tests*

	S	σs	p	Correlation (r)
Hybrids × total flies (2, 3)				
Cage 2	−70	30.8	.05 > but > .01	−.368
Cage 3	−21	18.3	> .05	−.231
Cage 4	−34	14.6	.05 > but > .01	−.515
Total flies × time (1, 2)				
Cage 2	122	30.8	< .01	.642
Cage 3	33	18.3	> .05	.363
Cage 4	38	14.6	< .01	.576
Hybrids × time (1, 3)				
Cage 2	−140	30.8	< .01	−.737
Cage 3	−19	18.3	> .05	−.209
Cage 4	−26	14.6	> .05	−.394

generation, as was done in the present experiments, no introgressive hybridization would be expected to occur. That such introgression is indeed lacking was established by Dobzhansky (1945).

Preliminary sexual isolation tests (see table 4) showed, for the original stocks, high sexual isolation using *pseudoobscura* males, but little or no sexual isolation using *persimilis males*. After outcrossing to wild strains and reextracting, the sexual isolation with *pseudoobscura* males was lowered somewhat, but with *persimilis* males was somewhat raised. This rise in isolation index is, it should be noted, non-significant, essentially random mating still taking place when *persimilis* males are used. Hence, in a cage containing both species, a considerable number of hybrids would be expected in the first generation. This is borne out by the first generation counts from the three population cages which could be carried to completion, the percentages being 50, 36, and 22. In earlier experiments, using other stocks, from population cages which had to be discarded early because of mite

infection, the hybrid percentages for the first generations were 60 and 27. In all population cages, however, which ran for more than four generations, a rather rapid decrease in the number of hybrids occurred. (See figs. 1–3 and tables 1, 2, and 3.) In all cases, within six generations, the percentage of hybrids had fallen to 5 per cent (though in some cases with some later temporary increase), and in certain cases reached as low as 1 per cent in later generations. This is in full agreement with Dobzhansky's work (1945), in which the percentage of hybrids in a population cage kept at 16° C. fell from 24 per cent on February 3 to 3.6 per cent on June 11.

A considerable heterogeneity may be noted in the percentage of hybrids after the first few generations; it may also be noted that in later generations a larger total number of flies was collected than earlier. It was therefore advisable to test the heterogeneity for significance and to determine whether the decrease in the percentage of hybrids could be explained by a correlation of percentages of hybrids

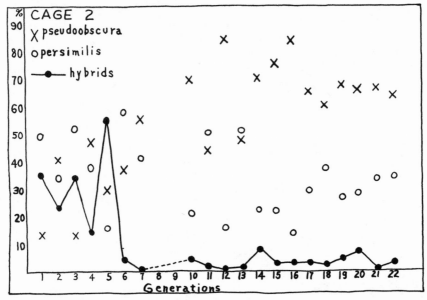

Fig. 1. Change in frequency of hybrids in cage 2, showing the percentage of the two pure species and the hybrids in each generation. (For additional data, see table 1.) No data for generations 8 and 9.

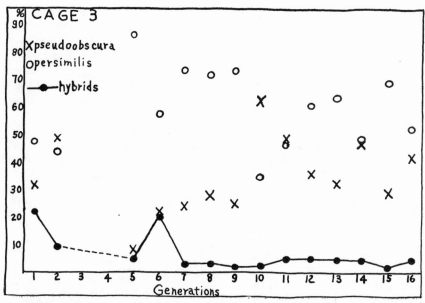

Fig. 2. Change in frequency of hybrids in cage 3, showing the percentage of the two pure species and their hybrids in each generation. (For additional data, see table 2.) No data for generations 3 and 4.

with the total numbers of flies. Such a correlation was possible, since the numbers of flies introduced each time the cage was reloaded were approximately the same, especially in later generations, and certainly showed no particular trend. The increase in total numbers of flies collected from generation to generation, therefore, was due to an increase in the percentage of eggs laid which later developed into adult flies. This meant a decrease in selection pressure for viability factors. Since the hybrids, being the only wild-type flies, were known to be superior in viability, reduced selection decreased their advantage over the mutant pure species. Hence their frequency would be reduced.

To test the heterogeneity, a χ^2 test was made for each cage, using the numbers of hybrids and pure species for each generation after a low value for the hybrids had been reached. The test, therefore, involved generations 6, 7, and 10–22 for cage 2, generations 7–16 for cage 3, and generations 3–12 for cage 4. The χ^2 obtained was very high for all three cages, 550 for cage 2, 138 for cage 3, and 1,680

for cage 4. The exceedingly high χ^2 for cage 4 was chiefly caused by the very large number of hybrids in generation 9. All three χ^2 values are highly significant, with a probability far below .01. It is evident, therefore, that even after the early generations, the frequency of hybrids was undergoing significant changes. The causes of these changes are, however, not clear.

To determine how the percentage of hybrids was correlated with time and with total number of flies per generation, rank correlation tests were performed. Three of these tests were made for each cage, percentage hybrids × time, percentage hybrids × total flies, and total flies × time. Time is considered variable 1, total flies as variable 2, and percentage hybrids as variable 3. The method used was that of Kendall (1943). The results may be seen in table 4.

It is evident that the conditions in the three cages are somewhat different. In cage 2, the percentage of hybrids shows a very significant decrease, and the total number of flies a significant increase, but the correlation of number of flies and hybrids is only on the borderline of significance. In cage 3, all three correlations are non-significant. In cage 4, conditions are essentially as in cage 2 except that the correlation of total flies × time is higher than the correlation of hybrids × time in cage 4, but not in cage 2.

In order to determine the partial correlation between percentage of hybrids and total, at the same time correcting for correlation of both with time, the formula

$$\tau_{23.1} = \frac{\tau_{23} - \tau_{13}\,\tau_{12}}{\sqrt{(1 - \tau_{12}^2)\,(1 - \tau_{13}^2)}}$$

(Kendall, 1942) was used. (Kendall gives no method for testing the significance of this partial rank correlation.) This formula gave a value of .20 for cage 2, − .17 for cage 3, and − .38 for cage 4. This shows that the partial correlation between total flies and percentage of hybrids may be either positive or negative and in two of the three cages is rather small. It therefore seems improbable that the correlation of percentage of hybrids with time can be explained by the correlation

of total flies with time and of total flies with percentage of hybrids. It must also be remembered that these correlations apply to the entire period during which flies were being kept in each cage. It was only during the early generations, however, with a very few exceptions, that the percentage of hybrids was undergoing much change. The rank correlation test used disregards the magnitude of the changes and reflects only the rank of the values for total flies, per cent hybrids, and time. A real decrease in frequency of hybrids formed seems indicated. Natural selection would appear to be building up new reproductive isolation.

The detailed history of the three cages, of course, differed considerably. Cage 4 showed a very rapid steady drop in the percentage of hybrids, whereas cages 2 and 3 took a longer time and showed considerable fluctuations. In the two earlier cages, the percentage of hybrids for certain generations is unknown; generations 8 and 9 for cage 2, generations 3 and 4 for cage 3. This unfortunate state of affairs arose from widespread contamina-

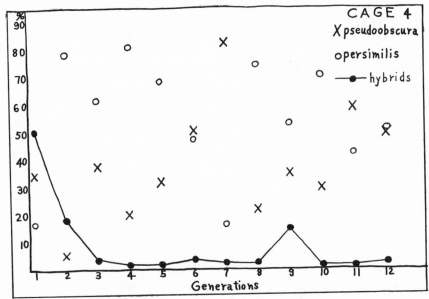

FIG. 3. Change in frequency of hybrids in cage 4, showing the percentage of the two pure species and their hybrids in each generation. (For additional data, see table 3.)

TABLE 5. *Source of hybrid males*

Generation	Cage 2		Cage 3		Cage 4	
	per. ♂ × *pseudo.* ♀	*pseudo.* ♂ × *per.* ♀	*per.* ♂ × *pseudo.* ♀	*pseudo.* ♂ × *per.* ♀	*per.* ♂ × *pseudo.* ♀	*pseudo.* ♂ × *per.* ♀
1	?	?	189	10	136	66
2	122	21	37	29	48	21
3	192	10	?	?	4	21
4	52	0	?	?	1	8
5	92	6	3	60	8	4
6	20	1	0	103	14	16
7	?	?	1	39	8	5
8	?	?	9	26	6	4
9	?	?	11	29	169	103
10	12	20	16	7	2	16
11	17	3	44	5	0	8
12	15	1	21	8	3	35
13	4	3	7	88		
14	84	14	45	37		
15	11	34	16	18		
16	42	17	72	6		
17	17	13				

tion of both cages by wild type *D. pseudoobscura* or *D. persimilis* which occurred at this time. Even after the percentage of hybrids had reached a low level, there was a certain amount of fluctuation, the extreme being in cage 4, where the frequency of hybrids rose from 2 per cent in generation 8 to 14 per cent in generation 9 and back to 1 per cent in generation 10, thereafter remaining at a low level. The causes of these earlier and later fluctuations are unknown. They could not be caused by contamination since this was ruled out by the examination of wild type male testes. These dissections showed no sharp rises in percentage of flies with large testes corresponding to high frequencies of wild type flies. (Compare tables 1, 2, and 3 with table 5.) This would have been the case if any appreciable contamination had occurred at these times. Indeed, in those generations in which data are lacking because widespread contamination was known to occur, almost all wild type males examined had full-sized testes. It might be argued that some of the later rise might be due to the contamination earlier, resulting in the introduction of unselected genes,

thereby reducing the reproductive isolation in the population. This, however, could only occur if appreciable numbers of the contaminants were *glass pseudoobscura* or *orange persimilis*. Otherwise, the F1 flies from the interbreeding of cage and contaminating flies would be wild type and would be discarded along with the species hybrids. The effects of contamination could therefore be confined to the generation immediately following the contamination. Reasons for the fluctuations must therefore be sought from other causes. Temperature was usually fairly constant, especially during the latter part of the experiments, but humidity was usually quite variable, and may have differentially affected the viability of the wild type hybrids, and even of the degree of reproductive isolation itself. These earlier and later fluctuations, however, do not in any way vitiate the clear demonstration that hybrids are in general much less frequent for the later generations than for the earlier ones in all three cages.

Another fluctuating variable was the relative number of pure *pseudoobscura* and *perisimilis* in each generation. Differences between generations, even in the same cage, were often extreme. The relative numbers of the two species might even undergo a radical shift in one generation. This may be seen by comparing the counts of generations 7 and 8 in cage 4. These fluctuations in the number of pure species flies also point to considerable environmental fluctuations, which caused natural selection to favor now one, now the other species.

From the examination of the hybrid male testes, an interesting fact emerges (see table 5). In the first two generations, the number of hybrids coming from the cross *persimilis* male × *pseudoobscura* female outnumbered and usually greatly outnumbered those from the cross of *pseudoobscura* male × *persimilis* female. This is to be expected, since, in the preliminary sexual isolation tests, *pseudoobscura* males already showed a strong preference for their own females, whereas the *persimilis* males showed little or no such preference. In the later generations, however, the hybrids seemed to be much more randomly distributed between the two types, often varying rather widely among cages and from generation to generation within the same cage, now one,

now the other kind of hybrid being more numerous. This was, to some extent, due to the small number of hybrid males which could usually be dissected in these later generations. In general, therefore, natural selection has acted mainly to reduce the number of fertilizations of *pseudoobscura* females by *persimilis* males, making their number roughly comparable to those of the reciprocal cross.

MULTIPLE-CHOICE EXPERIMENTS

When cage 2 had run for 10 generations and cage 3 for 5 generations, flies from each were subcultured in bottles and standard sexual isolation tests were made, using as a control the stocks from which the cages were originally made up. When the males were *persimilis,* the isolation index was not significantly different from zero when the original control stocks were used, but it was highly significant when the flies from cages 2 and 3 were used. As would be expected, the value of the isolation index for cage 2 (.52) was greater than the value (.30) for cage 3 (see table 6).

When cage 2 had run for 14 generations, cage 3 for 9 generations, and cage

TABLE 6.   *Sexual isolation tests*

Strains tested	No. of ♀ ♀ inseminated and not inseminated				Isolation index*	x^2	Probability
	Homogamic		Heterogamic				
	+	−	+	−			
persimilis ♂ ♂—Preliminary test 1	46	37	55	36	−.04	.7	.4
persimilis ♂ ♂—Preliminary test 2	31	17	30	29	.12	1.5	.2
persimilis ♂ ♂—Control 1	82	130	80	125	−.07	.02	.9
persimilis ♂ ♂—Cage 2, 10th generation	129	66	40	152	.52	98.68	<.01
persimilis ♂ ♂—Cage 3, 5th generation	99	84	54	132	.30	22.77	<.01
persimilis ♂ ♂—Control 2	107	71	68	108	.21	15.48	<.01
persimilis ♂ ♂—Cage 2, 14th generation	97	19	25	91	.60	87.15	<.01
persimilis ♂ ♂—Cage 3, 9th generation	75	15	23	66	.52	57.01	<.01
persimilis ♂ ♂—Cage 4, 5th generation	106	41	26	128	.62	89.74	<.01
pseudoobscura ♂ ♂—Preliminary test 1	81	14	3	86	.93	120.9	<.01
pseudoobscura ♂ ♂—Preliminary test 2	42	13	6	45	.73	42.0	<.01
pseudoobscura ♂ ♂—Control 1	75	32	11	88	.73	71.16	<.01
pseudoobscura ♂ ♂—Cage 2, 10th generation	120	9	2	126	.96	211.9	<.01
pseudoobscura ♂ ♂—Cage 3, 5th generation	87	11	6	92	.87	131.0	<.01
pseudoobscura ♂ ♂—Control 2	59	6	17	50	.57	55.12	<.01
pseudobscura ♂ ♂—Cage 2, 14th generation	60	7	7	60	.80	79.53	<.01
pseudoobscura ♂ ♂—Cage 3, 9th generation	75	3	21	59	.57	78.55	<.01
pseudoobscura ♂ ♂—Cage 4, 5th generation	57	9	4	62	.87	77.68	<.01

* The isolation index is calculated from the percentage of homo- and heterogamic females inseminated (see Dobzhansky and Mayr, 1944), + 1.00 indicating only homogamic mating, 0.00 random mating, and −1.00 completely heterogamic mating.

4 for 5 generations, a second series of sexual isolation tests were performed, using the same technique and again with the original stocks subcultured generation after generation as controls. In this second set of tests, using *persimilis* males, the controls as well as the experimental cultures gave a value highly significantly different from random mating, though the isolation indices were much lower than those for the flies from the cages (.21 as opposed to .60, .52, and .62). In order to determine whether the sexual isolation for the flies taken from the cages was significantly different from those of the controls, the procedure used by Snedecor (1946) for three sets of attributes (Section 9.8) was applied. Due to the extremely laborious nature of the procedure, the comparison was made only between the control and the cage test most like the control in χ^2 and isolation index, namely cage 3. The χ^2 for these two sets of tests was highly significant ($\chi^2 = 15.81$, probability $< .01$ for 1 degree of freedom). Since the other cages had each given a χ^2 and isolation index even more different from that of the controls, it was evident that for the second set of tests, as well as for the first, the flies from cages which had run for several generations displayed a definitely greater interspecific sexual isolation than did the controls. As would be expected, both control and experimental tests using *pseudoobscura* males showed strong sexual isolation (see table 4). From these results, it would certainly appear that at least part of the reproductive isolation observed in the cages is sexual.

In this connection, it was thought that certain comparisons of sexual isolation between different cages might prove interesting using *persimilis* males, of course. This could also be done using the procedure for three sets of attributes from Snedecor. The first such comparison was made between the sexual isolation in cage 2 generation 10 and cage 3 generation 5. Both of these series of tests come from the first set. At the time the flies used in

making up the stocks for this set of tests were taken from the cages, the percentage of hybrids in cage 2 stood at 6 per cent and had probably stayed at this point or lower for five generations. Never afterwards was the percentage of hybrids in this cage to go above 8 per cent. At the same time, however, cage 3, though it stood at 5 per cent, had probably never previously had such a small percentage of hybrids, and the fact that in the next generation it rose again to 21 per cent shows that the isolating mechanisms had not yet been stabilized. When the tests from these two cages, both from the first set, are compared statistically, we obtain a χ^2 of 7.67, which for one degree of freedom gives a probability of $< .01$.

The second comparison was made of the sexual isolation for cage 3 between generation 5 and generation 9. At generation 5, the isolating mechanisms had not yet been stabilized, as has already been mentioned, but by generation 9, the percentage of hybrids stood at 2 per cent and was never afterward to rise above 6 per cent. Hence, a difference might be expected. This comparison was, of course, not as valid as that between cage 2 and cage 3 from the first set of tests, since the two series of tests in this case were not done during the same period, and hence possibly not under strictly comparable conditions. Nevertheless, the results of this comparison might at least be suggestive. In this case, a χ^2 was obtained of 9.83, with a probability for one degree of freedom of $< .01$. These two comparisons would seem to give support to the idea that during the earlier generations, sexual isolation was increasing in all cages.

MIXED-CAGE EXPERIMENTS

In order to determine whether the isolation observed in the cages acts in general against all members of the other species, or is a more specific mechanism, isolating only the strains from the cage in which it is developed, mixed cage experiments were undertaken. In these

TABLE 7. *Mixed cage experiments*

(Equal numbers of each sex and species used as parents in each case)

Source of parents		Number of offspring			Per cent hybrids
pseudoobscura	*persimilis*	*pseudoobscura*	*persimilis*	hybrids	
Cage 3—10th generation	Cage 4—6th generation	889	840	85	5
Cage 4—6th generation	Cage 3—10th generation	314	1436	95	5
Cage 2—19th generation	Cage 4—9th generation	1143	731	270	13
Cage 4—9th generation	Cage 2—19th generation	1186	818	39	2
Cage 2—19th generation	Cage 3—13th generation	2535	873	117	3
Cage 3—15th generation	Cage 2—21st generation	838	1091	64	3

tests, *peudoobscura* and *persimilis* were taken from different cages, each of which had run for several generations with a very low percentage of hybrids, and were put together in one cage, which was permitted to proceed for one generation and then the number of pure species and hybred flies were counted. All combinations of the three cages were made. The results may be seen in table 7. In all cases but one, the percentages of the hybrids were quite low and approximately the same as those appearing in the unmixed cages. The only exception was when *pseudoobscura* from cage 2 were put together from cage 4. The percentage of hybrids obtained in this case, while not quite as high as one later count from one of the unmixed cages (cage 4 generation 9), was considerably higher than was usual in these later counts. On the other hand, it was a good deal lower than even the lowest of the first generation counts from the unmixed cages (13 per cent as compared with 22 per cent). From this it appears that these isolating mechanisms selected out in each of the three cages were very similar, so much so that they could be readily interchanged and probably were mechanisms which would react towards all individuals of the other species or at least that segment sampled by the original stocks, rather than with only the particular strain against which they had been developed. This was perhaps to be expected, inasmuch as all three cages had been made up from the same stocks, so that all initially carried the same store of

genetic variability for reproductive isolation, except for differences due to the sampling error involved in making up the cages. Under these circumstances, one might expect natural selection to fix essentialy the same gene complexes in each cage. An alternative hypothesis would be, of course, that different gene complexes having very similar phenotypic effects, or, at least, all acting effectively-against stock flies of the other species as a whole, were selected out in each cage. To me, at least, this would appear to be much less likely.

DISCUSSION AND CONCLUSIONS

Before attempting to evaluate these findings, it may be desirable to review briefly the effective isolating mechanisms between *Drosophila pseudoobscura* and *D. persimilis* existing in nature. Geographical isolation can hardly be said to exist, since the range of *D. persimilis* is entirely included in that of *D. pseudoobscura*. Ecological isolation, on the other hand, is considerable and is twofold. The two species have rather different macro-ecological or ecoclimatic preferences, *D. persimilis* being found, for the most part, at higher elevations in the mountains, *D. pseudoobscura*, to a greater extent, at lower elevations, including the lowlands (Dobzhansky and Epling, 1944). It is interesting to note that outside the range of *D. persimilis*, *D. pseudoobscura* is common in the mountains as well as in the lowlands, reaching the tree line, above 11,000 feet, on Pikes peak in Colorado.

Micro-ecological or ecotopic differences are also marked, *D. pseudoobscura* preferring warmer sunnier places. Whereas *D. persimilis* prefers the cooler shadier spots (Pittendrigh-unpublished). Sexual isolation seems to play an important part, newly captured strains having a rather high sexual isolation except at low temperatures. All these isolating mechanisms, however, are partial, and one would expect some hybrids to be formed in nature. This apparently does not occur, since of the thousands of salivary gland chromosomes which have been studied from flies caught in nature, not a single hybrid has been found, even from localities where both species occur together (Dobzhansky-unpublished). This total absence of hybrids is at present an unsolved problem. It may be due to other isolating mechanisms, not yet detected, which acting in conjunction with the known ones, completely prevent the appearance of hybrids. Those two isolating mechanisms, male hybrid sterility and backcross inviability, which are so important in keeping the species apart in the laboratory, apparently never have a chance to operate in nature, though of course they may have been important in preventing gene exchange in the past.

With these facts in mind, let us consider the central problem of whether natural selection can act to build up isolating mechanisms between distinct allopatric forms whose ranges meet. In the first place, there must already be some isolation before selection can act, both in a form which makes the hybrid less well adapted, and also as hereditary variability for further isolation. If the hybrid is as well adapted as either parental type for any availible environment, either parental or intermediate, the hybrids will not be discriminated against and the two original forms will be connected by a zone of subspecific intergradation. Hence it means that the first isolating mechanisms must arise as by-products of genetic divergence, but at least theoretically could be added to

and built into a "gene-tight" isolating system by selection.

Up until now, however, there has been no direct evidence that selection can and does do this. To the knowledge of the writer, no experimental evidence other than that here cited has been brought forward to show that natural selection can create or strengthen an isolating mechanism. Direct evidence of this occurrence from natural populations is also very scanty and often capable of interpretation on other grounds. Perhaps the best established case concerns sexual isolation between *D. pseudoobscura* and *D. miranda* (Dobzhansky and Koller, 1939). Here, strains of *D. pseudoobscura* coming from localities within or close to the range of at least the northern populations of *D. miranda* show in general a greater sexual isolation with northern strains of *D. miranda* than do strains of *D. pseudoobscura* coming from more distant localities. It is probable that in populations of *D. pseudoobscura* living in close proximity to *D. miranda*, natural selection has acted to prevent hybridization by means of greater sexual isolation, whereas in populations which are geographically remote from the range of *D. miranda*, increased sexual isolation has had no such selective advantage. However, even here the situation is not so simple, since this relation fails to hold when southern rather than northern strains of *D. miranda* are tested against the geographical strains of *D. pseudoobscura*.

A more disputed situation occurs in the cases of the crows, *Corvus coronecornix*, and the grackles, *Quiscalus quiscula-aeneus* discussed by Dobzhansky (1941). In both these cases, the hybrid zone between the ranges of the two incipient species is broad in northern regions in which the retreat of the glaciers has only recently permitted occupation by the parental forms, whereas the hybrid zone is narrow in the south where the two forms in each case have been able to occupy the habitat for a longer time. Dobzhansky interprets the facts as indicating a spread, with retreat of the glaciers, from geographically isolated refuges in the far south. As the two forms spread north, they came in contact first in the more southern regions, later in the north. In the south, natural selection has been able to build up reproductive isolation, preventing much hybridization, whereas in the north, not enough time has elaspsed for this to occur. This hypothesis has not been favored by Mayr (1942), who attributes the narrow hybrid zone in the more southern localities to local ecological factors preventing the two forms from coming in contact to as great a degree as in the north. It now seems probable, however, that an extensive study of cases where incipient species have come together, in different places, at different times, after being geographically isolated, would reveal undoubted cases of natural selection for reproductive isolation.

The evidence here presented shows, not only that natural selection can act to strengthen isolation between species, but it also brings out an important aspect of the difference between species and subspecies. When subspecies are involved, gene exchange between the two populations is always possible, the hybrid types are fitted for various intermediate habitats, geographical or ecological, between those of the two parental types, and fit into their population structure. Once the threshold has been passed, however, and the two populations have reached the status of full species, the relation between them becomes quite different. The hybrids are relatively ill-adapted for any available habitat. There are usually several isolating mechanisms which to a greater or lesser degree prevent gene exchange, and these are likely to be strengthened and added to by natural selection. Furthermore, if, because of a change in the environment, some of these isolating mechanisms are broken down, others are likely to take their place, due simply to the advantage of preventing the wastage of gametes which would otherwise result. *D. pseudoobscura* and *D. persimilis* have reached this stage of genetic divergence. In the experiments here described, ecological isolation was completely eliminated by keeping all flies in a small cage with only one type of culture medium. Existing sexual isolation was greatly weakened by keeping the cage at a low temperature. In this way, what are probably the two most important isolating mechanisms keeping the two species apart in nature were largely eliminated, yet in a surprisingly short time new isolation (in this case at least partly sexual) was built up, which brought the number of hybrids again to a low level. This change, of course, was aided by the practice of removing the hybrids entirely each generation, in this way simulating complete hybrid inviability. This, however, could hardly have had much effect, because of complete male hybrid sterility and strong backcross inviability under cage conditions. This seems to me to typify the true genetic relation of a good species to related forms. By virtue of its isolating mechanisms, in part at least maintained by selection, it is genetically independent of other organisms. In its further evolution, it is on its own, dependent entirely on its own mutations, since it is unable, as is a subspecies, ever to acquire advantageous genes from other populations.

Summary

Using artificial mixed populations of *Drosophila pseudoobscura* and *D. persimilis,* it has been possible to show, over a period of several generations, a very rapid increase in the amount of reproductive isolation between the two species as a result of natural selection. This isolation has been shown to be at least partly sexual. The implications of these findings for theories of speciation are discussed.

Acknowledgments

The author wishes to express his deep indebtedness to Dr. Th. Dobzhansky for suggesting the problem, for continual guidance and inspiration during the course of the work, and for many helpful technical suggestions throughout the experiments. The help very kindly given by Dr. Howard Levene in the statistical analysis of the data is also gratefully acknowledged.

BIBLIOGRAPHY

DOBZHANSKY, TH. 1935. Maternal effect as a cause of the difference between the reciprocal crosses in *Drosophila pseudoobscura*. Proceedings of the National Academy of Sciences, 31: 443–446.

DOBZHANSKY, TH. 1940. Speciation as a stage in genetic divergence. American Naturalist, 74, 312–321.

DOBZHANSKY, TH. 1941. Genetics and the origin of species. 2nd edition, New York, Columbia University Press.

DOBZHANSKY, TH. 1945. Genetic structure of natural populations. Carnegie Institution of Washington Year Book, 44: 127–134.

DOBZHANSKY, TH. 1947. Adaptive changes induced by natural selection in wild populations of *Drosophila*. Evolution, 1: 1–16.

DOBZHANSKY, TH., AND KOLLER, P. C. 1939. Sexual isolation between two species of *Drosophila*—A study in the origin of an isolating mechanism. Genetics, 24: 97–98.

DOBZHANSKY, TH. AND MAYR, E. 1944. Experiments on sexual isolation in *Drosophila*. I. Geographic strains of *Drosophila willistoni*. Proc. Nat. Acad. Sci., 30: 238–244.

KENDALL, M. G. 1942. Partial rank correlation. Biometrika, 32: 277–283.

KENDALL, M. G. 1943. The advanced theory of statistics. London, C. G. Griffen and Co.

LANCEFIELD, D. E. 1929. A genetic study of crosses of two races or physiological species of *Drosophila obscura*. Zeitscrift für induktives Abstammungs- und Vererbungslehre, 52: 287–317.

MAYR, E. 1942. Systematics and the origin of species. New York, Columbia University Press.

MAYR, E., AND DOBZHANSKY, TH. 1945. Experiments on sexual isolation in *Drosophila*. IV. Modification of the degree of isolation between *Drosophila pseudoobscura* and *Drosophila persimilis* and of sexual preferences in *Drosophila prosaltans*. Proc. Nat. Acad. Sci., 31: 75–82.

MULLER, H. J. 1939. Reversibility in evolution considered from the standpoint of genetics. Biol. Rev., 14: 261–280.

——. 1942. Isolating mechanisms, evolution, and temperature. Biol. Symposia, 6: 71–125.

SNEDECOR, G. W. 1946. Statistical methods. 4th edition.

WRIGHT, S., AND DOBZHANSKY, TH. 1946. Genetics of natural populations. XII. Experimental reproduction of some of the changes caused by natural selection in certain populations of *Drosophila pseudoobscura*. Genetics, 31: 125–156.

18

Reprinted from *Evolution* **9**:469–480 (1955)

MATING CALL AND STAGE OF SPECIATION IN THE *MICROHYLA OLIVACEA—M. CAROLINENSIS* COMPLEX [1]

W. Frank Blair

University of Texas

Received February 11, 1955

INTRODUCTION

This report deals with variations in mating call in a species group of narrow-mouthed frogs (genus *Microhyla*) [2] and with the possible evolutionary significance of these variations. Anurans were studied because differences in mating call serve as important isolation mechanisms in these animals. The particular species complex was selected because it has populations which appear to be in intermediate stages of speciation.

A western, xeric-adapted population that has been called *Microhyla olivacea* is distributed from the Gulf of California northeastward to eastern Texas and Oklahoma and northwestern Missouri. An eastern, mesic-adapted population that has been called *M. carolinensis* is distributed through the southern half of the eastern United States and reaches westward to eastern Texas and Oklahoma. The ranges of the two populations overlap in a strip running from the Gulf of Mexico into northeastern Oklahoma (fig. 1). Hecht and Matalas (1946) reported morphological intermediates between the unmottled *olivacea* and the dorsally and ventrally mottled *carolinensis* from a station in the overlap zone in southern Texas and from another in eastern Oklahoma. They hypothesized that the two are either approaching complete isolation or that previously existing isolating mechanisms have

broken down. Their treatment of the two populations as subspecies has been followed by most anuran taxonomists.

The present study was undertaken in an effort to determine just how the two populations were behaving toward each other in the overlap zone. One obvious possibility would be that isolation mechanisms were breaking down and that the two populations would be bound together in future evolution by gene flow between them. Another possibility would be that as hypothesized by Dobzhansky (1937, 1940) limited hybridization and selection were acting to reinforce incipient isolation mechanisms. If the latter were true the two populations would be trending toward eventual elimination of gene exchange. Measurements of call inside and outside of the overlap zone should provide critical information about the behavior of the two populations toward each other. This is true because call differences are important isolation mechanisms in most anurans. The males go to breeding pools and attract the females by their calls.

MATERIALS AND METHODS

Tape recordings have been made of the calls of 222 individuals at a total of 46 stations. The distribution of the recording stations is shown in figure 1 except for one station in southern Arizona and one in northern Florida. The distribution of the individuals in respect to the overlap zone is shown in table 1. All recordings were made in natural breeding aggregations. Recording equipment included a Magnecorder PT6 recorder and preamplifier powered by a storage battery and rotary converter with frequency controlled at 60 cps. An Altec dynamic

[1] This work was supported under National Science Foundation project No. NSF-G328.

[2] The generic name *Gastrophryne* has been resurrected from synonymy by de Carvalho (1954) to separate these frogs from the Asiatic genus *Microhyla*. The generic name has no bearing on the present problem, and I have followed Parker (1934) in retaining use of the name *Microhyla*.

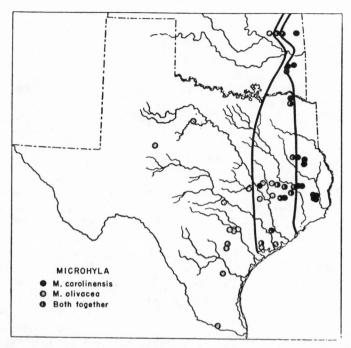

Fig. 1. Map showing approximate boundaries of overlap zone of *Microhyla carolinensis* and *M. olivacea*. Symbols represent stations at which recordings were made. The symbol "both together" is used for the three stations at which both species were recorded, the four at which one species and hybrids were recorded, and the three at which one species was recorded and the other was known to be present but could not be recorded for technical reasons.

microphone No. 660B was used with either a 100 or 200 foot cord. The microphone was placed close to the individual to be recorded in order to reduce background noise. All recordings were made at a tape speed of 15 inches per second. Air temperature near the ground and water temperature near the surface in the breeding pools were recorded. An attempt was made to collect the individuals recorded, but this was often unsuccessful with these tiny animals when certain types of vegetation filled the breeding pools.

In the laboratory, sound spectrograms of each individual call were made by use of a "Sona-Graph." With this instrument, the signal to be analyzed is recorded on a magnetic disc and then played back repeatedly into a scanning filter, the pass band of which is moved slowly across the frequency spectrum from 0 to 8,000 cycles. The output of the analyzing filter is recorded through a stylus on electrically

sensitive paper that is fixed to a drum which rotates synchronously with the magnetic disc. The "sonagram" produced on the recording paper is a graphic representation of the call in respect to time, frequency and intensity. Time is shown on the horizontal scale. Frequency up to 8,000 cps is shown on the vertical scale. The intensity of marking indicates the amount of energy involved at each frequency level. All analyses were made with narrow band filters having an effective band width of 45 cps.

CHARACTERISTICS OF THE CALL

The call in the two kinds of *Microhyla* studied is a simple buzz. As shown by the sonagrams (fig. 2), the call consists of a fundamental vibration and a large series of up to 40 or more harmonics. Certain harmonics or bands of harmonics are weakly expressed; others are stressed, as indicated by their heavy marking on the sonagram. The relative expression of the various harmonics and bands of harmonics is presumably a function of the vocal pouch. A few harmonic elements extend above the 8 kilocycle limit of the method used here, but the great bulk of the call and probably all of its significant parts fall within the limits of the present analysis.

Duration and frequency are the two most obvious variables in this kind of call. Duration has been measured from the sonagrams, where possible, by use of a plastic overlay scale calibrated in tenths of seconds. Where the call exceeded 2.4 seconds and therefore required the making of two sonagrams, the duration was determined from the tape recording by use of a stop watch calibrated to .10 seconds.

The best expression of frequency for the purposes of this comparison seems to be the mid-point of the emphasized band of harmonics. This usually falls between three and four kilocycles (fig. 2). It will be referred to as the emphasized frequency or mid-point frequency.

A comparison of frequency in the different samples must take into account the influence of temperature on frequency. Since these frogs almost always call from a partially submerged position, water temperature has been plotted against mid-point frequency to test the relationship between temperature and frequency (fig. 3). Separate regression lines have been plotted for the Texas-Oklahoma *olivacea* and *carolinensis,* using the method of least squares. Eight apparent field hybrids have been plotted on the scatter diagram, but they have not been used in calculation of the regression lines. Frequency is significantly correlated with temperature in both species. The correlation coefficient in *olivacea* is .883, and in *carolinensis* it is .273. The two regressions are obviously different; using the test of significance of Simpson and Roe (1939, p. 278) the probability that the two regression coefficients are the same is less than .0001.

Both the raw frequency data and the same data corrected to 25° C. are presented in table 1; in all other comparisons

TABLE 1. *Means and standard errors of duration and mid-point of emphasized frequency band in* Microhyla *calls*

Samples	Number of stations	Number of indi- viduals	Mid-point of emphasized band in CPS		Duration in seconds
			Uncorrected	Corrected to 25° C	
Carolinensis					
Florida (Welaka, Putnam Co.)	1	26	3531±28	3484±30	1.25±.04
East of overlap (Texas, Oklahoma)	14	44	3009±34	2968±29	1.31±.06
From overlap zone (Texas, Oklahoma)	10	36	3070±43	3060±41	1.14±.05
Hybrids					
Overlap zone (Texas)	5	8	3599±61	3575±43*	1.52±.11
Olivacea					
From overlap zone (Texas, Oklahoma)	12	56	4403±40	4394±31	2.15±.05
West of overlap (Texas, Oklahoma)	11	50	3974±50	4141±40	2.45±.08
Arizona (Pena Blanca Spring)	1	2	3352	3564	1.45

* Average of correction factor for two species used.

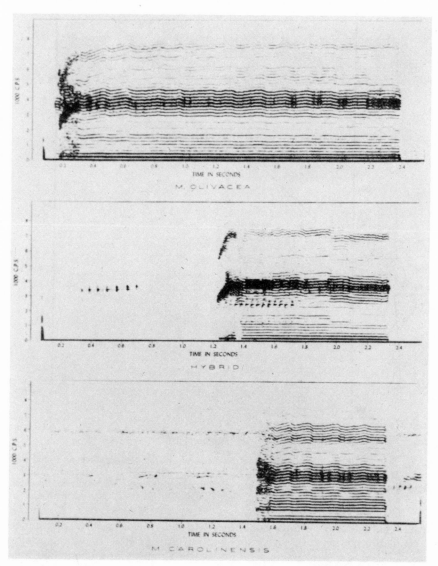

FIG. 2. Sonagrams of representative *Microhyla* calls from eastern Texas. Intensity of marking is proportional to energy involved at the frequency level. Note large number of harmonics, and emphasized band at about 3,000 cps in *M. carolinensis* and 4,000 cps in *M. olivacea*. Note differences in duration and note initial peep in *olivacea* and hybrid. Faint markings to left of call in hybrid and to left and right in *carolinensis* represent background noises.

the raw frequency data are used, because all differences between samples which are statistically significant in the raw data are also significant when the corrected frequencies are used. It is pertinent to the effectiveness of frequency difference as an isolation mechanism that the difference would be maintained in a mixed population and that it would actually increase as temperature increased.

In some cases there is a sharp rise in frequency at the start of the call. This is heard as a distinct peep. The presence or absence of this peep provides a significant

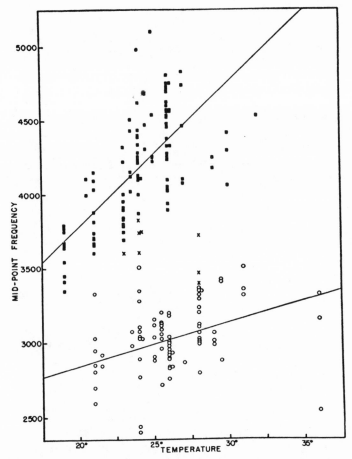

Fig. 3. Scatter diagrams showing relation between water temperature and mid-point frequency in *Microhyla*, with regression lines plotted by method of least squares. Solid squares represent Texas-Oklahoma *olivacea;* open circles show Texas-Oklahoma *carolinensis*. The symbol X shows presumed hybrids, which were not used in plotting regression lines.

qualitative character for comparison between populations.

COMPARISONS

The 222 individual calls available for analysis have been classified into seven groups (table 1). These are: (1) *olivacea* from the overlap zone in Texas and Oklahoma, (2) *carolinensis* from the overlap zone, (3) eight individuals from the overlap zone which were identified as probable hybrids on the basis of call and of morphological characters, (4) *olivacea* from west of the overlap zone in Texas and Oklahoma, (5) *carolinensis* from east of the overlap zone in Texas and Oklahoma, (6)

two individuals of *olivacea* from southern Arizona (Peña Blanca Spring, Santa Cruz County) and about 800 miles west of the overlap zone, (7) *carolinensis* from northern Florida (Welaka, Putnam County) about 800 miles east of the overlap zone.

In the Overlap Zone

One hundred individuals were recorded in the overlap zone and at a total of 19 stations. Both species were present together at three stations. One or the other species was found in company with apparent hybrids at four other stations. The eastern species was found alone at four stations. The western one was found alone at five localities, and at two others the eastern species was heard but could not be recorded for technical reasons. Absence of a species from a recording station does not necessarily mean that the species does not breed there. It means only that it was not calling there when the recordings were made or could not be recorded.

Disregarding the eight apparent hybrids for the moment, the remaining 92 individuals are clearly referable to one or the other of the two species. The call of *olivacea* is higher in pitch than that of *carolinensis;* the mid-point of the emphasized band averages 1,333 ± 58 cps higher in the former than in the latter species (table 1; fig. 4). The duration of the *olivacea* call averages nearly twice the length of the *carolinensis* call. The call of all of the 56 *olivacea* starts with a distinct peep which is seen on the sonagram as a sharp rise in frequency; the call in three of the 36 *carolinensis* has a slight initial inflection and that of the others is without evidence of the peep.

The eight presumed hybrids are intermediate between *olivacea* and *carolinensis* in both mid-point frequency and duration, although their means for both measurements fall somewhat closer to *carolinensis* than to *olivacea* (table 1; fig. 4). A slight to moderate peep is present in the call of six of the eight hybrids, and the other two show no initial rise in frequency.

Overlap with Non-overlap *olivacea*

Fifty *olivacea* were recorded at a total of 11 stations located from 50 to 300 miles west of the overlap zone in Texas and Oklahoma. The call of these western *olivacea* averages significantly lower in frequency than the call of *olivacea* in the overlap zone; the mid-point of the emphasized band averages 529 ± 64 cps lower in the former than in the latter group. The length of the call averages 0.30 ± .06 seconds longer in the western than in the overlap-zone *olivacea*. There is a distinct

peep in the initial part of the call of all of the 50 western *olivacea*.

Only two calls of *olivacea* could be obtained at the Arizona station, where this species is relatively rare. On the basis of these two individuals, the call of the *olivacea* living about 800 airline miles from the overlap zone is much lower in frequency and much shorter in duration than the call of *olivacea* both inside and outside the overlap zone in Texas and Oklahoma. In fact, the call of the Arizona *olivacea* resembles the call of *carolinensis* more than it does that of Texas and Oklahoma *olivacea*. The call of these Arizona *olivacea* seemed to be weaker in volume than that of any of the other *Microhyla* recorded, but this could not be measured with the equipment available. There is an initial peep in the call of the Arizona *olivacea*, but it is less distinct than in the Texas and Oklahoma *olivacea*.

Overlap with Non-overlap *carolinensis*

Forty-four *carolinensis* were recorded at a total of 14 stations located from five to 65 miles east of the overlap zone in Texas and Oklahoma. These average slightly but not significantly lower in frequency and longer in duration than do the *carolinensis* from the overlap zone (table 1; fig. 4). It should be noted that these *carolinensis* came from localities considerably nearer the overlap zone than did the *olivacea* from west of it. As in the overlap-zone frogs of the same species, the call of these *carolinensis* usually lacks the opening peep. Five of the 44 individuals showed a slight to moderate initial inflection.

Twenty-six *carolinensis* were recorded in northern Florida, about 800 airline miles from the overlap zone of the two species. The call of the Florida *carolinensis* is intermediate in frequency between the Texas-Oklahoma *carolinensis* and *olivacea* (table 1; fig. 4). In duration, the call of the Florida *carolinensis* does not differ significantly from that of the Texas-Oklahoma *carolinensis*. Four of the 26 Florida *carolinensis* show no initial

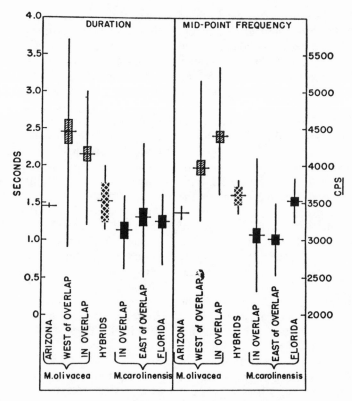

Fig. 4. Comparison of *Microhyla* calls by method of Dice and Leraas (1936). Vertical lines show range of variation; horizontal lines show mean. Failure of rectangles, representing twice the standard error on each side of mean, to overlap means that the difference between two means is at least four times the standard error of the difference. Note sharp differences between the two species in the overlap zone. Note intermediate position of presumed hybrids and of Arizona *olivacea* and Florida *carolinensis*.

rise in frequency. Three have pronounced rises, and the remainder have moderate ones.

DISCUSSION

Analysis of the mating calls leads to the following generalizations: (1) hybridization does occur in the overlap zone of *carolinensis* and *olivacea* as earlier reported by Hecht and Matalas (1946) on morphological evidence, (2) most overlap-zone individuals fall clearly into one species or the other, (3) calls of *olivacea* in the overlap zone differ more from those of *carolinensis* than do calls of *olivacea* from west of it; *carolinensis* from Florida are more like *olivacea* in call than are *carolinensis* from the overlap zone.

Distributional Relationships

Interpretation of the present relationships of *olivacea* and *carolinensis* in respect to gene interchange and speciational stage necessitates a reconstruction of the possible past history of the complex. It seems almost certain that the present contact of the two kinds is secondary as suspected by Hecht and Matalas (1946) and that it is post-Pleistocene. The general evidence for Pleistocene fragmentation of ranges in North America has been summarized by Deevey (1949) and that for the region and the species complex in question has been discussed by W. F. Blair (1951); this evidence does not need to be repeated here. There is no way of dating the contact beyond the strong circumstantial evidence that it is post-Wisconsin. There is evidence, however, that the present magnitude of the overlap zone has been influenced by clearing of the deciduous forest in this area. Except for the coastal prairie, the overlap zone roughly follows the western border of the eastern deciduous forest. Clearing for agricultural purposes along the forest border has resulted in the shift of terrestrial environmental conditions from humid toward xeric, and it has permitted the eastward spread of relatively xeric-adapted organisms.

The distributional pattern of the two species in the overlap zone strongly indicates a push eastward of *olivacea* into the cleared forest border. It also indicates a general withdrawal eastward of *carolinensis*. On the evidence from road logs of breeding choruses, the western species far outnumbers the eastern one in the overlap zone, and it is much more continuously distributed there. This is to be expected, as much of the area has been cleared of forest. The eastern species is discontinuously distributed in the overlap zone, and a few small disjunct populations exist in favorable localities west of what has been arbitrarily designated the western boundary of the overlap zone. One of these disjunct populations is in Gonzales County, Texas, in a peat bog known locally as Soefke's Swamp. A small collection of morphologically good *carolinensis* was taken there on April 24, 1949. Persistent efforts to locate *carolinensis* in Soefke's Swamp over the past two years have resulted in failure. Severe drought over the past five years has presumably depleted this population and may possibly have caused its extirpation. The species has never been found in apparently similar peat bogs in the same area nor in the mesic, post-climax deciduous forest of the flood-plain of the Guadalupe River there. Instead, enormous breeding congresses of *olivacea* have been found in rain pools on the heavily forested flood-plain. This is the only place in which we have found *olivacea* breeding in a situation which appeared ecologically more suitable for *carolinensis* than for it. One might argue that the small *carolinensis* population has been swamped through cross-breeding with the large *olivacea* population, but the mere existence of the small population of *carolinensis* until at least the spring of 1949 and the morphological distinctness of the specimens collected then make this explanation improbable. Depletion by drought seems the probable explanation of the apparent disappearance of this disjunct population of *carolinensis*. Another disjunct population has been reported to me by Ottys Sanders (oral communication) at a place locally called Bois d'arc Island on the Trinity River, just below Dallas, Texas. Blair and Laughlin (in press) have reported two apparently disjunct populations from mesic, flood-plain localities of the Verdigris River drainage in Wagoner and Tulsa counties, Oklahoma. The general distributional picture is one, then, of eastward expansion of the xeric-adapted *olivacea* into an area in which the eastward withdrawing *carolinensis* has left discontinuously distributed populations in favorable localities. These distributional changes were very possibly going on before disturbance of the forest border by man, and they have almost certainly been accelerated by clearing of the forest. The western, disjunct populations of *carolinensis* probably have been in contact with *olivacea* for a relatively long period of time, for they are in small areas of mesic environment well west of the historically known border of the deciduous forest and in which the regional environmental conditions have been relatively xeric for a long period.

The one place in the overlap zone where the distributional relationships of the two species could not have been affected by clearing of the forest is on the coastal prairie in Texas. This coastal strip is an area of relatively moist grassland with little or no water deficiency at any season (see map in Thornthwaite, 1948). Drainage is poor on the flat coastal prairie, and in many places irrigated rice fields provide even more moist conditions than the undisturbed prairie. It is possible that *olivacea* ranges eastward on the coastal prairie because it is a grassland and that *carolinensis* occurs there because it is moist.

Evolutionary Status

The relationships of the different samples in respect to mating call are shown graphically in figure 5. The greater difference in mating call of the two kinds of frogs in the overlap zone, where there is some hybridization, than where the two do not occur together is possibly explained as the result of selection against hybridization. The possibility that incipient isolation mechanisms could be reinforced through selection has been put forth by Dobzhansky (1937, 1940). Koopman (1950) has obtained convincing experimental evidence by use of population cages of *Drosophila*.

Certain weak isolation mechanisms other than difference in mating call probably operate to reduce the chance of interbreeding of the two species of *Microhyla*. Bragg (1950) and others have pointed out that *olivacea* is dependent on rainfall for breeding, while *carolinensis* is not, and that the latter is a "summer" breeder, while *olivacea* breeds on rain from April to September. From our own observations of the past two years in Texas, these differences appear to be of minor importance as isolation mechanisms. The earliest record of *olivacea* breeding was April 9 and the latest was September 3. The earliest record for *carolinensis* was May 2, and the latest was September 1. The latest record of large choruses of *carolinensis* was July 31, when large numbers of both species were breeding following torrential rains. Thus, *olivacea* starts breeding earlier than *carolinensis*, but large numbers of both species may breed over a span of three of the five months in which the former normally breeds.

Water and air temperatures at the recording stations indicate only a slight preference of *carolinensis* for warmer temperatures. Water temperatures where *olivacea* was breeding ranged from 19.0 to 32.0° C. (mean, 24.9), and the air temperatures ranged from 14.0 to 28.0° C. (mean, 23.7). Water temperatures where *carolinensis* was breeding ranged from 21.0 to 36.0° C. (mean, 25.6), and air temperatures ranged from 19.5 to 29.0° C. (mean, 24.3). The air temperatures for *carolinensis* are exclusive of those for two stations at which this species was recorded in chorus in mid-afternoon. Air temperatures at those times were 30.0 and 33.0° C., respectively. The daytime breeding of *carolinensis*, pointed out by Bragg (1950) and others, would reduce the probability of cross-mating with *olivacea*, which apparently breeds only at night. Our observations indicate, however, that these daytime breeding choruses usually continue into the night. The breeding of *carolinensis* in the absence of rain also is an incomplete isolation mechanism, as large breeding aggregations of both species have been found following heavy rain from May 2 to July 31.

Laboratory evidence shows that the two species can be crossed, but it does not show conclusively whether or not the hybrids are equally as viable as the parent species. A. P. Blair (1950) made reciprocal crosses between the two species from Oklahoma and reported virtually 100 per cent cleavage and apparently normal larval development in four of five crosses involving female *carolinensis* and in one cross involving a female *olivacea*. In one cross involving a female *carolinensis* and in two in which *olivacea* eggs were squeezed into a suspension of *carolinensis* sperm fertilization was reported to be somewhat lower. None of the hybrids metamorphosed, and failure of any to survive beyond 90 days was attributed to faulty technique. This worker regarded the reluctance of *carolinensis* males to clasp smaller females of *olivacea* as an incomplete isolation mechanism. Two crosses between overlap-zone *carolinensis* females and *olivacea* males in my laboratory showed a low percentage of cleavage by comparison with approximately 100 per

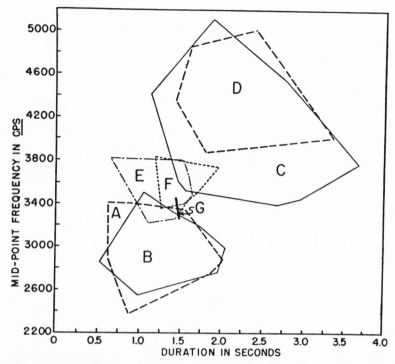

FIG. 5. Comparison of *Microhyla* calls by polygons constructed from scatter diagrams: (A) *carolinensis* from overlap zone, (B) Texas-Oklahoma *carolinensis* from east of overlap zone, (C) Texas-Oklahoma *olivacea* from west of overlap zone, (D) *olivacea* from overlap zone, (E) Florida *carolinensis*, (F) presumed hybrids from overlap zone, (G) Arizona *olivacea*.

cent cleavage in a control mating of *carolinensis*. The number of crosses is so small, however, that the lower development of the hybrids easily could have been due to condition of the eggs in females which had been in the laboratory for several days. A small number of both hybrids and controls metamorphosed and survived until they were about one-half to two-thirds grown, at which times they were lost apparently due to faulty technique.

Interbreeding of the two populations in the overlap zone is, then, restricted by a series of incomplete isolation mechanisms, most of which were presumably developed during geographic discontinuity of the two populations and as adaptations to different (xeric and mesic) environments. The total effect of the various mechanisms is insufficient, however, to prevent some cross-mating in the overlap zone. Perhaps

the most significant isolation mechanism of all is difference in the mating call. If the calls are sufficiently different that females recognize and respond only to the calls of their own species, then the two species can use the same breeding pools and respond to the same meteorological conditions with only slight chance of cross-mating. The striking divergence in mating call in the overlap zone (figs. 4, 5) suggests selection against hybridization. If hybrids are at a relative disadvantage in competition with the parental species there should be greater survival of the offspring of males with the greatest call differences and of the females which respond to them. There should be relatively less survival of the offspring of males with minimal call differences and of the females which respond to them. Under such a system, differences in call which possibly originated at random during spatial discontinuity of the populations would tend to be sharpened under present conditions of limited hybridization.

The argument for reinforcement of isolation mechanisms through selection against hybridization is premised on the hybrids being at a disadvantage in competition with the parental types. Direct evidence is not available, and it will be difficult, but not impossible, to obtain. The inconclusive results of laboratory hybridizations suggest but do not prove the possibility of reduced viability of the hybrids. The rather divergent behavioral adaptations of the two species to existence in contrasting xeric and mesic environments suggest that the hybrid genotype might be a disadaptive one. Morphologically, the relatively plain, olive-gray dorsum of *olivacea* provides good protective coloration in the muddy rain pools with scant vegetation other than grasses and sedges in which this species normally breeds and possibly at other times on the relatively vegetationless soils of its xeric environment. The dorsum of *carolinensis* is brown with blackish mottling, which makes it difficult to see against a background of dead leaves in the pools in which it normally breeds and at other times on the leaf-littered forest floor. The intermediate color and pattern of the hybrids would possibly provide relatively poor concealment on either type of background.

Judged from the evidence at hand, including characters of the mating call, the populations which have been called *Microhyla olivacea* and *M. carolinensis* are approaching final separation into separate breeding systems. If our interpretation of the evidence is correct, the relationships of these two populations are best represented by treating them as separate species.

Summary

Two species of narrow-mouthed frogs, *Microhyla olivacea* and *M. carolinensis,* have overlapping ranges in eastern Texas and Oklahoma. Limited hybridization occurs in the overlap zone. Contact of the two species is probably post-Pleistocene, and the present extent of the overlap appears to have been influenced by clearing of the forest.

The calls of 222 individuals have been compared by use of sound spectrograms in an effort to determine whether or not the isolation mechanism of call difference is being reinforced through selection against hybridization. In the overlap zone, the call of *olivacea* has a higher frequency as measured at the mid-point of the emphasized band of harmonics and is longer than the call of *carolinensis*. The calls of eight apparent hybrids are intermediate between those of the parent species in both frequency and duration. The call of *olivacea* from west of the overlap zone in Texas and Oklahoma averages significantly lower in mid-point frequency than that of *olivacea* from the overlap zone. The call of *carolinensis* from east of the overlap zone in Texas and Oklahoma does not differ significantly from that of overlap-zone *carolinensis*. The call of Arizona *olivacea* from about 800 miles west of the overlap zone is very similar to that of Florida *carolinensis* from about 800 miles east of the overlap, and both are intermediate in frequency and duration between the overlap-zone *olivacea* and *carolinensis*.

In addition to call difference, various weak isolation mechanisms affect interbreeding of the two species in the overlap zone. It seems likely that hybrids between the xeric-adapted *olivacea* and mesic-adapted *carolinensis* are at a disadvantage in competition with the parent species. Because of the role of call difference as an isolation mechanism, lower survival of offspring of males with minimal call differences and of females which respond to them would account for the markedly greater differences in call of the two species where they occur together than where they occur separately.

Acknowledgments

David Pettus has given valuable assistance in field work and in the sound and statistical analyses. Various people, particularly Hague L. Lindsay, William F. Meacham and William F. Pyburn, have contributed to the success of the field work. I am indebted to A. P. Blair for his cooperation during the work in Oklahoma and to W. A. Thornton and W. H. McCarley for cooperation during some of the work in eastern Texas. I am indebted to J. T. Patterson for reading the manuscript.

Literature Cited

Blair, A. P. 1950. Note on Oklahoma microhylid frogs. Copeia, 1950 (2) : 152.
—— and H. E. Laughlin. 1955. Range extension of Gastrophryne carolinensis. Copeia (in press).
Blair, W. F. 1951. Interbreeding of natural populations of vertebrates. Amer. Nat., 85: 9–30.
Bragg, A. N. 1950. Observations on Microhyla (Salientia: Microhylidae). Wasmann Jour. Biol., 8: 113–118.
de Carvalho, A. L. 1954. A preliminary synopsis of the genera of American microhylid frogs. Occas. Pap. Mus. Zool. Univ. Mich., No. 555: 1–19.
Deevey, E. S., Jr. 1949. Biogeography of the Pleistocene. Bull. Geol. Soc. Amer., 60: 1315–1416.
Dice, L. R., and H. J. Leraas. 1936. A graphic method for comparing several sets of measurements. Contrib. Lab. Vert. Genetics, Univ. Mich., No. 3: 1–3.
Dobzhansky, Th. 1937. Genetics and the Origin of Species. Columbia Univ. Press, New York, New York.
——. 1940. Speciation as a stage in evolutionary divergence. Amer. Nat., 74: 312–321.
Hecht, Max, and Bessie L. Matalas. 1946. A review of middle North American toads of the genus Microhyla. Amer. Mus. Novitates, No. 1315: 1–21.
Koopman, K. F. 1950. Natural selection for reproductive isolation between Drosophila pseudoobscura and Drosophila persimilis. Evolution, 4: 135–148.
Parker, H. W. 1934. A Monograph of the Frogs of the Family Microhylidae. British Museum, London, England.
Thornthwaite, C. W. 1948. An approach toward a rational classification of climate. Geogr. Review, 38: 55–94.

19

Reprinted from *Nature* 193:1164–1166 (1962)

ISOLATION BY DISRUPTIVE SELECTION

By J. M. THODAY and J. B. GIBSON

Department of Genetics, University of Cambridge

THOUGH speciation is one of the more striking features of evolution, direct experimental evidence concerning the origin of species is limited.

Artificial species have been made by allopolyploidy, but this, like any other process that involves the establishment of a new species from the hybrids between two pre-existing species, can only be secondary. The key process in speciation must involve the splitting of one population into two mutually isolated populations.

Our present theories of such speciation, based on considerable taxonomic, biogeographical and ecological evidence, implicate divergence during a period of geographical isolation and selection against hybridization after the geographical isolation has broken down[1]. Supporting evidence is available[2-4] demonstrating genetic variance affecting mating preference and showing that the frequency with which two genotypes form hybrids can be reduced by selection. However, the key demonstration that a single wild-type population can be converted by selection into two populations that are mutually isolated in the conditions in which they have to maintain themselves has not hitherto been made.

Mather[5] not only argued that disruptive selection should be able to establish two or more forms in one interbreeding population, but also suggested that in appropriate circumstances it should be able to promote isolating mechanisms. Thoday[6,7], Thoday and Boam[8] and Millicent and Thoday[9] have shown that polymorphisms are rather easily established and maintained by disruptive selection, but none of their experiments was of the kind in which isolation was to be expected.

The purpose of this article is to present a preliminary description of the results of an experiment in which a single wild-type population of *Drosophila melanogaster* has with astonishing rapidity been split into two populations that produce few hybrids in what to them is nature.

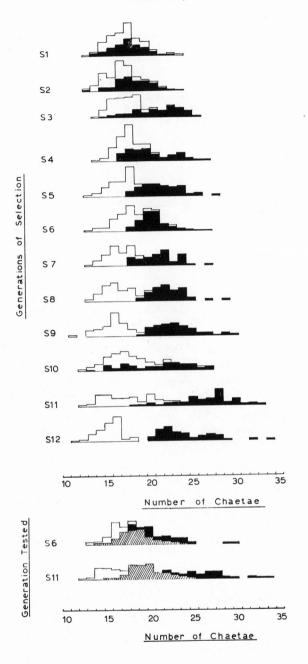

The experiment was started using the progenies of four wild females captured together in the same dustbin (garbage can) in an estate on the outskirts of Cambridge. The four progenies were combined as the 'Southacre' wild stock. Two generations later, 20 virgin females and 20 males from each of four cultures of this stock were assayed for sternopleural chæta number, and from each sex the 8 flies with the highest and the 8 flies with the lowest chæta numbers were selected regardless of the culture from which they came. (When one or two of several flies with the same chæta number had to be selected, random numbers were used to ensure against bias towards choosing flies from particular cultures.)

These 32 selected flies were placed together in a single 3 in. × 1 in. vial and left there to mate for 24 hr. They were then re-etherized, the males were discarded and the females separated once more into the 8 high and 8 low according to their chæta numbers. The 8 high females were divided at random into two lots of four and placed in two culture bottles. The 8 low females were likewise divided and placed in two other bottles. This process was repeated each generation thereafter.

Response to selection. The results are illustrated in Fig. 1 (top), which shows the distribution curves of chæta number obtained in each generation, and distinguishes the progeny of the high females from the progeny of the low females. There was rapid divergence of the two halves of the population, as a result of which from generation 4 onward almost all the high flies selected came from the progeny of high females and almost all the low flies selected came from the progeny of low females. Apart from generation 10, in which circumstances were unusual, partly owing to electric power cuts which affected the culture room temperature and partly inasmuch as special arrangements, which involved a 24-hr. delay in mating, were made to accommodate the Christmas holiday, there was a steady and remarkably rapid approach to discontinuity of the distributions which in the latest generation do not overlap.

The mating system permits random mating and ensures that unless there are departures from random mating or unless 'hybrids' differ in viability from

Fig. 1. Top, distribution curves of sternopleural chæta number in each generation of the selection experiment. White: progeny of low females. Black: progeny of high females; Bottom, distribution curves obtained in the test assays of the progeny of *S*6 and *S*11 flies. White: progeny of low × low mating. Hatched: combined progenies of high × low and low × high matings (which do not differ). Black: progeny of high × high mating. These curves should be compared with those for *S*7 and *S*12 in Fig. 1 (top) 'non-hybrids', half the flies in each half of the population will be 'hybrids' produced by the mating of high females with low males or of low females with high males. The rapid decrease in the overlap between the distribution curves and the discontinuity of the distribution curves in the latest generation clearly show that 'hybrids' must have occurred with very much lower frequencies than this, unless the hybrids are for some reason indistinguishable from one of the non-hybrid classes of fly.

Chæta numbers of hybrids. In generations $S6$ and $S11$ additional samples of flies were taken with the aim of obtaining information about the chæta number distribution of hybrids. These additional samples were assayed and selected exactly as for the continuance of the line, but set up under a different mating system. Four of the high females were placed in one mating tube with 4 of the high males; the other 4 high females were placed in another tube with 4 of the low males. Four of the low females were placed with the remaining 4 high males, and the remaining 4 low females were placed with the remaining 4 low males. After 24 hr. the males were destroyed and the four lots of four females were placed in 4 separate culture bottles to give progeny from the four classes of mating high × high, high × low, low × high and low × low that would occur with equal frequency in random mating. Twenty of each sex of each of these four progenies were assayed and provided the distribution curves given in Fig. 1 (bottom) which are to be compared with those for generations 7 and 12 in Fig. 1 (top).

It is immediately evident that the hybrid modes are intermediate between those of the non-hybrids and hence that the discontinuity of the distributions for the last generation in Fig. 1 (top), and the decline of the overlap between the distributions in the later generations of the selection experiment were the result of a rapid decline in the frequency of 'hybrids' in the selected line. Whether this arises from pronounced mating preferences or from inability of the hybrid flies to compete as larvæ in the same culture with the non-hybrids is not yet certain, but that hybrids have become very rare in the selection line is clear. The high and the low flies show a strong degree of reproductive isolation in the sense of Dobzhansky[10].

The condition under which Mather[5] proposed disruptive selection should give rise to polymorphism was that the two or more classes selected should be interdependent. This condition held in the earlier disruptive selection experiments in which genetic polymorphisms were produced and maintained[6-9]. Mather further argued that if the two classes that were selected could be independent the expected result would be reproductive isolation, assuming, of course, that suitable genetic variance were available.

The present experiment complements its predecessors, for by mating all the selected individuals together in the same vial the two selected classes have been given the opportunity to become independent should they be able to do so. The result is as Mather predicted. The only surprise is the remarkable rapidity with which the result was produced, despite the fact that 20 per cent of the flies assayed were selected, a rather low selection pressure for an artificial selection experiment.

Thoday and Boam[8] and Millicent and Thoday[9] have pointed out that their demonstrations that divergence is possible without isolation have a bearing on our assessment of the possibility of sympatric speciation. Streams and Pimentel[11] have since obtained consonant results. The present experiment, in which divergence and reproductive isolation have originated without any geographic or analogous isolation when the flies were mating, can only add strength to this point of view.

We do not, however, wish it to be thought that we regard this as a demonstration that sympatric speciation occurs in Nature, for such a conclusion cannot be drawn from the results of laboratory selection experiments. The evidence that most speciation in Nature is allopatric is very strong[1], and it is for the student of natural populations to determine whether and how often sympatric speciation occurs. However, sympatric speciation has frequently been supposed impossible on theoretical grounds, and these can no longer be regarded as sound. Though selection pressures as high as those used in the present experiment may be uncommon in Nature, the speed with which the present results were obtained clearly forces us to consider the possibility that natural selection pressures might readily induce divergence and complete isolation in an appropriately heterogeneous habitat.

[1] Mayr, E., *Systematics and Origin of Species* (Columbia Univ. Press, 1942).

[2] Merrell, D. J., *Evolution*, **4**, 326 (1950).

[3] Koopman K. F., *Evolution*, **4**, 135 (1950).

[4] Knight, G. R., Robertson, A., and Waddington, C. H., *Evolution*, **10**, 14 (1956).

[5] Mather, K., *Evolution*, **9**, 52 (1955).

[6] Thoday, J. M., *Nature*, **181**, 1124 (1958).

[7] Thoday, J. M., *Heredity*, **14**, 35 (1960).

[8] Thoday, J. M., and Boam, T. B., *Heredity*, **13**, 205 (1959).

[9] Millicent, E., and Thoday, J. M., *Heredity*, **16**, 199 (1961).

[10] Dobzhansky, Th., *Genetics and the Origin of Species* (Columbia Univ. Press, 1942).

[11] Streams, F. A., and Pimentel, D., *American Naturalist*, **95**, 201 (1961).

20

Reprinted from *Amer. Naturalist* **100**:99-118 (1966)

THE SELECTIVE ORIGIN OF INCOMPATIBILITY BARRIERS IN THE PLANT GENUS *GILIA*

VERNE GRANT

THE HYPOTHESIS OF SELECTION FOR REPRODUCTIVE ISOLATION

Isolating mechanisms which block or restrict interbreeding between species can originate in two ways: as by-products of evolutionary divergence, and as products of selection for reproductive isolation per se.

The development of reproductive isolation as a by-product of divergence is evidently the primary process in nature. This process was suggested by Darwin (1859, ch. 8; 1868, ch. 19) and by many later authors (i.e., Dobzhansky, 1937; Muller, 1940, 1942). It is supported by good evidence from many plant and animal groups (i.e., Clausen, 1951; Volpe, 1954, 1955; Moore, 1957; Santibañez and Waddington, 1958; Mecham, 1961; Rick, 1963; Thoday, 1964; Grant and Grant, 1964; Grun and Aubertin, 1965).

The hypothesis of a secondary and supplementary process of selection for reproductive isolation, considered as an advantageous situation in its own right for the species concerned, was advanced in the early period of evolutionary biology by Wallace (1889, pp. 173 ff.), who tried unsuccessfully to convince Darwin (see Mayr, 1959). It seems fitting and desirable to designate the process of selection for reproductive isolation as *the Wallace effect*.

The Wallace hypothesis was proposed again in the modern period by Fisher (1930, pp. 130 ff.), Dobzhansky (1941; 1951, pp. 209 ff.), and Huxley (1943, pp. 288 ff.). The subject has been reviewed recently by Mayr (1963, pp. 548 ff.) and Grant (1963, ch. 17).

It is argued that the individuals of two sympatric species populations which produce inviable or sterile hybrids will contribute fewer offspring to future generations than will sister individuals in the same parental populations which do not hybridize. Consequently the genetic factors determining some block or aversion to hybridization will tend to increase in frequency within each species over the course of generations. This process of selection is expected to lead to a reinforcement of the reproductive isolation which had developed as a by-product of divergence.

The hypothesis was formulated in very general terms in the earlier statements. Several later authors have spelled out the restrictive conditions under which selection for isolation can operate effectively.

The Wallace effect is expected to occur most readily in short-lived organisms, such as ephemeral flies or annual plants, in which a loss of reproductive potential is especially disadvantageous (Dobzhansky, 1958; Stebbins, 1958). Selection for reproductive isolation may be relatively ineffective in perennial plants or in dominant members of closed communities, where the number of seeds produced exceeds many times the number of seedlings which can become established (op. cit.).

It has been pointed out that selection for barriers between species can have reference only to isolating mechanisms which act in the parental generation (Latimer, 1958; Grant, 1963; Rick, 1963). Evidence regarding later-generation blocks like hybrid inviability (Stephens, 1946; Dobzhansky, 1951, pp. 209–210) should probably be excluded from consideration.

Among the different isolating mechanisms which operate in the parental generation, moreover, a pre-mating barrier like ethological isolation will conserve the reproductive potential more effectively than will a post-mating barrier like incompatibility. Consequently, we would expect selection to favor ethological isolation over incompatibility wherever there is a choice between these two mechanisms. The salient role of ethological isolation in animals is probably accounted for on this basis. In plants, on the other hand, ethological isolation is rarely sufficient by itself to prevent hybridization, because of periodic lapses in the flower-constant behavior of pollinating insects, whereas incompatibility can be highly effective. In plants, and especially in annuals, therefore, we may expect selection for isolation to build up not only ethological but also supplementary incompatibility barriers.

Selection for isolation, finally, will not necessarily lead to a complete blocking of hybridization (Ehrman, 1962). The isolating mechanisms built up by this process will become only as strong as they need to be to safeguard the populations from net deleterious effects of hybridization, and this level of strength is relative to the multifarious circumstances of the populations. The minimum required degree of reproductive isolation, as Ehrman (1962) states, is that where ''the gene exchange between the species population[s does] not exceed the rate at which the diffused genes can be eliminated by natural selection.''

EVIDENCE FROM PREVIOUS STUDIES

Four lines of evidence have been advanced in support of the Wallace effect. These are: (1) Selection experiments in artificial mixtures of species or strains. (2) Observed historical changes in the frequency of hybridization in hybrid zones. (3) Geographical variation in the strength of reproductive isolation within a pair of species having overlapping distribution areas, such that the sympatric races of the two species are more strongly isolated than the allopatric races. (4) Comparisons between allopatric and sympatric species with regard to the strength of isolation.

(1) Artificial selection against hybrids and for parental genotypes which do not hybridize freely has been carried out in mixed cultures of Drosophila containing two species or strains. Koopman (1950) used a mixture of D. pseudoobscura and D. persimilis in his experiment, while Wallace (1954) and Knight, Robertson, and Waddington (1956) used combinations of mutant strains of D. melanogaster. In these experiments a response to selection

for reproductive isolation was manifested in a marked enhancement of ethological barriers between species or strains and a lowering of the frequency
of hybrids during a series of generations.

(2) In zones of overlap and hybridization between two species it may be
possible to compare the frequency of hybrid formation at different times in
history. Vaurie (1957) has made such a comparison for the titmice *Parus
caeruleus* and *P. cyanus* in their zone of overlap in western Russia. Hybrids were common when these two species first came into contact in the
period 1870 to 1890. By 1950 hybrids had become rare and were restricted
to one part of the zone of overlap (Vaurie, 1957; Mayr, 1963).

(3) In several pairs of intersterile species in Drosophila which have
overlapping distribution areas, Dobzhansky and his co-workers have compared the strength of ethological isolation between sympatric representatives with that between allopatric representatives of the two species. This
comparison has been made for *Drosophila pseudoobscura* and *D. miranda*
(Dobzhansky and Koller, 1938; Dobzhansky, 1951, p. 210); for *D. willistoni*
and *D. insularis* (Dobzhansky, Ehrman and Pavlovsky, 1957); and for species belonging to the *D. paulistorum* group (Dobzhansky et al., 1964). In
each case the races from the sympatric zone of a species pair are isolated
ethologically to a stronger degree than races from the allopatric parts of
the areas of the same two species.

Blair (1955) has made a similar comparison in a pair of species of tree
frogs, *Microhyla carolinensis* and *M. olivacea*, in the southern United
States. The call notes of the two species are very different in their sympatric
zone but are much alike in the allopatric parts of the ranges. The call
notes of frogs belonging to the *Pseudacris nigrita* group in the eastern
United States (Mecham, 1961) and the *Hyla ewingi* group in southeastern
Australia (Littlejohn, 1965) are likewise most strongly differentiated in the
zones of sympatric overlap. These differences in call notes play an important role in ethological isolation in frogs.

Strains of *Zea mays* and *Tripsacum spp.* from Mexico and Central America,
where these species are sympatric, are separated by very strong incompatibility barriers; but strains from the eastern and southern United States,
where maize and *Tripsacum* are apparently less closely associated, are
easy to cross (Randolph, 1953). Sympatric races of *Gilia modocensis* and *G.
sinuata* are isolated by a strong incompatibility block, whereas allopatric
races of the same species can be crossed with relative ease (Grant, 1964).

(4) A geographically isolated species can be compared with two or more
sympatric species belonging to the same natural group in respect to the degree of reproductive isolation in the parental generation. Such comparisons
have been made in two species groups in Drosophila, in one group of butterflies, and in a group of fish.

The cases studied are as follows: (A) The *Drosophila guarani* group
which has two sympatric species in Brazil and one allopatric species in
Mexico (King, 1947). (B) The *Drosophila willistoni* group which is represented by four sympatric species in the American tropics and by one periph-

eral and nearly allopatric species in the Lesser Antilles (Dobzhansky, Ehrman, and Pavlovsky, 1957). (C) The *Erebia tyndarus* group (Satyridae) with two sympatric and one allopatric species in the Alps (Lorkovič, 1958). (D) The *Gambusia affinis* group in the southern United States and Mexico (Hubbs and Delco, 1960). The F_1 hybrids of allopatric × sympatric species crosses, as well as of sympatric × sympatric species crosses, are known to be sterile in the Drosophila and Erebia groups.

In each of the species groups mentioned above the sympatric species are separated from one another by strong ethological barriers. By contrast the ethological barriers between the geographically isolated species and the central species are relatively weak.

CRITIQUE OF THE EVIDENCE

(1) The selection experiments dealing with the Wallace effect are good, though few in number and restricted to ethological barriers in *Drosophila*, and indeed more work could be done along these lines. The experimental results obtained to date show that hybridization, if selectively disadvantageous, can actually be reduced in amount by selection as predicted by the hypothesis. The main problem then becomes one of determining the reality and assessing the importance of this selective process in natural situations.

(2) Adequate quantitative evidence of long-term historical changes in the frequency of hybrids in a natural area is exceedingly difficult to obtain, and is not in fact available for the one case on record. This line of evidence cannot be said to have made any important contribution to the problem so far. It is an approach well worth following up, however, if situations can be found which are favorable for making the necessary observations.

(3) The reported cases of correlation between geographical distribution and strength of reproductive isolation in species pairs which have overlapping areas are of unequal value. Some of the evidence, particularly in the earlier studies, was apparently obtained as a product of investigations of other problems. The facts regarding crossing barriers between *Zea* and *Tripsacum* were not only gathered but were considered in relation to a different problem—the center of origin of maize.

Such incidental or anecdotal evidence suffers from several defects. Some relevant pieces of information are likely to be missing; there may be too few points of comparison; the danger exists that cases favorable to the hypothesis will be singled out of a larger body of data.

The latter point can be illustrated by examples in *Gilia*. It is undoubtedly true, as mentioned in the preceding section, that sympatric races of *Gilia modocensis* and *G. sinuata* are more difficult to cross than allopatric races. But in some other species pairs in *Gilia* this correlation does not hold true; and in two cases, which will be discussed later in this paper, we find the opposite pattern of higher crossability between the sympatric races. Cases unfavorable to the hypothesis of reinforcement of isolation also exist in *Drosophila* and amphibians, as pointed out by Patterson and Stone (1952, pp. 357-358, 549-550), Volpe (1955), and Moore (1957).

The proper remedy is of course to carry out *ad hoc* studies of geographical variation in strength of isolating mechanisms between the same species, with as many separate points of comparison as possible, and to take all the results into account. The finding of consistently repeated geographical trends in degree of isolation would then constitute strong evidence for the hypothesis. This is the approach and the result in the most recent studies, those on the *Drosophila paulistorum* and the *Hyla ewingi* groups (Dobzhansky et al., 1964; Littlejohn, 1965).

(4) The available comparisons of degree of isolation between sympatric species and geographically isolated species are of the type illustrated diagrammatically in Fig. 1 A. Crosses of sympatric species *inter se* are compared with crosses of sympatric species × geographically isolated species. In such comparisons at least one species in each class of interspecific cross has been exposed to the challenge of sympatry and hence to possible selection for enhanced isolation, which complicates the picture. Better evidence could be obtained from comparisons of the strength of isolating mechanisms in crosses of sympatric species *inter se* vs. crosses of allopatric species *inter se* (Fig. 1 B). Comparative data of the latter type will be presented in this paper (also Grant, 1965b).

To sum up this critique, the evidence on record for the occurrence of the Wallace effect in nature is suggestive but not overwhelming in amount and not critical in many or most of the cases cited in support. As a result evolutionists are not in agreement about the reality of this secondary process, and a number of students have expressed skeptical views (i.e., Moore, 1957; Clausen, Channell, and Nur, 1964). The purpose of the present paper

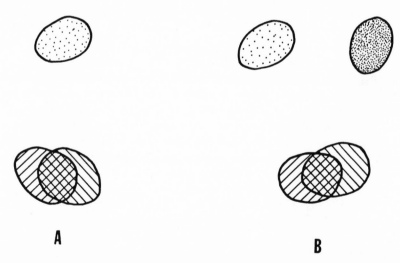

A   **B**

FIG. 1. Two types of distribution pattern of a species group containing both sympatric and geographically isolated species. It is possible to compare different classes of interspecific crosses with respect to degree of isolation in the two patterns, as follows. (A) Sympatric species *inter se* vs. sympatric × geographically isolated species. (B) Sympatric species *inter se* vs. allopatric species *inter se*.

is to consider some new evidence from the herbaceous plant genus *Gilia*
(Polemoniaceae) which strongly supports the Wallace hypothesis.

NATURE OF INCOMPATIBILITY BARRIERS IN *GILIA*

Considered embryologically, cross-incompatibility in flowering plants is
a complex of pre-fertilization and post-fertilization blocks (Avery, Satina,
and Rietsema, 1959; Grant, 1963, pp. 370–379; Rick, 1963). Latimer's
(1958) study of the cross of *Gilia splendens* × *australis* shows that both
pre-fertilization and post-fertilization blocks occur between species of
Gilia.

In the cross, *G. splendens* ♀ × *australis* ♂, the pollen tubes usually fail
to reach the ovules (Latimer, 1958). In the reciprocal cross, *G. australis* ♀ ×
splendens ♂, the pollen tubes reach the embryo sac but frequently fail to
effect fertilization. Or if fertilization does take place, the endosperm develops in an abnormal manner, with deleterious effects on the growth of the
embryo, and the ovule aborts at an early stage of development (op. cit.).

From the standpoint of the Wallace effect, either pre- or post-fertilization
incompatibility blocks might be adaptively valuable in annual plants. The
value of pre-fertilization blocks is evident—they conserve a given supply
of ovules for intra-specific matings. The possible selective value of post-
fertilization blocks is less obvious and requires elucidation.

An annual *Gilia* or other ephemeral plant puts virtually all its excess
photosynthetic production into its crop of seeds. There is a great difference between a young ovule and a ripe seed as regards the parental plant's
investment of stored food. The number of mature seeds which the plant can
produce is definitely limited, whereas whole flowers and batches of ovules,
if lost for one reason or another, can be replaced by new flowers with comparative ease. Therefore a post-fertilization block which prevents the
formation of mature hybrid seeds would have a high selective advantage
over no such block in an annual plant.

The degree of compatibility between individuals, races, or species of
Gilia varies continuously from high to low. A good measure of the incompatibility is the output of hybrid seeds by a fair number of flowers emascu-
lated and cross-pollinated under insect-free conditions. The hybrid constitution of these seeds is confirmed by identification of the F_1 plants grown
from them. The average number of plump hybrid seeds produced per flower
pollinated will be designated as S/Fl in this paper.

EVIDENCE FOR THE ORIGIN OF INCOMPATIBILITY BARRIERS
IN *GILIA* AS BY-PRODUCTS OF EVOLUTIONARY DIVERGENCE

In several species of *Gilia* a definite but surmountable barrier to crossing
is developed between particular geographical races which produce highly
fertile F_1 hybrids. This is the case in *Gilia capitata*, *G. achilleaefolia*,
and *G. ochroleuca* (Grant, 1950, 1952a, 1954a; Grant and Grant, 1960). In
Gilia ochroleuca, for example, the races *G. o. bizonata* and *G. o. vivida*

cross freely (8.8 *S/Fl*), whereas the races *G. o. bizonata* and *G. o. ochroleuca* cross with difficulty (0.2 *S/Fl*) (Grant and Grant, 1960).

The interracial incompatibility barriers are usually weak. This is indicated by a comparison of interracial with interspecific crosses in the Cobwebby Gilias (*Gilia* section Arachnion). Table 1 shows that in this branch of the genus, all species crosses combined have 3.6 *S/Fl*, the race crosses have 13.4 *S/Fl*, and control crosses between different biotypes of the same population yield 15.2 *S/Fl*. In certain exceptional cases, as within *Gilia achilleaefolia* in a different branch of the genus (*Gilia* section Gilia), strong crossing barriers may exist between particular races which produce fully fertile F$_1$ hybrids (Grant, 1954a). These exceptional incompatibility barriers between interfertile races are comparable in strength to those between some intersterile species.

TABLE 1

Average number of hybrid seeds produced per flower cross-pollinated (*S/Fl*) for numerous crosses at different levels of divergence in the Cobwebby Gilias. Data compiled from Grant and Grant (1960) and Grant (1964).

Level of divergence	No. hybrid combinations	No. flowers	*S/Fl*
Biotype crosses	7	173	15.2
Race crosses	45	1002	13.4
Species crosses	179	3568	3.6

In favorable instances we can see the primary adaptive value of racial differences which lead, incidentally, to reduced crossability. Let us return to the case of *Gilia ochroleuca*.

This species ranges from the coastal mountains to the interior desert in southern California. The western mountain races (*G. o. bizonata* and *G. o. vivida*) have large, colorful, insect-pollinated flowers with a long style. The desert race (*G. o. ochroleuca*) has small, whitish, short-styled, autogamous flowers. These differences in flower size and mode of pollination are adaptive in relation to the environmental conditions in the mountains and desert, respectively. Style length is an integral part of the adaptive character combination in each race.

But style length also has important side effects on crossability, inasmuch as fertilization depends, among other factors, on a proper coordination between pollen tube growth and length of style. We find, in fact, that the long-styled races of *Gilia ochroleuca* cross freely with one another (8.8 *S/Fl*), whereas crosses of long-styled × short-styled races are difficult to make in either direction (0.4 *S/Fl* on long-styled ♀, 0.1 *S/Fl* on short-styled ♀).

The long- and short-styled races of *G. ochroleuca* also differ as to ease of crossing with a foreign species, *G. cana*. The cross *G. o. bizonata* (long style) ♀ × *G. cana speciosa* (long style) yielded 1.9 *S/Fl*; that of *G. o.*

ochroleuca (short style) ♀ × *G. cana speciosa* (long style) 0.04 *S/Fl* (Grant and Grant, 1960).

We thus see that incompatibility barriers can, and sometimes do, develop as by-products of divergence at the racial level. It is important to note that such barriers are not an inevitable by-product of racial differentiation. In several species of Cobwebby Gilia, geographical races can be crossed as easily as biotypes of the same population, as shown by the figures in Table 2.

TABLE 2

Number of hybrid seeds per flower (*S/Fl*) in biotype and race crosses in three species of Cobwebby Gilia. Data from Grant and Grant (1960) and Grant (1964).

Species	Biotype crosses		Race crosses	
	S/Fl	No. flowers	*S/Fl*	No. flowers
G. latiflora	26.5	23	30.8	140
G. minor	17.9	39	19.7	67
G. inconspicua	11.2	28	13.1	21

EVIDENCE FOR THE ORIGIN OF INCOMPATIBILITY BARRIERS IN THE LEAFY STEMMED GILIAS AS PRODUCTS OF SELECTION FOR ISOLATION

Although incompatibility barriers may arise as by-products of divergence in *Gilia*, this is not the whole story, as we shall now attempt to show by some comparative data on interspecific crossability in the Leafy-stemmed Gilias. This phylogenetic branch of the genus possesses characteristics which enable us to make a significant comparison between sympatric and geographically isolated species with respect to the strength of incompatibility barriers.

The Leafy-stemmed Gilias (*Gilia* section Gilia) form a natural group of ten species, nine of which have been studied genetically. They are listed in Table 3. The nine species are all more or less well differentiated morphologically and ecologically.

Twenty-two of the 36 possible crosses between the nine species have been attempted. Nine of the crosses failed, and the remaining 13 yielded F_1 hybrids. These hybrids were highly or completely sterile with reduced chromosome pairing and other disturbances of meiosis. It is possible to demonstrate from indirect evidence that the paired combinations of species which could not be crossed also differ genomically and hence would be intersterile in the F_1 generation. All of the genetically known species of Leafy-stemmed Gilia are thus intersterile (Grant, 1954b, 1965a).

The Leafy-stemmed Gilias are annual herbs which bloom in the spring and die as individuals when they go to seed. The loss in seed output involved in the production of sterile hybrids must therefore have a high selective disadvantage in these plants.

The pattern of geographical distribution of the nine species is favorable for our present purpose. Five of the species—*G. tricolor, angelensis,*

TABLE 3

The species of Leafy-stemmed Gilia.

Species group and species	Ploidy ($x = 9$)	Geographical distribution
Gilia tricolor group		
1. *G. tricolor*	2 x	California foothills and valleys
2. *G. angelensis*	2 x	— ditto —
Gilia capitata group		
3. *G. capitata*	2 x	— ditto —
4. *G. achilleaefolia*	2 x	— ditto —
Gilia laciniata group		
5. *G. clivorum*	4 x	— ditto —
6. *G. millefoliata*	2 x	California coast line
7. *G. nevinii*	4 x	California islands
8. *G. lomensis*	4 x	Peruvian coast line
9. *G. valdiviensis*	2 x	Chilean coast line
10. *G. laciniata*	?	Peruvian Andes to Patagonia

capitata, achilleaefolia, clivorum—occur in the foothills and valleys of coastal California and adjoining regions. The areas of these species overlap extensively (Fig. 2), and individuals belonging to two or more species grow side by side in many places (Fig. 3). Four other species—*G. millefoliata, nevinii, lomensis, valdiviensis*—occur on the coastal strand in four widely separated areas of North and South America (Fig. 2). The maritime species are completely allopatric with respect to one another, and come into contact rarely or not at all with the foothill-and-valley species (Fig. 3).

The areas of these species have probably undergone migrational shifts with climatic changes during the Pleistocene and since. However, maritime habitats have always occupied a peripheral position in relation to mediterranean habitats in the general area in which the Leafy-stemmed Gilias have developed. It is likely, therefore, that the broad geographical relationships now found in this group, though not necessarily the detailed ranges, have prevailed during the phylogenetic history of the group. The foothill-and-valley species probably have a long history of frequent sympatric contacts, while the maritime species by contrast probably have a long history of geographical isolation.

Let us now compare the strength of incompatibility barriers between species in the two geographical classes of Leafy-stemmed Gilias. The data for 20 interspecific crosses, many of which have been carried out in both reciprocal directions and replicated with different strains, are summarized in Table 4.

Table 4 shows that hybridization between the sympatric foothill-and-valley species is blocked by strong incompatibility barriers. The seed output ranges from 0.0 to 1.2 *S/Fl* in different combinations and averages 0.2 *S/Fl* for all interspecific crosses combined (Grant, 1965b). One species in this class, *Gilia tricolor*, is isolated from all other species by an incompatibility block which has never been breached in numerous attempts (Grant, 1952b).

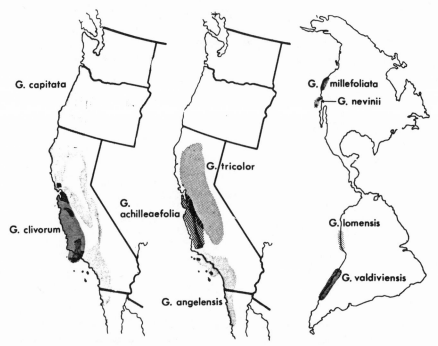

FIG. 2. Geographical distribution of the nine genetically studied species of Leafy-stemmed Gilia. Left: the California foothill-and-valley species. Right: the strictly maritime species (Grant, 1965b).

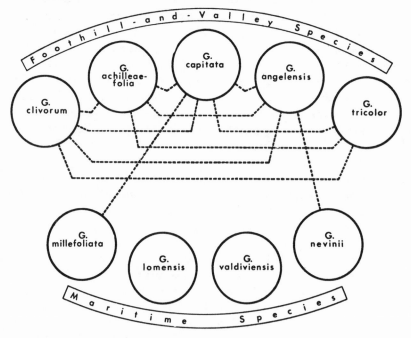

FIG. 3. Paired combinations of species of Leafy-stemmed Gilia which are known to grow side by side in nature (Grant, 1965b).

TABLE 4

Comparative crossability of species with different geographical
relationships in the Leafy-stemmed Gilias.

Geographical relationship of parental species	No. combinations of parental species	Values of *S/Fl* in magnitude array		Mean of means, *S/Fl*
Foothill species *inter se*	9	0.0	0.1	0.2
		0.0	0.1	
		0.0	0.4	
		0.0	1.2	
		0.0		
Maritime species *inter se*	5	7.7		18.1
		16.7		
		19.6		
		21.9		
		24.8		
Foothill species × maritime species	8 (complete data for 6)	0.0	4.2	3.2
		0.1	5.1	
		2.8	6.8	

The allopatric maritime species, on the other hand, are not separated by
any significant incompatibility barrier at all (Grant, 1965b). The values of
S/Fl range from 7.7 to 24.8 and average 18.1 for five interspecific combinations (Table 4). These values are comparable to those obtained in intraspecific crosses. For example, *Gilia millefoliata*, a diploid on the California coastal strand, and *G. lomensis*, a tetraploid of the Peruvian coast,
will cross in either direction as easily as two sister plants from the same
population (Grant, 1965a).

Crosses between the two geographical classes of species, finally, show
incompatibility barriers of intermediate strength. The average for all
crosses of foothill species × maritime species is 3.2 *S/Fl*. The variation
from cross to cross is considerable as shown by the figures in Table 4.

The differences between the means of the three classes of interspecific
crosses as given in Table 4 are statistically significant in all paired combinations (P < 0.01). In fact, the seed output in species crosses in the
maritime class could be only 20% of the observed amount, and the difference in mean values between the maritime and foothill classes would
still be significant at the 1% level.

The degree of evolutionary divergence between the maritime species is
about the same as that between the foothill-and-valley species on the
criteria of chromosomal differentiation and hybrid sterility. In terms of
morphological characters and ecological preferences, certain pairs of foothill species, like *Gilia capitata* and *G. tricolor*, have reached a more advanced level of divergence than have any combinations of species in the
maritime group. The amount of morphological and ecological differentiation
between other pairs of foothill species—such as *G. capitata* and *G. achilleaefolia*, or *G. tricolor* and *G. angelensis*—is on a par with that found between
the maritime species.

We expect the primary divergence to bring about some cross-incompatibility, as pointed out in the preceding section; and, consequently, we can expect the crossing barriers to have developed further between the foothill species in certain particular cases than between the maritime species. However, the difference between the two geographical classes of *Gilia* species in level of primary divergence is not sufficiently great in itself to account for all of the observed differences in crossability.

This conclusion is supported by the finding of strong incompatibility barriers between those foothill species which are as similar morphologically and ecologically as any combination of maritime species. Thus *Gilia capitata* and *G. achilleaefolia*, which were once placed in the same taxonomic species, yield only 0.06 *S/Fl* on crossing, and crosses between *G. tricolor* and *G. angelensis* yielded 0.00 *S/Fl* (Grant, 1965b).

After due allowance is made for the role of primary divergence in reducing crossability, therefore, we are left with a large component of cross-incompatibility among the foothill species which is best explained as a product of the Wallace effect.

GEOGRAPHICAL DIFFERENCES IN DEGREE OF INTERSPECIFIC INCOMPATIBILITY IN THE COBWEBBY GILIAS

The results obtained from our analysis of interspecific crossability barriers in the Leafy-stemmed Gilias make it desirable to search for similar patterns in other groups. Extensive data are available on the crossability of intersterile species in the Cobwebby Gilias (Grant and Grant, 1960; Grant, 1964; Day, 1965). These data have been analyzed with reference to the hypothesis of selection for hybridization-preventing mechanisms.

There are 27 known biological species of Cobwebby Gilia in North America. The collective area of the whole group and the number of species per local area are shown in Fig. 4. As is evident from this map, several or many species of Cobwebby Gilia occur sympatrically throughout a large region in western North America. Only on the periphery of the collective distribution area do we find local areas inhabited by one species alone. These peripheral species all range to the interior of the collective area and have sympatric contacts in the more central parts of their ranges.

We have, in other words, numerous sympatric species but no entirely allopatric species in the Cobwebby Gilias, in contrast to the situation in the Leafy-stemmed Gilias, and, consequently, we cannot make the comparison that would be most significant for our present purpose. There are, however, differences of a relative sort between the central species of Cobwebby Gilia, which have numerous sympatric contacts with several or many other species, and the peripheral species with few sympatric contacts. We will compare the strength of incompatibility barriers in central species × central species crosses and in crosses of peripheral species × central species.

A large number of crosses of central species *inter se* yield an average of 3.4 *S/Fl*, as indicated in Table 5.

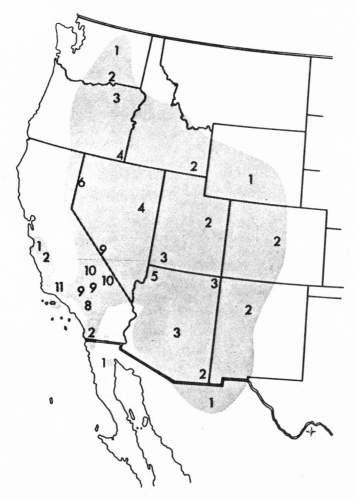

FIG. 4. The collective area of 27 species of Cobwebby Gilia in western
North America, and the number of species per local area.

Three peripheral species are *Gilia flavocincta* and *G. mexicana* in southern Arizona and New Mexico and *G. tenuiflora* in west-central California.
Table 5 shows that crosses between these species and central species with
flowers of the same general size yield a distinctly higher average seed set
(7.6 *S/Fl*). The difference in means between the two classes of crosses is
statistically significant at approximately the 2% level.

The case of *Gilia flavocincta* is particularly revealing. This species
lives in relative geographical isolation from other Cobwebby Gilias in the
Sonoran Desert. It is a tetraploid. Nevertheless it has proven to be easy
to cross with various distantly related diploid species of southern California. *Gilia flavocincta* × *G. exilis* yielded 17.9 *S/Fl*; × *G. ochroleuca
bizonata*, 11.6 *S/Fl*; × *G. cana*, 7.5 *S/Fl*; and × *G. tenuiflora* in one direction but not the other, 7.4 *S/Fl*. These figures are unusually high for tetra-

TABLE 5

Comparative crossability of species with different geographical relationships in the Cobwebby Gilias. From data of Grant and Grant (1960) and Grant (1964).

Geographical relationship of parental species	No. combinations of parental species	No. flowers pollinated	Mean of means for different combinations, S/Fl	Standard deviation
Central species *inter se*	68	2363	3.4	4.69
Peripheral species × central species*	13	413	7.6	5.97

*Excluding crosses of large-flowered × small-flowered species.

ploid × diploid crosses in the Cobwebby Gilias, which often fail completely and average 3.3 S/Fl.

The evidence from the Cobwebby Gilias thus provides support for the conclusions reached on the basis of the evidence in the Leafy-stemmed Gilias.

POLYMORPHISM FOR CROSSABILITY

A prerequisite for response to selection for incompatibility is the occurrence of polymorphism in a plant population with respect to ease of crossing with a foreign species. Polymorphism of this sort has been found in populations of two species of Cobwebby Gilia. In both cases individual differences in crossability were associated with morphological differences. It was the latter indeed which led to the detection of the former.

A population of *Gilia exilis* near Dripping Springs (in the coastal mountains of Riverside County, California) contains individuals which differ genetically in pattern of leaf dissection. The pinnate leaves have simple lateral lobes in biotype II and more complex, divided lobes in biotype I. Biotypes I and II cross easily with one another (12.7 S/Fl) to produce a fully fertile F_1 hybrid. They differ, however, as to crossability with the related but intersterile species, *G. ochroleuca bizonata*. Using the same strain of *G. o. bizonata* for crosses carried out in the same year, under the same conditions, and in the same direction, biotype II of *G. exilis* yielded 2.1 S/Fl (22 flowers) and biotype I 0.0 S/Fl (24 flowers) (Grant and Grant, 1960).

A population of *Gilia ophthalmoides* in Westgard Pass (Inyo Mountains, eastern California) is polymorphic for flower color and form. Biotypes Y and P differ in having a yellow or purple corolla tube respectively. They also differ in crossability with an intersterile population from the Sweetwater Mountains farther north. The cross of Sweetwater × biotype Y produced 8.1 S/Fl (19 flowers); that of Sweetwater × biotype P yielded 0.0 S/Fl (20 flowers) (Grant, 1964).

The barriers to crossing which are found between species (and occasionally races) of plants in nature are complex developmentally and probably have a complex genetic basis. Rick (1963) has studied the incompatibility barrier between certain Peruvian races of *Lycopersicon peruvianum* in both the parental generation and in later-generation test crosses. He found continuous variation for strength of the incompatibility barrier in the F_2 and B_1 generations, suggesting that the block is determined by several or many genes (Rick, 1963). This is not inconsistent with the idea that such barriers could begin as simple polymorphic variants, however, for a single-gene change bringing about greater incompatibility with a foreign population could, if selectively valuable, be established first, and later stabilized and enhanced in its action by the addition of modifiers.

CONVERGENCE IN CROSSABILITY

There is another pattern of geographical distribution of incompatibility barriers in *Gilia* which runs counter to expectation on the Wallace hypothesis. Where two species have overlapping distribution areas, the sympatric populations are sometimes distinctly easier to cross than are allopatric populations of the same parental species. This situation has been found in *Gilia capitata* between the marginally sympatric races *G. c. abrotanifolia* and *G. c. pedemontana* (Grant, 1952a), and again between *Gilia splendens* and *G. australis* (Grant and Grant, 1954). It is best documented in the latter case by virtue of the detailed study of Latimer (1958).

Gilia splendens and *G. australis* are two annual diploid species of Woodland Gilia (*Gilia* section Saltugilia) which form semisterile and sometimes inviable hybrids. *Gilia splendens* occurs in the pine belt of the mountains from central to southern California and ranges onto the western edge of the desert (Fig. 5). *Gilia australis* lives in the chaparral zone and on the desert in southern California (Fig. 5).

Most populations of the two species are mutually allopatric. In the desert slopes and valleys of the Little San Bernardino Mountains, however, *G. splendens* and *G. australis* are sympatric, and individuals of the two species frequently grow intermixed in the same local territory.

Latimer (1958) intercrossed a series of populations of *G. splendens* and *G. australis* in numerous combinations. Some of his results—those which are most significant for our present discussion—are presented in Table 6. It will be seen that the allopatric populations of *G. splendens* and *G. australis* are consistently separated by a pronounced incompatibility barrier, forming an average of 0.07 *S/Fl*. By contrast, the sympatric populations can be crossed fairly easily with one another in five of the six combinations attempted (ave. 6.1 *S/Fl*). The difference in means is highly significant statistically.

A similar pattern is found at the species level in the Melanium violets (Clausen, Channell, and Nur, 1964). Several sympatric species of this group in Europe—*Viola tricolor*, *V. arvensis*, *V. kitaibeliana*, and others—cross readily with one another (Clausen, 1931). The geographically isolated species *V. rafinesquii* in eastern North America, on the other hand, is separated by a strong incompatibility barrier from the three European species mentioned above (Clausen, Channell, and Nur, 1964).

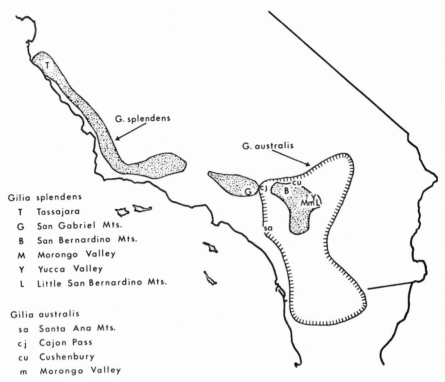

Gilia splendens

T Tassajara
G San Gabriel Mts.
B San Bernardino Mts.
M Morongo Valley
Y Yucca Valley
L Little San Bernardino Mts.

Gilia australis

sa Santa Ana Mts.
cj Cajon Pass
cu Cushenbury
m Morongo Valley

FIG. 5. Distribution areas of *Gilia splendens* and *G. australis*. The key letters indicate the geographical positions of the local populations which were intercrossed with the results given in Table 6.

TABLE 6

Racial differences in crossability of *Gilia australis* ♀ × *G. splendens* ♂. Data compiled from Latimer (1958).

Population of *G. australis*	Population of *G. splendens*	No. flowers pollinated	S/Fl	Mean of means, S/Fl
(A) Crosses between sympatric populations				6.1
Morongo Valley × Morongo Valley		289	6.3	
Morongo Valley × Yucca Valley		30	8.1	
Morongo Valley × Little San Bernardino Mts.		25	7.0	
Cushenbury × Morongo Valley		31	0.3	
Cushenbury × Yucca Valley		30	8.1	
Cushenbury × Little San Bernardino Mts.		25	7.0	
(B) Crosses between allopatric populations				0.07
Santa Ana Mts. × Tassajara		28	0.0	
Santa Ana Mts. × San Gabriel Mts.		31	0.1	
Santa Ana Mts. × San Bernardino Mts.		30	0.2	
Cajon Pass × Tassajara		28	0.0	

Clausen, Channell and Nur state (1964): "Certain evolutionary generalities are contradicted by the fact that the partially sympatric European species of the *Melanium* section have retained compatibility and the geographically highly isolated *Viola rafinesquii* acquired genetic isolation from its morphologically close relatives on the other side of the Atlantic Ocean."

A possible explanation of this pattern may be suggested. The geographically remote populations of two species (or the widely separated species in a species group) will frequently live under very different environmental conditions, insofar as the environment changes along geographical transects, and the allopatric populations (or species) will therefore be differentiated physiologically and morphologically to a great extent. Their reduced crossability may be a side effect of their high degree of differentiation. The sympatric populations, having been selected for fitness in the same environment, are likely to be similar in many physiological and morphological traits which, incidentally, increase the ease of crossing. This convergence in characters affecting crossability may be enhanced still further by introgressive hybridization between the sympatric populations.

The case of *Gilia splendens* and *G. australis* can be explained in these terms. The pine belt races of *G. splendens* and the chaparral or desert races of *G. australis* are far more strongly differentiated than are the desert races of the same two species. In fact, introgressive hybridization from *G. australis* into *G. splendens* in their area of sympatry has brought about a relatively close genetic relationship and a close morphological and ecological similarity between the desert populations of the two species. Now, the differences between *G. splendens* and *G. australis* in flower size and style length, to name one obvious factor affecting crossability, are great between the allopatric races of these species, but are slight between the sympatric desert populations. No doubt other more covert embryological differences which influence cross-compatibility have a similar ecogeographical trend.

In conclusion, it is not necessary to discard the Wallace hypothesis because of contrary cases of this sort. Diverse and often opposing processes are at work during speciation.

SUMMARY

Nine species of annual Gilias in Pacific North America and South America, belonging to the same section of the genus—the Leafy-stemmed Gilias, fall into two classes with regard to geographical distribution. Five species in the California foothills and valleys are sympatric. Four maritime species on the coasts of North and South America are completely allopatric in relation to one another and either completely or mainly allopatric in relation to the foothill-and-valley species. The sympatric foothill species are isolated from one another by very strong incompatibility barriers, forming an average of 0.2 hybrid seeds per flower pollinated in interspecific crosses, whereas the allopatric maritime species can be crossed *inter se* with the greatest of ease, forming an average of 18.1 hybrid seeds per flower.

A somewhat similar geographical distribution pattern of crossing barriers is found in another branch of the genus, the Cobwebby Gilias, which occur in western North America and are also annual herbs. The sympatric species from the central part of the distribution area of this group yield an average of 3.4 hybrid seeds per flower in interspecific crosses. By comparison, crosses between central and peripheral species yield an average of 7.6 hybrid seeds per flower.

The species hybrids are highly sterile in all combinations in the two groups of annual Gilias. The formation of such sterile hybrids represents a loss of reproductive potential on the part of their seed parents in the parental species population, a loss which must be especially disadvantageous in short-lived annuals.

The inverse correlation between interspecific geographical and crossing relationships provides critical evidence in the case of the Leafy-stemmed Gilias, and supporting evidence in the case of the Cobwebby Gilias, for the hypothesis of a selective origin of hybridization-preventing mechanisms in annual plants under conditions of sympatry.

It is proposed to name the process of selection for reproductive isolation the Wallace effect.

ACKNOWLEDGMENTS

The work reported here has been aided by research grants from the National Science Foundation. Mrs. Karen A. Grant and Dr. Richard C. Lewontin read the manuscript and made a number of very helpful suggestions.

LITERATURE CITED

Avery, A. G., S. Satina, and J. Rietsema. 1959. Blakeslee: The genus Datura. Ronald Press, New York.

Blair, W. F. 1955. Mating call and stage of speciation in the *Microhyla olivacea-M. carolinensis* complex. Evolution 9: 469–480.

Clausen, J. 1931. Cyto-genetic and taxonomic investigations on Melanium violets. Hereditas 15: 219–308.

_____. 1951. Stages in the evolution of plant species. Cornell Univ. Press, Ithaca, New York.

Clausen, J., R. B. Channell, and U. Nur. 1964. *Viola rafinesquii*, the only Melanium violet native to North America. Rhodora 66: 32–46.

Darwin, C. 1859. On the origin of species by means of natural selection. 1st ed. John Murray, London.

_____. 1868. The variation of animals and plants under domestication. 2 vols. John Murray, London.

Day, A. 1965. The evolution of a pair of sibling allotetraploid species of Cobwebby Gilias (Polemoniaceae). Aliso 6: 25–75.

Dobzhansky, Th. 1937, 1941, 1951. Genetics and the origin of species. 1st, 2nd, 3rd ed. Columbia Univ. Press, New York.

_____. 1958. Species after Darwin, p. 19 to 55. *In* S. A. Barnett [ed.], A century of Darwin. Heinemann, London.

Dobzhansky, Th., L. Ehrman, and O. Pavlovsky. 1957. *Drosophila insularis*, a new sibling species of the willistoni group. Studies in the genetics of Drosophila. Univ. of Texas Publ. 9: 39–47.

Dobzhansky, Th., L. Ehrman, O. Pavlovsky, and B. Spassky. 1964. The superspecies *Drosophila paulistorum*. Proc. Nat. Acad. Sci. 51: 3–9.

Dobzhansky, Th., and P. C. Koller. 1938. An experimental study of sexual isolation in Drosophila. Biol. Zentralbl. 58: 589–607.

Ehrman, L. 1962. Hybrid sterility as an isolating mechanism in the genus Drosophila. Quart. Rev. Biol. 37: 279–302.

Fisher, R. A. 1930. The genetical theory of natural selection. Clarendon Press, Oxford.

Grant, K. A. and V. Grant. 1964. Mechanical isolation of *Salvia apiana* and *Salvia mellifera* (Labiatae). Evolution 18: 196–212.

Grant, V. 1950. Genetic and taxonomic studies in Gilia. I. *Gilia capitata*. Aliso 2: 239–316.

———. 1952a. Genetic and taxonomic studies in Gilia. II. *Gilia capitata abrotanifolia*. Aliso 2: 361–373.

———. 1952b. Genetic and taxonomic studies in Gilia. III. The *Gilia tricolor* complex. Aliso 2: 375–388.

———. 1954a. Genetic and taxonomic studies in Gilia. IV. *Gilia achilleaefolia*. Aliso 3: 1–18.

———. 1954b. Genetic and taxonomic studies in Gilia. VI. Interspecific relationships in the Leafy-stemmed Gilias. Aliso 3: 35–49.

———. 1963. The origin of adaptations. Columbia Univ. Press, New York.

———. 1964. Genetic and taxonomic studies in Gilia. XII. Fertility relationships of the polyploid Cobwebby Gilias. Aliso 5: 479–507.

———. 1965a. Species hybrids and spontaneous amphiploids in the *Gilia laciniata* Group. Heredity 20: 537–550.

———. 1965b. Evidence for the selective origin of incompatibility barriers in the Leafy-stemmed Gilias. Proc. Nat. Acad. Sci. 54: 1567–1571.

Grant, V. and Grant, A. 1954. Genetic and taxonomic studies in Gilia. VII. The Woodland Gilias. Aliso 3: 59–91.

———. 1960. Genetic and taxonomic studies in Gilia. XI. Fertility relationships of the diploid Cobwebby Gilias. Aliso 4: 435–481.

Grun, P., and M. Aubertin. 1965. Evolutionary pathways of cytoplasmic male sterility in Solanum. Genetics 51: 399–409.

Hubbs, C., and E. A. Delco. 1960. Mate preference in males of four species of gambusiine fishes. Evolution 14: 145–152.

Huxley, J. S. 1943. Evolution: The modern synthesis. George Allen and Unwin, London.

King, J. C. 1947. Interspecific relationships within the guarani group of Drosophila. Evolution 1: 143–153.

Knight, G. R., A. Robertson, and C. H. Waddington. 1956. Selection for sexual isolation within a species. Evolution 10: 14–22.

Koopman, K. F. 1950. Natural selection for reproductive isolation between *Drosophila pseudoobscura* and *Drosophila persimilis*. Evolution 4: 135–148.

Latimer, H. 1958. A study of the breeding barrier between *Gilia australis* and *Gilia splendens*. Thesis, Claremont Graduate School, Claremont, Calif.

Littlejohn, M. J. 1965. Premating isolation in the *Hyla ewingi* complex (Anura: Hylidae). Evolution 19: 234–243.

Lorković, Z. 1958. Some peculiarities of spatially and sexually restricted gene exchange in the *Erebia tyndarus* group. Cold Spring Harbor Symp. Quant. Biol. 23: 319–325.

Mayr, E. 1959. Isolation as an evolutionary factor. Proc. Amer. Phil. Soc. 103: 221–230.

————. 1963. Animal species and evolution. Harvard Univ. Press, Cambridge, Mass.

Mecham, J. S. 1961. Isolating mechanisms in anuran amphibians, p. 24 to 61. *In* W. F. Blair [ed.], Vertebrate speciation. Univ. of Texas Press, Austin, Texas.

Moore, J. A. 1957. An embryologist's view of the species concept, p. 325 to 338. *In* E. Mayr [ed.], The species problem. Amer. As. Advance. Sci., Washington, D. C.

Muller, H. J. 1940. Bearings of the "Drosophila" work on systematics, p. 185 to 268. *In* J. Huxley [ed.], The new systematics. Oxford Univ. Press, London.

————. 1942. Isolating mechanisms, evolution and temperature. Biol. Symp. 6: 71–125.

Patterson, J. T., and W. S. Stone. 1952. Evolution in the genus Drosophila. Macmillan Co., New York.

Randolph, L. F. 1953. Crossability of maize and Tripsacum in relation to theories of the origin of maize. Proc. 7th Internat. Bot. Congr. (Stockholm), 179–180.

Rick, C. M. 1963. Barriers to interbreeding in *Lycopersicon peruvianum*. Evolution 17: 216–232.

Santibañez, S. K., and C. H. Waddington. 1958. The origin of sexual isolation between different lines within a species. Evolution 11: 485–493.

Stebbins, G. L. 1958. The inviability, weakness, and sterility of interspecific hybrids. Advances in Genet. 9: 147–215.

Stephens, S. G. 1946. The genetics of "corky." I. The New World alleles and their possible role as an interspecific isolating mechanism. J. Genet. 47: 150–161.

Thoday, J. M. 1964. Genetics and the integration of reproductive systems, p. 108 to 119. *In* K. C. Highnam [ed.], Insect reproduction. Royal Entomological Society, London.

Vaurie, C. 1957. Systematic notes on palearctic birds. 26. Paridae: the *Parus caeruleus* complex. Amer. Mus. Novit. no. 1833.

Volpe, E. P. 1954. Hybrid inviability between *Rana pipiens* from Wisconsin and Mexico. Tulane Stud. in Zool. 1: 111–123.

————. 1955. Intensity of reproductive isolation between sympatric and allopatric populations of *Bufo americanus* and *Bufo fowleri*. Amer. Natur. 89: 303–317.

Wallace, A. R. 1889. Darwinism: An exposition of the theory of natural selection. Macmillan, London.

Wallace, B. 1954. Genetic divergence of isolated populations of *Drosophila melanogaster*. Proc. Ninth Internat. Congr. of Genet., Caryologia, suppl. vol., p. 761–764.

Part V

THE NATURE OF THE SPECIATION PROCESS

Editor's Comments
on Papers 21 Through 27

As discussed earlier speciation can occur through a variety of processes. Asexual species and obligatory self-fertilizers are comparable in that they produce lineages unable to exchange genetic material. The problem of identification and understanding of speciation in these forms requires different definitions than those that we have used in this volume. Among diploid sexually reproducing species the gradual evolution of geographically isolated populations may be the most frequent process.

The origin of species by gradual processes was described by Darwin and Wallace. Their papers have been reprinted in the *Evolutionary Genetics* volume of the Benchmark Papers in Genetics. While most of their discussion concerns anagenesis, they do comment on the divergence of populations. Darwin says (pp. 52–53):

Another principle, which may be called the principle of divergence, plays, I believe, an important part in the origin of species. . . . it follows, I think, from the foregoing facts, that the varying offspring of each species will try (only few will succeed) to seize on as many and as diverse places in the economy of nature as possible. Each new variety of species, when formed, will generally take the place of, and thus exterminate its less well-fitted parent. This I believe to be the origin of the classification and affinites of organic beings always *seem* to branch and sub-branch like the limbs of a tree from a common trunk, the flourishing and diverging twigs destroying the less vigorous—the dead and lost branches rudely representing extinct genera and families.

Wallace says (p. 59):

But this new, improved, and populous race might itself, in course of time, give rise to new varieties, exhibiting several diverging modifications of form, any of which, tending to increase the facilities for preserving existence, must, by the same general law, in their turn become predominant. Here, then, we have *progression and continued divergence* deduced from the general laws which regulate the existence of animals in a state of nature, and from the undisputed fact that varieties do frequently occur.

Anderson and Stebbins (Paper 22) discuss the role of introgression in contributing to the observed bursts of evolutionary activity. They suggest that man contributes under domestication and by disturbing the habitats in which organisms live.

Lewis (Paper 24) discusses the origin of species which results from saltational chromosomal reorganization in plants and contrasts this with the more common process. He notes the multiple structural differences in adjacent populations. Hybrid plants have low fertility and the probability that they will persist is rare. He discusses various processes in *Clarkia* and the conditions which promote this mode of evolution, and summarizes the processes.

Other positions concerning speciation during the past century have already received comment. During the first third of this century the genetic basis of the process of speciation received little emphasis. Perhaps this is reasonable. The main thrust of early genetics was to understand the nature of inheritance, which must precede its application to the process of speciation. This accumulating knowledge did provide significant understanding to the problem. Haldane (Paper 21) considered the species problem and noted that species differences could be attributed to known genetic phenomena. He summarized the differences but offered little information on the conditions which might promote their occurrence or fixation in a population.

Dobzhansky (Paper 9) reviewed the role of genetics in the origin of the species and provided a volume (1937) which truly stimulated several generations of investigators. He reviewed the literature from natural and experimental populations on variation, selection, isolating mechanisms, and hybridization.

Mayr (1942, 1947, 1949, 1963) has presented the most exhaustive case in support of the role of geographic isolation in the origin of species. He has been most dogmatic in the assertion that sympatric speciation plays only a minor role in the origin of species, if in fact it plays a role. His point is that geographic isolation can explain all cases and thus serve as a universal rule. This, of course, is more satisfactory than having a separate rule for each speciation event.

White (Paper 25) noted that some morabine grasshoppers with low vagility and contiguous ranges have chromosome numbers which differ. The seventeen-chromosome form appears to have chromosomes which result from the fusion of chromosomes of the more common nineteen-chromosome presumed progenitor. White presents a stasipatric model which explains observations in some species and allows a new chromosomal rearrangement to be established and spread throughout a continuous population. The situation is reminiscent of Wright's (Paper 2) discussion of the method of origin of species in his three-phase shifting balance theory.

Carson (Paper 26) examined the chromosome banding sequences in a number of "picture winged" *Drosophila* species in Hawaii. He found that more than 100 inversions have been fixed among the diverse species and that deletions were extremely rare. He found that some homosequential species (with identical arrays of fixed inversion sequences) were reproductively isolated. He suggests that "speciation results from a single founder individual" invading a new island. This observation, if universal among diploid forms, would contribute to the explanation of why there are such large numbers of closely related species on islands while the total diversity of mainland fauna is not present.

Dobzhansky (Paper 27) summarized the recent advances in the speciation of *Drosophila*. He noted the variety of processes which contribute to the variety of species and of speciation, and that reproductive isolation can precede or follow adaptive divergence.

21

Reprinted from *Nature* 124:514–516 (1929)

The Species Problem in the Light of Genetics.[1]

By J. B. S. Haldane.

DARWIN held that the differences between species were due to the accumulation of such smaller differences as distinguish varieties within a species. Since the rediscovery of Mendel's papers, a vast amount of work has been done on the genetical basis of intra-specific varieties, and a smaller, but still considerable amount, on the genetics of specific differences.

Intra-specific differences, so far as they are hereditary, can be classified as due to one of the following causes :

1. Extra-nuclear 'factors', or plasmons. These are inherited entirely or almost entirely through the mother. They cause many of the differences in chloroplasts between different plant varieties, the plastids being handed on maternally as more or less independent units. They may also interact with nuclear factors to alter such characters as the development of the anthers. They are not certainly known in animals.

2. Single intra-nuclear factors, or genes. An enormous number of varietal differences, in both wild and domesticated organisms, have been shown to be due to one, or a small number of genes.

3. Multiple genes. Quantitative differences are often due to the action of a number of genes. In some cases an apparently continuous varying character can be shown by careful analysis of individuals to be determined in this way. Moreover, Fisher has shown that the correlations found for human stature between relatives by Pearson and his pupils are in quantitative agreement with expectation on the hypothesis that they are due to multiple genes.

4. Differences in the arrangement of genes within a chromosome. Sturtevant has shown that different geographical races of *Drosophila melanogaster* differ in the order of the genes in a chromosome, as determined by linkage experiments. A section of a chromosome of one race appears to have been reversed in the other. Similar results have been produced by Muller with X-rays.

5. Differences in chromosome attachment. A chromosome of one variety may be represented by two smaller bodies in another, as in *Zea Mays*, or a fragment may be attached to different larger chromosomes in different varieties, as in *Drosophila melanogaster*.

6. Unbalanced differences in the amount of chromatin. One or more chromosomes, or portions of them, may be represented once, thrice, or four or more times in a variety, as compared with twice in the type. This is not only the genetical basis of sex in most organisms, and of intersexuality and other abnormalities in some, but also occurs in varieties of other types. For example, some fatuoid oats, and most cultivated sweet cherries, have one or two chromosomes in addition to the set characteristic of the species. In this condition some genes are represented three or four times, the

majority twice. This generally produces a greater effect on the visible character than results from a trebling or quadrupling of the haploid number of all the genes at once.

7. Polyploidy. The number of chromosomes is here two, three or more times as great in one variety as in the other. This generally results in an increase of size, but often the visible effect is very small indeed, far less than that of many single factors or of an unbalanced difference in chromosome number. But it invariably results in a certain degree of physiological isolation. Not only is there often difficulty in crossing a diploid and a tetra, ploid, but also, if the union is fertile, the hybrid is generally a triploid, and therefore much more sterile than either parent owing to irregularities in meiosis.

Differences of all these types have arisen in animal and plant races under observation, and all but the first have been produced experimentally. So far as I know, there is no clear evidence that any intra-specific hereditary variations are due to causes other than these, though it is possible that the list is not yet complete, and some of the cases ascribed to multiple genes demand much further study.

The assertion is still occasionally made that characters inherited in a Mendelian manner are pathological. This may, I take it, mean one of two things. The character may be supposed to be disadvantageous to its bearer. Much of the variation in shell pattern of wild *Cepea nemoralis* is due to two factors. Diver has shown that the four races produced by the interaction of these factors have been in existence in England since Neolithic times, and although it is conceivable that one race may have some slight advantage in a particular environmental niche, there can be no such advantage in the country as a whole, or selection would have eliminated certain of the types. Naturally, however, most variations from the normal are disadvantageous in a normal environment, and are therefore eliminated by natural selection. Many mutants are definitely shorter lived or less fertile than the type. But Pearl and his pupils have shown that in artificial conditions some of the mutant types of *Drosophila melanogaster* are more fertile than the type, others longer lived. Such mutants cannot be called pathological.

Secondly, it may be meant that a Mendelian character is pathological because it is due to injury. Mutants are produced in large quantities by X-rays, and it may be that much of normal mutation is due to the β- and γ-rays from potassium, other radioactive substances, and cosmic radiations. I can see no reason why such mutation should be regarded as more pathological than photosynthesis or sunburn. It is probably a prerequisite of evolution, and its effects are not necessarily harmful either to the individual or the species, though often so to the individual.

[1] Paper read to the Society for Experimental Biology on June 15.

Inter-specific differences are largely due to the same causes as intra-specific. In general, they can only be analysed genetically where the species can be crossed. But this is not always the case. For example, the order of the genes in the chromosomes of different species of *Drosophila* can be shown to be nearly, but not quite, the same. The linkage values of homologous genes are somewhat different in the mouse and rat. Since the yellow *Primula acaulis* and related species differ from the purple *P. Juliae* by the loss of a gene needed for anthocyanin formation, it is very plausible that other yellow Primulas also lack this gene.

Differences in chromosome number and arrangement can, of course, also be observed apart from crossing. A few examples of inter-specific differences will now be given under the same classification as that adopted for intra-specific.

1. In a number of plant species crosses, one of the F_1 hybrids is vigorous, while the reciprocal has defective plastids, and is yellow or variegated. Renner regards this as due to the inviability of the maternally inherited plastids in the presence of the hybrid nucleus. A very clear case of a plasmon causing sexual abnormality after species crossing occurs in *Geranium* (unpublished work of the late Mr. Newton). There are probably analogous cases in animals; indeed, wherever adult reciprocal hybrids of the homogametic sex differ, extra-nuclear inheritance may be suspected.

2. Mendelian segregation for some characters in F_2 is very common. Apart from cases where varietal characters of one species still behave in a Mendelian manner after the crossing, some of the actual specific characters are so inherited. Sometimes, however, the ratios in F_2 diverge markedly from expectation.

In plants the genes by which species differ often cause striking differences. Thus Chittenden showed that the purple *Primula Juliae* had no gene for plastid pigments, the primrose none for anthocyanin. Hence white flowers appeared in F_2. On the other hand, the colour genes distinguishing crossable rodent species cause rather smaller changes, and are multiply allelomorphic with genes causing the sharp differences distinguishing domestic varieties. Thus *Cavia porcellus* has a gene for yellow-bellied agouti, *C. rufescens* for agouti-bellied agouti, both allelomorphic with the gene found in the well-known black variety.

3. When species are crossed the F_1 is generally uniform, the F_2 variable, often differing among themselves more than do the parent species. This fact is, of course, the principal reason why hybridisation is employed in horticulture to obtain striking new forms. The phenomena can be exactly paralleled in varietal crosses, and are probably due to multiple gene differences.

4. The order of the genes is slightly different in *Drosophila melanogaster* and *D. simulans*, and probably in other *Drosophila* species which cannot be crossed.

5. There is strong cytological evidence for this when the chromosomes of different species are compared, and fairly good genetical evidence both in *Drosophila* and mammals. Thus the gene the loss of which converts a grey mammal into a yellow is sex-linked in cats but not so in rodents, suggesting that a corresponding gene is carried by the X-chromosome in the cat, by another chromosome in rodents.

6. Unbalanced differences of this type between species probably occur in *Viola* and some other genera. They are not, however, quite so well authenticated as types 5 and 7.

7. This type of difference is very common in plants, and extremely rare in animals. For example, in *Rosa*, species with 14, 28, 42, and 56 chromosomes are known, besides species with intermediate numbers, which are probably hybrids.

It is obviously impossible to state that all inter-specific differences can be explained on these lines. It is, however, doubtful whether any differences are known which cannot be so explained. In view of the very great morphological and physiological differences produced by single genes, there is no reason to doubt their capacity for causing inter-specific differences of these kinds, which are often less striking than varietal differences. The stumbling-block in the past has been the failure to find, between varieties, the physiological barrier which often prevents the effective crossing of species. This failure was regarded as a serious but not fatal objection to Darwinism by such men as Huxley and Romanes. It has now been completely overcome. Let us consider, for example, *Primula sinensis* and its tetraploid variety *gigas*. Every plant of these forms in England is descended from the same few seeds brought over from China in 1819–26. The giant tetraploid form has originated on several occasions in cultivation since 1900. Tetraploid pollen on the diploid stigma has never produced a single seed. The reciprocal cross, though very extensively made, has produced about a dozen hybrids. These hybrids are often triploids, and hence have irregular reduction divisions, and are far less fertile than either parent. We have thus a complete analogy to the case of true species, and indeed some geneticists regard such tetraploids as new species. Such tetraploidy can sometimes be produced by injury of the diploid plant. This produces a tetraploid branch, and if this branch is self-fertilised, the seedlings are tetraploids. Incidentally, this is the only case known to me in which a *somatically* acquired character is transmitted by sexual reproduction.

Phenomena similar to those found in the F_2 of species crosses may be produced by the action of small numbers of genes. Thus Gonsalez found the following expectations of life in days for *Drosophila melanogaster* females. The characters are recessives and combinations of recessives two or three at a time.

Wild	.	.	.	40·6
Purple (eye)	.	.	.	21·8
Arc (wing)	.	.	.	28·2
Speck (axilla)	.	.	.	38·8
Purple, arc	.	.	.	32·0
Purple, speck	.	.	.	23·0
Arc, speck	.	.	.	34·7
Purple, arc, speck	.	.	40·7

274

Clearly this last combination represents a physiological balance as good (under the artificial culture conditions) as the normal. All other combinations are below the viabilities of the triple dominant or the triple recessive. It is well known that when species are crossed, the F_1 generation, though itself often vigorous, produces gametes and zygotes less vigorous than those of the parental types. In some cases I conceive that related species are simply those genotypes, out of a large possible number, which possess the highest viability.

I contend, then, that all specific differences so far analysed may be due to the cumulative action of known types of varietal difference. Whether they actually are so is another question, but. on the principle that *entia non sunt multiplicanda praeter necessitatem*, we are justified in assuming, as a provisional working hypothesis, that they are. The question as to how species arise in Nature is a much more complicated one. Natural selection undoubtedly occurs ; on the other hand, the environment may influence the rate of mutation, and it is probable that mere chance plays a certain part in establishing new types. Many other causes of evolution have of course been postulated. Which of these processes is the more important is a matter which can only be decided by observation of Nature, and not by experiment alone.

22

Reprinted from *Evolution* 8:378-388 (1954)

HYBRIDIZATION AS AN EVOLUTIONARY STIMULUS

E. Anderson and G. L. Stebbins, Jr.

Missouri Botanical Garden and University of California, Davis

Received July 1, 1954

One of the most spectacular facets of the newer studies of evolution has been the demonstration that evolution has not proceeded by slow, even steps but that seen in the large there have been bursts of creative activity. Some of the evidence for these bursts is from paleontology; Simpson (1953) has recently assembled a wealth of data concerning them and has discussed in detail their possible causes. Paleobotanists are equally aware of such events as the great upsurge of angiosperms in the Cretaceous, and of primitive vascular plants in the Devonian period. Other evidence for evolutionary bursts comes from the existence of large clusters of related endemic species and genera in the modern fauna and flora of certain regions, particularly oceanic islands and fresh water lakes. The snails (Achatinellidae) and honey sucker birds (Drepanidae) of Hawaii are classical examples, as are also the Gammarid crustaceans of Lake Baikal, and the fishes of Lakes Tanganyika and Nyasa in Africa, and particularly of Lake Lanao in the Philippines (see Brooks, 1950 for a summary and discussion of the data). It is true that some of these examples may represent normal rates of evolution occurring in a restricted area which has been isolated for a very long time, but there can be little doubt that in the case of others evolution has been phenomenally rapid.

As Simpson (1944, 1953) has clearly stated, the cause of this rapid evolution is to be sought in the organism-environment relationship. Along with most authors, however, he has tended to emphasize the peculiar environment present during these evolutionary bursts, and has suggested that one need not postulate any unusual type of population structure as a contributing factor. Zimmermann (1948) has given a plausible account of the environmental factors operating in the case of oceanic islands; reduction of competition, frequent migration to new habitats, and populations repeatedly reduced to a very few individuals, giving a maximum opportunity for the operation of chance as well as for the rapid action of selection.

To the student of hybridization, however, another factor which may have contributed largely to these evolutionary bursts presents itself. Hybridization between populations having very different genetic systems of adaptation may lead to several different results. If the reproductive isolation between the populations is slight enough so that functional, viable and fertile individuals can result from segregation in the F_2 and later generations, then new adaptive systems, adapted to new ecological niches, may arise relatively quickly in this fashion. If, on the other hand, the populations are well isolated from each other so that the hybrids between them are largely sterile, then one of two things may happen. The hybrids may become fertile and genetically stabilized through allopolyploidy, and so become adapted to more or less exactly intermediate habitats, or they may back cross to one or both parents, and so modify the adjoining populations of the parental species through introgression. This latter phenomenon has now been abundantly documented in the higher plants, and several good examples are known in animals (see bibliographies in Anderson, 1949; Heiser, 1949; Anderson, 1953). By introgressive hybridization elements of an entirely foreign genetic adaptive system can be carried over into a previously stabilized one, permitting the rapid reshuffling of varying adaptations and complex modifier systems. Natural selection is presented not with one or two new alleles but with segregating blocks of genic material belonging to entirely different adaptive systems. A simple analogy will show the comparative effectiveness of introgression.

Let us imagine an automobile industry in which new cars are produced only by copying old cars one part at a time and then putting them together on an assembly line. New models can be produced only by changing one part at a time. They cannot be produced *de novo* but must be built up from existing assembly lines. Imagine one factory producing only model 'T' Fords and another producing model 'T' Fords and also modern station wagons. It will be clear that if changes could only be brought about by using existing assembly lines these would have to proceed slowly in the factory which had only one assembly line to choose from. In the other factory, however, an ingenious mechanic, given two whole assembly lines to work with, could use different systems out of either and quickly produce a whole set of new models to suit various new needs when they arose.

Just as in the example of the two assembly lines, hybrids between the same two species could produce various different recombinations, each of which could accommodate itself to a different niche. When a big fresh water lake was formed *de novo,* hybrids between the same two species could rapidly differentiate into various new types suitable for the various new niches created in the big new lake. A technical point of much significance is that each of the various heterozygous introgressive segments brought in by hybridization would (by crossing over) be capable of producing increased variation generation after generation for periods running into whole geological eras (Anderson, 1939). The enhanced

plasticity due to crossing over in introgressed segments has been shown on theoretical grounds to be present for many generations. Such studies as those of Woodson on Asclepias (1947, 1952), of Hall on Juniperus (1952) and of Dansereau on Cistus (1941) indicate that this does actually happen and that introgressive segments may persist for geological periods and produce effects of continental magnitude.

To students of introgressive hybridization it would seem like an excellent working hypothesis to suppose that when Lake Baikal was formed, and when each new island of the Hawaiian archipelago arose from the ocean, species belonging to different faunas and floras were brought together and that physical and biological barrier systems were broken down. There were increased chances for hybridization in an environment full of new ecological niches in which some new recombinations would be at selective advantages. There is a growing body of experimental data to support such an hypothesis. These data fall largely in two groups (1) Evolution under domestication, (2) Evolution in disturbed habitats.

(1) For evolution under domestication the evidence is overwhelming that by conscious and unconscious selection, man has created forms of plants and animals which are specifically distinct from their wild progenitors. This large body of evidence demonstrates that given a habitat in which novelties (or at least some of them) are at a great selective advantage, evolution may proceed very rapidly. There is presumptive evidence that many of these domesticates originated through introgression but the process began so early that getting exact experimental evidence for the history of any one of them will entail long-continued cooperative research (see, however, Mangelsdorf and Smith (1949), Alava (1952), and Nickerson (1953) for evidence that modern Zea is greatly different from the maize of five thousand

years ago and that much of this differentiation may well be the result of introgression from Tripsacum). For some ornamentals, domestication is such a recent event that critical evidence is easier to assemble. Anderson (1952) has presented in elementary detail the case of *Tradescantia virginiana*. He shows that in four hundred years by introgression from *T. ohiensis* and *T. subaspera* (unconsciously encouraged by man) it has evolved under cultivation into a variable complex quite distinct from *T. virginiana* as a genuinely wild species.

(2) Evolution in disturbed habitats. It has been repeatedly shown (Anderson, 1949; Heiser, 1949; Epling, 1947) that species which do not ordinarily produce hybrids and backcrosses may readily do so when man or any other agent disturbs the habitat. This phenomenon was referred to as "Hybridization of the Habitat" by Anderson (1948). After citing the work of several authors who have emphasized the role of man in promoting and creating habitats favorable for the perpetuation of hybrids and hybrid derivatives, he reached the following conclusion (1948, p. 6). "Does this mean that introgression as a phenomenon is limited to the areas disturbed by man and that its results are mere artifacts and not genuine natural phenomena? I think not. Though freely admitting that nearly all the introgression which has been studied experimentally (for one exception see Dansereau, 1941) is of the nature of an artifact, I believe that at particular times, and in particular places, introgression may have been a general evolutionary factor of real importance."

The great frequency of hybrid derivatives in disturbed habitats is only in part due to the breaking down of barrier systems, allowing previously isolated species to cross. It can and does occur when the barrier systems are not broken down (see for instance Heiser, 1951). Much more important is the production of new and varying ecological niches; more or less open habitats in which some of the almost

infinitely various backcrosses and occasional types resulting directly from segregation in F_2 and later generations will be at a selective advantage. A particularly significant example was investigated by Anderson (unpublished) who studied *Salvia apiana* and *Salvia mellifera* in the San Gabriel mountains, confirming and extending Epling's (1947) previous studies. He found hybrid swarms not in the chaparral itself where both of these species are native but adjacent to it in cutover live oaks amidst an abandoned olive orchard. In this greatly disturbed area, new niches were created for the hybrid progeny, which are apparently always being produced in the chaparral but at a very low frequency. In this strange new set of various habitats some of the mongrels were at a greater selective advantage and the population of the deserted olive orchard was composed of hybrids and back-crosses to the virtual exclusion of *S. apiana* and *S. mellifera*.

It has been customary to dismiss the evidence of introgression under the influence of man as relatively unimportant to general theories of evolution because nothing quite like it had previously occurred. A little reflection will show that this is not so. Man at the moment is having a catastrophic effect upon the world's faunas and floras. He is, in Carl Sauer's phrase, an ecological dominant but he is not the first organism in the world's history to achieve that position. When the first land vertebrates invaded terrestrial vegetation they must have been quite as catastrophic to the flora which had been evolved in the absence of such creatures. When the large herbivorous reptiles first appeared, and also when the first large land mammals arrived in each new portion of the world there must have been violent readjustments and the creation of new ecological niches.

The last of these (the arrival of the large land mammals) is close enough to us in geological time so that we have witnessed the very end of the process. The vegetation of New Zealand had had no experience with mammals until the arrival of the Maori in the fourteenth century followed by Europeans in the 18th and 19th centuries. Man, pigs, horses, cattle, rats, sheep, goats, and rabbits were loosed upon a vegetation which had had no previous experience with simians or herbivores. The effect was catastrophic. Hybrid swarms were developed upon the most colossal scale known in modern times. A succession of New Zealand naturalists have occupied themselves with the problem and it has been treated monographically by Cockayne (1923) and by Allen (1937).

The extent to which disturbance of the habitat combined with reorganization of adaptive systems through hybridization could have been responsible for evolutionary bursts, "proliferation," "tachytely" or "quantum evolution" (Simpson 1953) can best be estimated by summarizing the geological and paleontological evidence concerning the time of occurrence of habitat disturbances, and comparing this with probable evolutionary changes in certain groups of organisms which were most likely initiated by hybridization. In such a survey, all three of the possible results of hybridizations—introgression, segregation of new types without backcrossing and allopolyploidy—must be considered. Reference to allopolyploids is particularly important, since hybrid derivatives of this type can easily be distinguished from their parental species by their chromosome numbers, and the time and place of hybridization can often be indicated with a high degree of probability (Stebbins, 1950, Chap. 9).

Preceding the advent of man, the most revolutionary event in the history of the northern continents was the Pleistocene glaciation and the contemporary pluvial periods of regions south of the ice sheet. This involved not only radical oscillations in climate, but also great disturbances of the soil, both in the glaciated regions and in areas to the south of them. In the latter, the extensive deposits of loess im-mediately south of the ice margin and the masses of alluvium carried for miles down the river valleys must have disturbed these areas almost as much as the ice sheets churned up the areas which they covered.

The activity of hybridization in developing plant populations adapted to these new habitats is amply evident from the frequency of allopolyploids in them. Specific examples are *Iris versicolor* and *Oxycoccus quadripetalus* (Stebbins, 1950); the polyploid complexes of *Salix, Betula, Vaccinium, Antennaria, Poa, Calamagrostis,* and many others can also be cited. The best example of introgression among species which have invaded the ice-free areas in post-Pleistocene time is in the complex *Acer saccharophorum* (Dansereau and Desmarais, 1947). The numerous examples cited by Anderson (1953) of hybrid and introgressant types which occupy the central Mississippi Valley between the Appalachian, Ozark, and central Texas highlands probably represent late Pleistocene or post-Pleistocene invasion of these areas which were strongly affected by outwash from the ice sheet and from the postglacial lakes. The origin of *Potentilla glandulosa* subsp. *Hanseni* in the post-Pleistocene meadows of the Sierra Nevada is discussed by Stebbins (1950, p. 279).

During the Tertiary and earlier geological periods three types of changes in the inanimate environment can be singled out which probably gave rise to disturbed habitats favorable to the establishment of hybrid derivatives. These were mountain building movements, advance and retreat of epicontinental seas, and radical changes in the earth's climate.

Some of the direct effects of mountain buildings are the rapid creation of raw, unoccupied habitats (such as lava flows, for instance), in which plants belonging to very different ecological associations may temporarily mingle and gain a chance to hybridize. In central California the canyon of the Big Sur River is a typical example of the mixing together of species belonging to very different floras in a region of recent uplift which has a rugged, youthful topography. Here yuccas and redwoods grow within a stone's throw of each other. An example of hybridization in this area is between two species of *Hieracium; H. albiflorum,* which is typical of northern California, the Pacific Northwest, and the Rocky Mountains, and *H. argutum,* a Southern California endemic which here reaches its northern limit except for one known station in the Sierra foothills. Examples such as this could undoubtedly be multiplied by a careful study of any youthful mountain region.

The retreat of epicontinental seas in the latter part of the Pliocene period, plus faulting in the Pleistocene and recent times, has been largely responsible for the present topography of coastal California with its flat valleys and abrupt mountain ridges. One hybrid polyploid which appears to have spread as a result of these changes is the octoploid *Eriogonum fasciculatum* var. *foliolosum* (Stebbins, 1942); another is probably the tetraploid *Zauschneria californica* (Clausen, Keck, and Hiesey, 1940). A series of hybrid swarms which may have arisen in response to the same topographical changes is that of *Quercus Alvordi* (Tucker, 1952). *Delphinium gypsophilum* is a relatively well stabilized species, probably of hybrid origin, endemic to this same recently emerged area of California (Epling, 1947), and the species of *Gilia* considered by Grant (1953) to be of hybrid origin have the same general distribution. In the Old World, Dansereau (1941) has suggested that *Cistus ladaniferus* var. *petiolatus,* which occupies the recently emerged coast of North Africa, is a product of hybridization between typical *C. ladaniferus* and *C. laurifolius* both of which occur in the more ancient land mass of the Iberian Peninsula.

Among the radical changes in the earth's climate which occurred recently enough so that their effect on the vegeta-tion can be recorded, is the advent of the Mediterranean type of climate with its wet winters and dry summers in most of California. The time of this climatic change is now fully documented by the fossil record; it took place during the middle part of the Pliocene period. It was preceded by a general decrease in precipitation, with biseasonal maxima (Axelrod, 1944, 1948).

The effects of this climatic change on the woody vegetation of the area are also well documented by the fossil record. One very probable example of a hybrid swarm exists in a fossil flora. In the Remington Hill Flora, which was laid down in the Sierra foothills at the beginning of the Pliocene, there is a great abundance of oak leaves corresponding to the modern *Q. morehus,* a hybrid between the mesophytic, deciduous *Q. Kelloggii,* and the xerophytic, evergreen *Q. Wislizenii* (Condit, 1944). That these fossil leaves were borne by hybrid trees is evidenced not only by their very unusual and characteristic shape, but also by their great variability and the fact that no similar leaves are found in any of the numerous Miocene and Pliocene floras of California. Furthermore, the Remington Hill is the only one of these fossil floras which contains the counterparts of both parental species. At present, the *Q. Kelloggii* × *Wislizenii* hybrid is frequent in the Sierra foothills, but it usually grows as single trees in company with dense stands of *Q. Wislizenii* and *Q. Kelloggii.* The populations of the parental species growing in the vicinity of the hybrids appear little or not at all different from those occurring by themselves, far from any other species of this complex. On the other hand, *Q. Wislizenii* shows considerable geographic variation, with the more northernly and more coastal variants, i.e., those adapted to increasingly mesic climates, possessing an increasingly greater resemblance to *Q. Kelloggii* in habit, leaves, buds, and fruits. This suggests that the present variation pattern in *Q. Wislizenii* is the result chiefly of extensive introgression from *Q. Kelloggii,* which began with the hybrid swarms of Mio-Pliocene time, and has since been ordered into a regular, clinical series of variants by the selective action of the changing Pliocene and Pleistocene climates. Tucker (oral comm.) has suggested that *Q. Douglasii,* a completely unrelated oak with a similar geographical distribution, may have also originated from one or more hybrid swarms of a similar geological age. The modern variation pattern of the common chaparral species *Adenostoma fasciculatum* (Anderson, 1952) could be interpreted on the same basis, while less thorough observations by the junior author suggest that several other examples can be found in the California flora.

Conditions favorable for the origin and spread of hybrid derivatives are made not only by changes in the inanimate environment, but also by the advent and disappearance of various types of animals. Previous to man and his associated domesticates, some of these disturbances were as follows. In the Eocene and Oligocene periods, large grazing mammals made their first appearance on the earth. Their effect on the woody vegetation cannot be detected in the fossil record, and probably was not great. The herbaceous plants, however, must have been greatly affected by their inroads, and if these smaller plants had been abundantly preserved as fossils, we might be able to record a burst of evolution in them during these early Tertiary epochs. Babcock (1947, p. 132), after careful consideration of all lines of evidence, has suggested the latter part of the Oligocene as the time of origin of the genus *Crepis,* one of the larger, more specialized, and probably more recent genera of Compositae. On this basis, one might suggest that the greatest period of evolution of genera in this largest of plant families was during late Eocene and Oligocene time. The junior author, from his studies of various grass genera of temperate

North America, believes that many facts about their present distribution patterns could best be explained on the assumption that they began their diversification during the Oligocene epoch. They appear to have attained much of their present diversity by the middle of the Miocene, by which time many of the now extensive polyploid complexes, such as those in *Bromus, Agropyron,* and *Elymus,* had begun to be formed. The extensive Miocene record of species belonging to the relatively advanced tribe Stipeae (Elias, 1942) would support such an assumption.

At an earlier period, namely the beginning of the Cretaceous, the world saw for a relatively short time the dominance of the largest land animals which have ever existed, the great herbivorous dinosaurs. These monsters must have consumed huge quantities of the fern and gymnosperm vegetation which prevailed at the time, and it is difficult to see how these plants, with their relatively slow growth and reproduction, could have kept up with such inroads. It is very tempting, in fact, to speculate that over grazing on the part of giant dinosaurs contributed toward the extinction of the Mesozoic gynmospermous vegetation, as well as of the larger dinosaurs themselves, during the middle of the Cretaceous period. At the same time, shallow epicontinental seas were advancing and retreating, leaving coastal plain areas open for plant colonization; other significant events during this period were the rise of modern birds and of Hymenoptera, particularly bees.

The writers venture to suggest that these four nearly or quite concurrent events—retreat of seas, overgrazing by dinosaurs, advent of a diversified avifauna which transported seeds long distances, and rise of flower pollinating bees and other insects—all contributed to the greatest revolution in vegetation which the world has even seen; the replacement of gymnosperms by the predominant angiosperm flora of the upper part of the Cretaceous period. One should note that all of these conditions would favor hybridization and the spread of hybrid derivatives, by giving unusual opportunities for previously separated types to be brought together by wide seed dispersal, by permitting cross pollination between types previously isolated from each other, and by opening up new areas for colonization by the hybrid derivatives. The suggestion has been made elsewhere (Stebbins, 1950, p. 363) that differentation of genera and sub-families among primitive angiosperms took place partly via allopolyploidy; the time of origin of this polyploidy may well have been during the Cretaceous period. Evidence of introgression at so remote a time is probably impossible to obtain; by an analogy we should assume that in the past as now, conditions favorable for allopolyploidy also promoted introgression.

Going still further into the past, let us speculate on the events which must have taken place at the time when vascular plants and vertebrates first spread over the land. The principal geological period involved is the Devonian. At the beginning of this period comes the first extensive fossil record of vascular plants, all belonging to the primitive order Psilophytales. By the end of the Devonian, forms recognizable as club mosses (Lycopsida), ferns (primitive Filicales), and seed plants (Pteridospermae) were already widespread. We shall, of course, never know what chromosome numbers existed in these extinct groups of primitive vascular plants. But their nearest living descendants are nearly all very high polyploids, as has now been most elegantly demonstrated by Manton (1950, 1953). She has suggested that the living Psilotales, which have gametic numbers of about 52, 104, and over 200, "are the end-products of very ancient polyploid series which date back to simple beginnings. . . ." The relationship between the modern Psilotales and the Devonian Psilophytales is not clear, but to the present authors they appear to resemble each other nearly enough so that they could belong to the same complex

network of allopolyploids, which developed its greatest diversity in the Devonian period. In the genus *Ophioglossum,* generally regarded as one of the three most primitive genera of true ferns, we have the highest chromosome numbers known to the plant kingdom, namely n = ca. 256 in the northern *O. vulgatum* and n = ca. 370 in the tropical *O. pendulum.* These ferns are not preserved in the fossil record because of their soft texture, but their origin during the Devonian period is a fair inference. There is very good reason to believe, therefore, that the great proliferation of genera and families of vascular plants during this earliest period of their dominance was accompanied by allopolyploidy just as it has been in the more recent periods of very active evolution. Where allopolyploidy was widespread, we can also suspect abundant introgression.

The reader may well ask at this point whether any of this evidence contributes to the central theme of the present discussion, namely the hypothesis that these extensive hybridizations, both ancient and relatively modern, gave rise to really new types, which formed the beginnings of families, orders, and classes having different adaptive complexes from any plants previously existing. It is undoubtedly true that the results of introgression and allopolyploidy are chiefly the blurring of previously sharp distinctions between separate evolutionary lines, and the multiplication of variants on adaptive types which were already established during previous cycles of evolution. Nevertheless, the fact must not be overlooked that conditions favorable for introgression and allopolyploidy, namely the existence of widely different and freely recombining genotypes in a variety of new habitats, also favor the establishment and spread of new variants. Establishment of new adaptive systems is under any circumstances a relatively rare event; in any group of organisms we have hundreds of species and subspecies which are variants of old adaptive types to one which represents a really new departure. Hence we cannot expect to recognize introgressive or polyploid complexes which have given rise to such new types until we have carefully analyzed hundreds of those which have not. Furthermore, our methods of recognizing these complexes almost preclude the chance of identifying the new types which have arisen from them. We make the assumption that hybrid derivatives, whether introgressants or allopolyploids, have characteristics which can all be explained on the basis of intermediacy between or recombination of the characteristics of the putative parents, and then devise methods of verifying this assumption. The new types, falling outside of this assumption, would be rejected by our methods.

The junior author can suggest two examples known to him of new and distinctive morphological characteristics which may have arisen in recent hybrid derivatives. One of these is the presence in *Ceanothus Jepsonii,* a species narrowly endemic to the serpentine areas of northern California, of flowers with six and seven sepals, petals, and anthers (Nobs, 1951). This characteristic is not known anywhere else in the family Rhamnaceae or even in the entire order Rhamnales, an order which almost unquestionably dates back to the Cretaceous period. Mason (1942) has given strong evidence for the recent origin of *Ceanothus Jepsonii.* It inhabits an environment which is certainly recent, since the mountains on which it occurs were covered by a thick layer of volcanic rocks even as late as the end of the Pliocene epoch, and the serpentine formations to which it is endemic were not exposed until after the faulting which occurred at the beginning of the Pleistocene (Mason, 1942). It belongs to a complex of closely related species and subspecies, among which hybridization is still very actively taking place (Nobs, 1951). In characteristics other than sepal and petal number, it is intermediate between various ones of its relatives rather than an extreme type.

Hence there is a good reason to suspect that *Ceanothus Jepsonii* represents a species of relatively recent (i.e. Pleistocene) hybrid origin which has evolved a morphological characteristic previously unknown in its family, and in fact one which is relatively uncommon in the entire subclass of dicotyledons.

The other example is in the grass species *Sitanion jubatum.* This species is distinguished by possessing glumes which are divided into a varying number of linear segments, a characteristic not found elsewhere in the tribe Hordeae, and one which is the basis of a distinctive mechanism for seed dispersal (Stebbins, 1950, p. 141). *Sitanion jubatum* is endemic to Pacific North America, being most abundant in the coast ranges and foothills of central California. Its nearest relative is *S. hystrix,* a species found in the montane areas of the same region, and extending far eastward and southeastward. The two species are distinguished only by the degree of division of the glumes, and in fact appear to grade into each other. Field observations suggest that they actually consist of a large swarm of genetically isolated microspecies, such as has been demonstrated experimentally to exist in the related *Elymus glaucus* (Snyder, 1950).

Cytogenetically, both species of *Sitanion* are allotetraploids (Stebbins, Valencia, and Valencia, 1946). Extensive chromosome counts from various parts of the ranges of both species plus still more numerous measurements of sizes of pollen and stomata have failed to reveal any form of *Sitanion* which could be diploid. Furthermore, the chromosomes of both species are strongly homologous with those of *Elymus glaucus,* as evidenced by complete pairing in the F_1 hybrid. All of this evidence suggests that *S. jubatum* did not have any diploid ancestors which possessed its distinctive glumes, but has evolved out of a complex of allopolyploids which has existed in western North America for a long time, probably since the middle of the Tertiary period.

The forms of *S. jubatum* which have the most extreme division of the glumes occupy habitats which are recent, and which in some ways are intermediate between the most extreme habitats occupied by *Sitanion* and those characteristic of *Elymus glaucus*. They are known from the shore of San Francisco Bay, in northeastern Marin County, from the eastern edge of the Sacramento Valley north and east of Sacramento and from the Sierra foothills in Mariposa county. In growth habit, these races of *S. jubatum* could be regarded as intermediate between the most extreme xerophytes found in *Sitanion* on the one hand, and *E. glaucus* on the other.

Experimental evidence (Stebbins, unpublished) has now indicated that the complex of microspecies within the taxonomic species *Elymus glaucus* originated partly if not entirely through introgression. The probability is strong that *Sitanion* consists of a similar swarm of microspecies which originated also by introgression. The extensive subdivision of the glumes in some of these microspecies, therefore, may well have originated through the establishment of new mutations, or of new types of gene interaction, in genotypes produced by hybridization and introgression between morphologically very different and genetically well isolated species.

When all of this evidence has been considered, the writers can hardly escape the conclusion that hybridization in disturbed habitats has produced the conditions under which the more familiar processes of evolution, mutation, selection, and the origin of reproductive isolation barriers, have been able to proceed at maximum rates. Far from being insignificant because much of it is in habitats greatly disturbed by man, the recent rapid evolution of weeds and semi-weeds is an indication of what must have happened again and again in geological history whenever any species or group of species became so ecologically dominant as greatly to upset the habitats of their own times.

SUMMARY

(1) It has been established by recent work in Palaeontology and Systematics that evolution has not proceeded at a slow even rate. There have instead been bursts of evolutionary activity as for example when large fresh water lakes (Baikal, Tanganyika, and Lanao) were created *de novo*.

(2) Recent studies of introgression (hybridization and subsequent back-crossing) have demonstrated that under the influence of man evolution has been greatly accelerated. There has been a rapid evolution of plants and animals under domestication and an almost equally rapid evolution of weed species and strains in greatly disturbed habitats.

(3) The rapidity of evolution in these bursts of creative evolution may well have been due to hybridization. At such times diverse faunas and floras were brought together in the presence of new or greatly disturbed habitats where some hybrid derivates would have been at a selective advantage. Far from being without bearing on general theories of evolution, the repeated demonstrations of accelerated introgression in disturbed habitats are of tremendous significance, showing how much more rapidly evolution can proceed under the impact of a new ecological dominant (in this case, Man). Such an agent may bring diverse faunas and floras into contact. Even more important is the creation of various new, more or less open habitats in which novel deviates of partially hybrid ancestry are at a selective advantage. The enhanced evolution which we see in our own gardens, dooryards, dumps and roadsides may well be typical of what happened during the rise of previous ecological dominants. The first vertebrates to enter isolated continents or islands, the first great herbivorous reptiles, the first herbiv-

orous mammals must have created similar havoc upon the biotae of their own times. Introgression must have played the same predominant role in these disturbed habitats as it does today under the impact of man. These arguments are supported by a homely analogy (page 379) and by various kinds of experimental and taxonomic data.

LITERATURE CITED

ALAVA, REINO O. 1952. Spikelet variation in *Zea Mays L.* Ann. Mo. Bot. Gar., **39**: 65–96.

ALLAN, H. H. 1937. Wild species-hybrids in the phanerogams. Bot. Rev., **3**: 593.

ANDERSON, E. 1939. Recombination in species crosses. Genetics, **24**: 688.

———. 1948. Hybridization of the habitat. Evolution, **2**: 1–9.

———. 1949. Introgressive Hybridization. Wiley & Sons, New York, 109 pp.

———. 1952. The ecology of introgression in Adenostoma. Nat. Acad. Sci.: Abstracts of papers presented at the autumn meeting, Nov. 10–12, 1952 (Sci., **116**: 515–516).

———. 1952. Plants, Man and Life. Little, Brown & Co., Boston, 245 pp.

———. 1953. Introgressive hybridization. Biol. Rev., **28**: 280–307.

AXELROD, D. I. 1944. The Pliocene sequence in central California. Carnegie Inst. Wash. Publ., 553: 207–224.

———. 1948. Climate and evolution in western North America during Middle Pliocene time. Evolution, **2**: 127–144.

BABCOCK, E. B. 1947. The genus *Crepis*. Part I. The taxonomy, phylogeny, distribution and evolution of *Crepis*. Univ. Calif. Publ. Bot., 21: 1–198.

BROOKS, J. L. 1950. Speciation in ancient lakes. Quart. Rev. Biol., **25**: 131–176.

CLAUSEN, J., D. D. KECK AND W. HIESEY. 1940. Experimental studies on the nature of species. I. Effect of varied environment on western North American plants. Carnegie Inst. Wash. Publ., 520, vii, 452 pp., figs. 1–155.

COCKAYNE, L. 1923. Hybridism in the New Zealand flora. New Phytol., **22**: 105–127.

CONDIT, C. 1944. The Remington Hill flora. Carnegie Inst. Wash. Publ., 553: 21–55.

DANSEREAU, P. 1941. Etudes sur les hybrides de Cistes. VI. Introgression dans la section Ladanium. Can. Jour. Research, **19**: 59–67.

—— AND Y. DESMARAIS. 1947. Introgression in sugar maples. II. Amer. Midl. Nat., **37**: 146–161.

ELIAS, M. K. 1942. Tertiary prairie grasses and other herbs from the high plains. Spec. Papers Geol. Soc. Amer., 41: 176 pp.

EPLING, C. 1947. Actual and potential gene flow in natural populations. Am. Nat., **81**: 81–113.

———. 1947. Natural hybridization of *Salvia apiana* and *S. mellifera*. Evolution, **1**: 69–78.

GRANT, V. 1953. The role of hybridization in the evolution of the leafy-stemmed *Gilias*. Evolution, **7**: 51–64.

HALL, M. T. 1952. Variation and hybridization in *Juniperus*. Ann. Mo. Bot. Gard., **39**: 1–64.

HEISER, C. B., JR. 1949. Natural hybridization with particular reference to introgression. Bot. Rev., **15**: 645–687.

———. 1951. A comparison of the flora as a whole and the weed flora of Indiana as to polyploidy and growth habits. Indiana Acad. Sci., Proc., **59**: 64–70.

MANGELSDORF, P. C., AND C. E. SMITH, JR. 1949. New archeological evidence on evolution in maize. Bot. Mus. Leaflets, Harvard Univer., **13**: 213–247.

MANTON, I. 1950. Problems of Cytology and Evolution in the Pteridophyta. 316 pp., Cambridge University Press.

———. 1953. The cytological evolution of the fern flora of Ceylon. Soc. Exp. Biol., Symp., **7**: Evolution, 174–185.

MASON, H. L. 1942. Distributional history and fossil record of *Ceanothus*. pp. 281–303 in Van Rensselaer, M., and H. E. McMinn. *Ceanothus*, publ. by Santa Barbara Bot. Gard., Santa Barbara.

NICKERSON, N. H. 1953. Variation in cob morphology among certain archaeological and ethnological races of maize. Ann. Mo. Bot. Gard., **40**: 79–111.

NOBS, M. 1951. Ph.D. Thesis, Univ. California, Library.

SAUER, C. O. 1952. Agricultural origins and dispersals. Am. Geogr. Soc., Bowman memorial lectures Ser. II, v. 110 pp., 4 pls. New York.

SIMPSON, G. G. 1944. Tempo and Mode in Evolution. xiii, 237 pp., New York.

———. 1953. The Major Features of Evolution. Columbia University Press, New York, 434 pp.

SNYDER, L. A. 1950. Morphological variability and hybrid development in *Elymus glaucus*. Amer. Jour. Bot., **37**: 628–636.

STEBBINS, G. L., JR. 1942. Polyploid complexes in relation to ecology and the history of floras. Am. Nat., **76**: 36–45, figs. 1–2.

——. 1950. Variation and Evolution in Plants. Columbia University Press, New York, 643 pp.

——, J. I. VALENCIA AND R. M. VALENCIA. 1946. Artificial and natural hybrids in the Gramineae, tribe Hordeae I. *Elymus, Sitanion* and *Agropyron.* Am. Jour. Bot., **33**: 338–351.

TUCKER, M. 1952. Evolution of the California oak *Quercus alvordiana.* Evolution, **6**: 162–180.

WOODSON, R. E., JR. 1947. Some dynamics of leaf variation in *Asclepias tuberosa.* Ann. Mo. Bot. Gard., **34**: 353–432.

——. 1952. A biometric analysis of natural selection in *Asclepias tuberosa.* Nat. Acad. Sci.: Abstracts of papers presented at the autumn meeting, Nov. 10–12, 1952 (Sci., **116**: 531).

ZIMMERMAN, E. C. 1948. Insects of Hawaii. Vol. I. Introduction. University of Hawaii Press, Honolulu, 206 pp.

23

Reprinted from *Proc. Amer. Phil. Soc.* **103**:221-230 (1959)

ISOLATION AS AN EVOLUTIONARY FACTOR

ERNST MAYR

Professor of Zoology, Harvard University

(*Commemoration of the Centennial of the Publication of* The Origin of Species *by Charles Darwin,*
Annual Meeting of the American Philosophical Society, April, 1959)

CONTENTS

INTRODUCTION

THE fact that isolation plays a role in evolution was recognized long before Darwin (Buch, 1825). What this role is, however, was frequently misunderstood. Even today there is so much difference of opinion on this point that it would be hasty to assert that a complete solution is within our grasp.

One might treat this important subject by giving a straightforward analysis of the various problems associated with isolation and the current attempts at solution. I prefer a different treatment. Most of the great pioneers of modern evolutionary thinking, Darwin, Wallace, Huxley, Weismann, Wagner, de Vries, and others, grappled with this difficult theme, and it would seem a fascinating task to trace their steps and to determine where they advanced our understanding and where they "missed the boat" and why. There are few other subjects in biology which lend themselves as well to historical treatment as the subject of isolation. An analysis of the questions asked by each generation of investigators and of the reasons for some of the wrong answers they gave, time after time, will lead to a much fuller understanding of the problems than would a systematic treatment of isolation.

Darwin's [1] voyage on the *Beagle* gave him abundant opportunity to observe isolation at work:

. . . barriers of any kind, or obstacles to free migration, are related in a close and important manner to the differences between the production of various regions . . . on the opposite sides of lofty and continuous mountain-ranges, of great deserts and even of large rivers, we find different productions (Darwin, 1872: 414).

When chided by M. Wagner for underestimating the role of isolation in speciation, Darwin defended himself with the words: "It would have been a strange fact if I had overlooked the importance of isolation, seeing that it was such cases as that of the Galapagos Archipelago, which chiefly led me to study the origin of species" (*Life and Letters of Darwin* 3: 159, letter of October 13, 1876). Yet, there is no doubt that Wagner's criticism was justified. Darwin admitted the occurrence of speciation on islands, but he emphasized again and again that incipient species could evolve into full species also without any spatial isolation:

I can by no means agree [with Wagner] that migration and isolation are necessary elements for the formation of new species (1872: 106). . . . I believe that many perfectly defined species have been formed on strictly continuous areas (1872: 175).

All the evidence that has accumulated since Darwin indicates that this assumption is unwarranted as far as higher animals are concerned. It is of more than historical interest to determine how Darwin arrived at his erroneous conclusion. An analysis of his publications and letters indicates that responsible for it was his failure to understand clearly four evolutionary phenomena or concepts.

(*a*) *The Meaning of the Term "Variety."* Since species to Darwin were the result of gradual evolution they had to pass through an intermediate stage, such as the "incipient species" and the

---

[1] Darwin's contribution to the subject is particularly difficult to evaluate since he was more plagued with doubts on this than on almost any other evolutionary question. As Barzun (1948) has remarked, not without justification, Darwin was often loath to commit himself too definitely, and if he made an emphatic statement in one sentence, he tended to take part or most of it back in the next. This is surely true for his stand on isolation and makes a balanced account quite difficult. I believe, however, that the quoted sentences represent Darwin's basic views.

"variety." "A well-marked variety may be called an incipient species" (Darwin, 1872: 54). With the variety occupying such a key position in the problem of the origin of species, one might expect that Darwin would have devoted a great deal of effort to a definition of the concept and to an investigation of the circumstances under which varieties are being formed, but this is not the case. Darwin simply took over term and concept as it was current among the naturalists and systematists of his period. He never seems to have realized that since Linnaeus (and even before) the term had been applied indiscriminately to two very different kinds of phenomena, deviating individuals and deviating populations. Weismann, as we shall presently see, fell into the same error. For a typologist any deviation from the type is a "variety." For a biologist, on the other hand, it is of vital importance to know whether such a deviant is merely an intrapopulation variant or a different population. If Darwin had made a clear distinction, he would not have said: "If a variety were to flourish so as to exceed in numbers the parent species, it would then rank as the species, and the species as the variety; or it might come to supplant and exterminate the parent species; or both might coexist, and both rank as independent species" (1872: 54).

(b) *A Morphological Species Concept.* In view of Darwin's great insight into biological processes and evolutionary phenomena, one is somewhat shocked to realize how completely his species definition is based on degree of difference:

. . . I look at the term species as one arbitrarily given, for the sake of convenience, to a set of individuals closely resembling each other, and that it does not essentially differ from the term variety, which is given to less distinct and more fluctuating forms (1872: 54) . . . the amount of difference is one very important criterion in settling whether two forms should be ranked as species or varieties (1872: 58).

Weismann (1872: 19), who argued along exactly the same lines as Darwin expressed the matter as follows: "The species is nothing absolute, and the differences among various species are of exactly the same nature as the differences between the sexes of one and the same species." It is on the basis of views like this that de Vries eventually developed his theory of speciation by mutation. I have looked in vain in Darwin's writings for an indication that he ever considered the species as anything but a "more distinct variety." Not

realizing that the species is a "reproductively isolated population," a concept which was definitely familiar to many of his contemporaries (Mayr, 1957a), Darwin was quite unable to focus on the essential aspects of speciation and on the role of isolation. And yet, the same Darwin had extremely sound ideas on the development of sterility in incipient species (see below).

(c) *Failure to Distinguish Between Phyletic Evolution and Multiplication of Species.* Evolutionary change within a lineage will, given enough time, produce sufficient change to justify ranking the descended population as a species different from the ancestral one. This is the "formation of a new species" of which Darwin spoke most frequently in his work. But this process of evolutionary change fails to account for the steady increase in the number of species which seems to have occurred in geological history. The splitting off of one lineage from another, the "multiplication of species," includes an evolutionary factor (the acquisition of reproductive isolation) which is not implicit in mere evolutionary change. Owing to his essentially morphological species definition, Darwin failed to give sufficient emphasis to the problem of the origin of reproductive isolation. Where he was concerned with the origin of sterility among species, it was in connection with "natural selection" rather than with speciation.

The failure of Darwin, and later of Weismann, to understand the real scientific problems of the origin of species, because of their failure to understand the biological nature of species, should be an object lesson to those who attempt to minimize the species problem. Even though we have made great progress in this field during the past thirty to fifty years, it would be premature to believe and to assert that we understand the nature of species of all kinds of organisms, or on the other hand, to claim that it is useless to seek an understanding.

(d) *A Desire for a Single Factor Explanation.* Evolutionists prior to about 1930 were singularly reluctant to consider the interaction of various factors in the causation of evolutionary phenomena. Weismann (1872) bases his entire discussion on the alternative "natural selection *or* geographical isolation" as the factor responsible for the origin of new species. Darwin states, "Although isolation is of great importance in the production of new species, on the whole I am inclined to believe that largeness of area is still more important" (1872: 107). He supports this claim by arguing that in large areas there are more individuals and, thus, "there will be a better chance of favorable variations" and also, "the conditions of life are much more complex from the large number of already existing species" (1872: 107), and that this also will favor the origin and spread of new "varieties." Admittedly all this would favor phyletic evolution, but it does not shed light on the origin of reproductive isolation. In acknowledging Wagner's volume on geographic isolation (*Life and Letters of Darwin* 3: 157), Darwin admits the importance of this factor but then continues,

I must still believe that in many large areas all the individuals of the same species have been slowly modified, in the same manner, for instance, as the English race horse has been improved, that is by the continued selection of the fleetest individuals, without any separation.

Did Darwin not see that there is no stricter isolation of gene pools than exercised by the animal and plant breeders? What would have happened to the selection of race horses, if they had been permitted to interbreed freely with ponies, jumping horses, draft horses, and all sorts of utility horses? This very example should have convinced Darwin completely of the indispensibility of isolation, yet he used it to argue against the importance of isolation because he felt he had to make a choice between either isolation or selection. And this is the same Darwin who said elsewhere (1868: 185):

On the principle which makes it necessary for man, whilst he is selecting and improving his domestic varieties, to keep them separate, it would clearly be advantageous to varieties in a state of nature, that is to incipient species, if they could be kept from blending. . . .

One would expect Darwin to continue "by spatial segregation." Instead he concludes, "either through sexual aversion, or by becoming mutually sterile." The mechanism by which coexisting varieties might acquire sexual aversion or mutual sterility is not indicated. Darwin concludes his rejection of Wagner's thesis with the emphatic statement: "My strongest objection to your theory [of geographic speciation] is that it does not explain the manifold adaptations in structure in every organic being" (*Life and Letters* 3: 158), as if speciation and adaptation were exclusive phenomena.

WAGNER, HIS FOLLOWERS AND OPPONENTS

The most ardent champion of isolation in the evolutionary literature is the great naturalist Moritz Wagner (1813–1887). During his travels in Asia, Africa, and the Americas, he had observed that, almost invariably, closely related forms or species occupy adjacent ranges, separated from each other by rivers, mountain ranges, valleys (in the case of mountain species) or, indeed, by any barrier to dispersal. He first published this observation in 1841, elaborated it in a major essay in 1868 and added to it in a number of later essays, republished posthumously in 1889. While Darwin had readily agreed that geographic isolation favors speciation, Wagner insisted that it was a *conditio sine qua non*:

The formation of a genuine variety which Mr. Darwin considers an "incipient species," will succeed in nature only when a few individuals can spatially segregate themselves for a long time from the other members of the species by transgressing the confining barriers of their range (1889: 64).

It is crucial for an understanding of the controversy between Wagner and Weismann to realize that Wagner, when speaking of a variety as an incipient species, referred without exception to geographic races while Darwin and Weismann in similar arguments more often than not referred to intrapopulation variants. In view of Wagner's incessant repetition of the two terms migration and colonization as the principal factors responsible for the origin of new species, it may be pertinent to quote a modern author, who has probably never read Wagner: "Thus, migration and colonization favour the origin of discontinuity" (Darlington, 1956: 362).

Wagner's original observation (the geographic relation of incipient species) and the empirical conclusion he drew from this observation (the importance of geographic isolation for speciation) are as true today as they were when first published. Wagner, however, was not quite so successful when he tried to find reasons for the need of geographic isolation. He advances two reasons. The first is, to prevent the new population from being swamped by the parental one:

The origin and continued evolution of a race will always be endangered where numerous reinvading individuals of the same species disturb this process by general mixing and, thus, usually suppress it altogether. . . . Without a long continued separation of the colonists from the other members of their species the formation of a new race cannot succeed in my opinion (1889: 65).

This first conclusion is not only substantiated by observation but has been confirmed by much recent work in population genetics which has established the overriding importance of integrating factors in an isolated gene pool.

Wagner was less successful in the second half of his explanation. He firmly believed that a change of environment was necessary for natural selection to become active. "Organisms which never leave their ancient area of distribution will never change" (1889: 82). Even though it is, of course, true that there is less probability of evolutionary change in a stable environment, natural selection (even if only normalizing selection) will always be active and phyletic evolution will frequently take place. These marginal and ill-conceived comments on the relation between isolation and natural selection served Weismann (1872) as the basis for a severe criticism of Wagner's theory of geographic speciation. The original question, "Can species multiply without geographic isolation?" was changed into the questions, "Is isolation itself the factor which is responsible for the changes in isolated populations?" and, "Is isolation necessary for varieties to become constant?" Weismann's refutation of Wagner, like Darwin's, is based on a morphological species definition and on the assumption that a morphologically different variety is an incipient species. He states that, on the basis of Wagner's theory, on one hand all isolated populations of species should be different varieties and, on the other hand, different varieties should not be able to originate in the same area as the normal type of species. Both of these postulates can, of course, be easily disproved. Failure of geographic speciation, he says, is indicated by the many cosmopolitan species, particularly among the tardigrades and the fresh-water crustaceans, but also among higher organisms (for instance, the butterfly *Vanessa cardui*). On the other hand, Weismann continues, there are numerous cases of polymorphism, particularly among the butterflies, which prove that varieties can originate without isolation. How much in his argument he equates morphological change with origin of new species may be documented by some quotations. He asks, is it possible "that newly arising characters can become constant only through isolation and subsequent colony formations and thus give cause to the origin of a new species?" (1872: 6) and

asserts in a statement of *non sequiturs*: ". . . it would be a fatal mistake if one were to assume . . . that isolation were an indispensable prerequisite to the modification of species, that not selection, but isolation alone would make possible the change of a species, that is its splitting into several forms" (1902: 319). One final quotation may demonstrate how completely Weismann missed the essential point in the problem of the multiplication of species:

In this it is quite unimportant how they [endemic species that originated in isolated areas] originated, whether by Amixia in a period of variation or by natural selection, which tried to adjust the immigrants to the new environmental conditions of the isolated area. The change can even have been caused by influences which had nothing to do with the isolation, as for example the direct influence of the physical environment or the process of sexual selection (1872: 107).

The main reason for Weismann's inability to evaluate properly the role of isolation was his failure to determine what an incipient species is. This was seen much more clearly by his successors and explicitly or implicitly it forms the basis of most discussions of isolation during the 1880's and 1890's. From the very beginning to the present day there has been a clear separation of two schools of thought. On one side there are those who, with Wagner, insist that geographic isolation is an indispensable prerequisite for the multiplication of species in sexually reproducing organisms (excluding the special situation of polyploidy); on the other side are those who insist with equal determination that in addition to geographic speciation there exist various modes of sympatric speciation. The sympatrists claim that varieties with all the properties of incipient species often coexist. Their argument was, for the first time, clearly stated by Darwin himself:

I can bring forward a considerable body of facts showing that within the same area, two varieties of the same animal may long remain distinct, from haunting different stations, from breeding at slightly different seasons, or from the individuals of each variety preferring to pair together (1872: 105).

Wallace (1889: 150) enthusiastically supports this contention and concludes

that geographical or local isolation is by no means essential to the differentiation of species, because the same result is brought about by the incipient species acquiring different habits or frequenting a different station;

and also by the fact that different varieties of the same species are known to prefer to pair with their like, and thus to bring about a physiological isolation of the most effective kind.

Catchpool, Dahl, Romanes, Kellogg, and Petersen were other early authors endorsing the theory of sympatric speciation, as I have pointed out in a partial historical review of the field (Mayr, 1955). The first author who can be credited with full understanding of the difference between phyletic evolution and the multiplication of species, and who has stated the case in a thoroughly modern manner seems to have been the ornithologist Seebohm. He points out with great logical acuity that natural selection and variation alone cannot account for the multiplication of species (1888: Chap. 3):

There is no reason why evolution should not go on indefinitely modifying a species from generation to generation until a pre-glacial monkey becomes a man, and yet no second contemporary species be originated. The origin of a second species is prevented by interbreeding. So long as the area of distribution of the species is continuous and not too large, the constant intermarriage which takes place between the males of one family and the females of another distributes the inherited and transmittable modifications throughout the race or species; which may advance or retrograde according to circumstances, but is prevented by interbreeding from originating a second species. . . . In order to originate a second species, it is necessary to counteract the leveling effect of interbreeding by isolating some of the individuals comprising the species, so that there may be two colonies, which are unable to communicate with each other, and consequently unable to interbreed. . . . In every species there is a tendency to vary in definite directions: the variations are hereditary and cumulative, so that evolution goes on steadily, though slowly, from generation to generation. If a part of the species be isolated from the rest, the evolution of the two colonies does not proceed in exactly the same direction, and the rapidity with which differentiation takes place is exactly in proportion to the difference in the circumstances in which the two colonies are placed.

How highly Seebohm rated isolation is evident from his amusing criticism of Romanes:

It is a remarkable circumstance that only once in the seventy-five pages of Mr. Romanes's paper does the word isolation occur, and then in a footnote. In a paper relating to the origin of species it is like the play of Hamlet with the part of Hamlet omitted.

It was around this time that the concept of the species as an interbreeding community became general among naturalists and systematists. It is this concept which is taken for granted by K. Jordan in 1896 and 1905 (Mayr, 1955) and of which Poulton (1903, 1908: 68) says: "The idea of a species as an interbreeding community is, I believe, the more or less acknowledged foundation of the importance given to transition" (when in doubt whether or not two isolated populations are conspecific). This permitted a reasonable explanation of the origin of reproductive isolation during geographic isolation:

The individuals of an interbreeding community form a biological whole, in which selection inevitably keeps up a high standard of mutual compatibility between the sexual nuclei. As soon, however, as a group of individuals ceases, for any reason, to breed with the rest of the species, there is no reason why the compatibility of the sexual nuclei of the two sets should be retained. Within each set, selection would work as before and keep up a high standard of compatibility; between the sets compatibility would only persist as a heritage of past selection, gradually diminishing as life changes of structure in either or both of the sets rendered them less and less fitted to produce fertile combinations (Poulton, 1903, 1908: 81).

Similar views were expressed by K. Jordan, D. S. Jordan, and by far the majority of systematists publishing about speciation during the first half of this century.

THE IMPACT OF MUTATIONISM

The theory of geographic speciation seemed to receive a fatal setback from the newborn science of genetics. Bateson, de Vries, and other early Mendelians believed that "species arise by mutation, by a sudden step in which either a single character or a whole set of characters together becomes changed" (Lock, 1906: 144). De Vries said at the same time, "The theory of mutation assumes that new species and varieties are produced from existing forms by certain leaps. The parent type itself remains unchanged throughout this process and may repeatedly give birth to new forms" (1906: vii). These saltationist views swayed the thinking of contemporaries so completely that D. S. Jordan (1905) was forced to complain: Wagner's theory of geographic speciation "is accepted as almost self-evident by every competent student of species or of the geographical distribution of species . . . but in the literature of evolution of the present day the principles set forth by Wagner have been almost universally ignored." The result was a tragic schism between experimentalists on one hand and naturalists on the other. Its ultimate bridging was made possible by the realization that most genetic changes are small and that mutations as such do not make new species. This cleared the way for a balanced treatment of the problem of geographic speciation by Rensch (1933), Dobzhansky (1937), Huxley (1942), and Mayr (1942).

THE MODERN SYNTHESIS

The development of the past ten or twenty years is characterized by the contribution from genetics of a firm foundation for the empirical findings of the naturalists of the preceding generation. The naturalists had discovered that isolation is necessary for speciation; the geneticists found out why. But one more step was necessary before this could be done successfully. The term and concept of isolation itself had to be re-examined. It turned out that it was applied to two entirely independent biological phenomena; just as in German the word *Entwicklungsgeschichte* is applied by some authors to ontogeny, by others to phylogeny. The two evolutionary meanings of isolation are geographic isolation and reproductive isolation. Both are equally important in the evolutionary process, but they play very different roles. *Geographic isolation* refers to the division of a gene pool in two by strictly extrinsic factors. It is a reversible phenomenon which in itself has no effect whatsoever on the two separated gene pools. However, it guarantees their independent development and permits the accumulation of an ever-increasing amount of genetic differences. *Reproductive isolation*, however, refers to what we might call the protective devices of a well-integrated and harmoniously coadapted gene pool against pollution by other gene pools. This is achieved by what Dobzhansky calls "isolating mechanisms," of which sterility is the best known but among higher animals by no means the most important. As soon as one clearly discriminates between the two kinds of isolation their respective roles at once become apparent. Geographic isolation is a necessity to permit the gradual building up of the genetic basis for the reproductive isolating mechanisms (polyploidy, as always, is an exception). To repeat once more: The genes within a gene pool form a harmonious whole which can evolve only as a whole. The first step

then, in the multiplication of species, is a physical separation of a portion of the species, permitting it to go its own way genetically. What happens after this isolation depends on the genetic contents of the isolated population, on the totality of the selective forces working on it and on numerous chance phenomena (mutation, recombination, etc.). Divergence and the acquisition of isolating mechanisms in the separated gene pool may happen rapidly or may be delayed for millions of years. Speciation may be considered as essentially completed when the isolating mechanisms have reached that stage of perfection where the geographic isolation can be removed without resulting in genetic swamping of the new daughter species by the parental species.

In spite of essential agreement among evolutionists on the role of isolation, there is still divided opinion on a number of aspects of the isolation problem. Among these three may be singled out as perhaps occupying the greatest amount of attention in the recent literature:

(1) Are there as yet undiscovered forms of sympatric speciation? The search for proven cases of sympatric speciation, initiated by Darwin, still continues. I have myself reviewed the evidence *pro* and *con* in two recent summaries (Mayr, 1947, 1957b). It appears to me that this quest is becoming increasingly hopeless. The realization of the genetically highly complex nature of the isolating mechanisms and, more broadly speaking, of the intricate integration of the total gene pool of a population, makes it exceedingly difficult to conceive of a mechanism that would permit the building up of genetic isolating mechanisms within a physically undivided gene pool. The bridging effects of heterozygosity and the swamping effects of dispersal militate against the possibility of a lasting role of temporary conditioning.

(2) What role does selection play in the perfection of isolating mechanism? Two opposing theories can be found in the contemporary literature. According to one, isolating mechanisms are strictly an incidental by-product of the genetic changes occurring in geographically isolated populations and are perfected during this isolation without any *ad hoc* selection. According to the other, the development of isolating mechanisms is only started in isolation, but their perfection is achieved through natural selection after the incipient species has reestablished contact with the parental species.

It is not realized by most contemporary students

that this argument goes back to Darwin and Wallace. They used the term "sterility" where we would use the term "isolating mechanisms," but the essential part of the argument, the role of selection, has remained unchanged. Darwin first stated his views in *The Origin of Species* in the chapter on hybridism (1872: 320 ff.):

At one time it appeared to me probable, as it has to others, that the sterility . . .[between species] might have been slowly acquired through the natural selection of slightly lessened degrees of fertility, which, like any other variation, spontaneously appeared in certain individuals of one variety when crossed with those of another variety. For it would clearly be advantageous to two varieties or incipient species, if they could be kept from blending. . . .

But, he continues, there are a number of facts known which do not fit with this hypothesis:

In the first place, it may be remarked that species inhabiting distinct regions are often sterile when crossed; now it could clearly have been of no advantage to such separated species to have been rendered mutually sterile, and consequently this could not have been effected through natural selection; but it may perhaps be argued, that, if a species was rendered sterile with some one compatriot, sterility with other species would follow as a necessary contingency.

But, of course, this would not explain how it became sterile with this "compatriot." Darwin continues saying that the drastic differences so often observed between reciprocal crosses (e.g., ♂A × ♀B fertile, ♂B × ♀A sterile) is another phenomenon not explicable by selection, "for this peculiar state of the reproductive system could hardly have been advantageous in either species." He then continues:

In considering the probability of natural selection having come into action, in rendering species mutually sterile, the greatest difficulty will be found to lie in the existence of many graduated steps from slightly lessened fertility to absolute sterility. It may be admitted that it would profit an incipient species, if it were rendered in some slight degree sterile when crossed with its parent form or with some other variety; for thus fewer bastardised and deteriorated offspring would be produced to commingle their blood with the new species in process of formation.

But Darwin is much too critical a thinker to be satisfied with a solution that is nothing but wishful thinking, and so he comes to the conclusion that such a scheme cannot operate (*op. cit.*, 321–322):

But he who will take the trouble to reflect on the steps by which this first degree of sterility could be increased through natural selection to that high degree which is common with so many species . . . will find the subject extraordinarily complex. After mature reflection it seems to me that this could not have been effected through natural selection. Take the case of any two species which, when crossed produce few and sterile offspring; now, what is there which could favor the survival of those individuals which happened to be endowed in a slightly higher degree with mutual infertility, and which thus approached by one small step toward absolute sterility?

The same argument is presented, in part with identical phrases, in *The Variation of Animals and Plants Under Domestication* (1868). Here he states his conclusions even more unequivocally (p. 188):

We may conclude that with animals the sterility of crossed species has not been slowly augmented through natural selection . . . . As species have not been rendered mutually infertile through the accumulative action of natural selection . . . we must infer that it has arisen incidentally during their slow formation in connection with other and unknown changes in their organisation,

a conclusion which is now quite generally accepted.

Wallace, on the other hand, was not willing to let natural selection take the back seat so completely. After having read what Darwin had stated in the 1868 work, he writes (in February, 1868, *More Letters* 1: 288):

I do not see your objection to sterility between allied species having been aided by Natural Selection. It appears to me that, given a differentiation of a species into two forms, each of which was adapted to a special sphere of existence, every slight degree of sterility would be a positive advantage, not to the individuals who were sterile, but to each form,

and continues to explain this in detail. This started an active exchange of letters (letters 209–214, *More Letters* 1: 288–297) on the subject of the origin of sterility. Darwin, however, sticks by his guns:

I feel sure that I am right about sterility and Natural Selection . . . . If sterility is caused or accumulated through Natural Selection, then, as every degree exists up to complete barrenness, Natural Selection must have the power of increasing it. Now take two species A and B, and assume that they are (by any means) half-sterile, *i.e.*, produce half the full number of offspring. Now try and make (by Natural Selection) A and B absolutely sterile when crossed, and you will find how difficult it is . . . .

This was a challenge to Wallace which he took up at once. He developed a most detailed thesis, consisting of nineteen propositions or theorems by which he thought he could do what Darwin considered impossible (March 1, 1868). In retrospect it is clear that Wallace made so many assumptions "to avoid complication," as he says, that he already starts out with virtually reproductively isolated species. Darwin's reaction is sufficiently amusing to be reproduced in full (March 17, *More Letters* 1: 293):

I do not feel that I shall grapple with the sterility argument till my return home; I have tried once or twice, and it has made my stomach feel as if it had been placed in a vice. Your paper has driven three of my children half mad—one sat up till 12 o'clock over it. My second son, the mathematician, thinks that you have omitted one almost inevitable deduction which apparently would modify the result. He has written out what he thinks, but I have not tried fully to understand him. I suppose that you do not care enough about the subject to like to see what he has written.

In this he misjudged Wallace, for only a week later Wallace writes (letter 212A) : "I return your son's notes with my notes on them," and on goes the argument! Darwin's anguish is real (letter 213, p. 294):

I have been considering the terrible problem. Let me first say that no man could have more earnestly wished for the success of Natural Selection in regard to sterility than I did, and when I considered a general statement (as in your last note) I always felt sure it would be worked out, but always failed in detail. The cause being, as I believe, that Natural Selection can not effect what is not good for the individual, including in this term a social community.

In the end Darwin apparently felt what he had said to Huxley a year earlier (*More Letters* 1: 277) : "Nature never made species mutually sterile by selection, nor will men." Wallace once more summarized his views in his *Darwinism*, 1889, p. 174–179. In retrospect it is clear that in spite of the brilliance of analysis on both sides, the problem at that time was an insoluble one, without an understanding of genetics, of population structure, and of the nature of all the other isolating mechanisms, in addition to sterility. It was though, while it lasted, a noble debate.

All the recent work indicates that by far the greatest part of the genetic basis of the isolating mechanisms is an incidental by-product of the genetic divergence of isolated gene pools and acquired during this isolation. There is no argument about this conclusion; indeed, it is obvious that there would be complete hybridization after the breakdown of geographic barriers if such isolating mechanism had not previously developed. The frequency of hybrid belts between formerly isolated portions of species fully substantiates this conclusion. The only remaining argument concerns one point: Will it lead to an improvement of the isolating mechanisms of the populations that are sympatric in the zone of overlap of two newly-formed species if an occasional hybrid is formed? Logically, the answer would have to be yes. Hybrids, at least in animals, are normally of decreased fitness as far as their contribution to the gene pool of the next generation is concerned. Since the fact of their occurrence indicates that the genetic isolating mechanisms of their parents were less than perfect, such hybridization should lead to an elimination of these less than perfect genes from the gene pool. Moore (1957) points out correctly that on the whole the effects of such selection will be confined to the zone of overlap. Furthermore, such a production of hybrids will strengthen the isolating mechanisms only if the hybrids are effectively sterile or inviable, because otherwise introgression between the two parental species would occur and, with it, an accelerating weakening of the reproductive isolation. Ecological and behavioral isolating mechanisms should be the ones most easily strengthened in such zones of overlap. This conclusion is supported by the available observational evidence, as cited by Dobzhansky (1951), which indicates an increased reproductive isolation between certain pairs of species in areas of geographical overlap. Lorković (1958) reports an additional case for the butterfly genus *Erebia* in the Alps.

(3) What is the effect of isolation on the genetic structure of populations? Virtually all work in genetics and animal breeding is done on completely isolated, closed populations. Geneticists have, on the whole, not been conscious of the fact that the conclusions at which they arrived on the basis of work on these closed populations are not necessarily equally true for the open populations of wild species. In a closed population the genetic input is restricted to a minimum, consisting of a few mutations; homozygosity is considerable and usually increasing, and the selective value of any gene is essentially constant. In open populations there is a high and (owing to immigration)

qualitatively variable genetic input, most loci (among those that are genetically variable within the species) are in the heterozygous state, and the selective value of a gene varies considerably with its genetic background (Mayr, 1954). The full consequences of the effects of the presence or absence of isolation on the genetic structure of gene pools have not yet been determined.

OTHER EVOLUTIONARY ASPECTS OF ISOLATION

The two most important evolutionary aspects of isolation are those we have discussed: geographic isolation in the process of the multiplication of species on the one hand, and reproductive isolation in the course of the origin of isolating mechanisms on the other. A third important aspect of isolation is its role in ecological interaction, particularly as determining degree and kind of competition. When an entire fauna or flora is isolated, as those of South America and Australia during the Tertiary, the effects of such isolation become apparent only when it breaks down. At a lower level, we find an isolation of associations and communities separated by ecological barriers and habitat preferences. No systematic treatment of the ecological consequences of presence or absence of such isolation is available nor will it be attempted here. It is mentioned mainly for the sake of completeness. On the whole, the effects of such isolation are self-evident and not controversial.

CONCLUSION

It will be evident from the above account that considerable clarification in our understanding of the evolutionary role of isolation has occurred during the last one hundred years. In the synthetic theory of evolution isolation plays its role in conjunction with natural selection, mutation, and other evolutionary factors rather than in competition with them as was believed by some of the founding fathers of the evolutionary theory. Indeed, it is .the understanding of the genetic structure of populations which has finally provided the reasons for need for isolation during speciation which had long previously been established empirically.

REFERENCES

BARZUN, J. 1941. Darwin, Marx, Wagner. Critique of a heritage. Boston, Little, Brown and Co.

BUCH, L. VON. 1825. Physicalische Beschreibung der Canarischen Inseln. Berlin, Kgl. Akad. Wiss.

DARLINGTON, C. D. 1956. Natural populations and the breakdown of classical genetics. Proc. Royal Soc., B, 145: 350–364.

DARWIN, CHARLES. 1868. The variation of animals and plants under domestication. London, John Murray.

——. 1872. The origin of species. Sixth edition. Oxford University Press, reprinted 1956. (The World's Classics.)

DARWIN, FRANCIS (editor). 1888. The life and letters of Charles Darwin. London, John Murray.

——. 1903. More letters of Charles Darwin. New York, D. Appleton.

DE VRIES, HUGO. 1906. Species and varieties, their origin by mutation, (Lectures delivered at the University of California.) D. T. MacDougal, editor. Second edition. Chicago.

DOBZHANSKY, T. 1937. Genetics and the origin of species. First edition. New York, Columbia University Press.

——. 1951. Genetics and the origin of species. Third edition, New York, Columbia University Press.

HUXLEY, J. S. 1942. Evolution, the modern synthesis. New York, Harper.

JORDAN, D. S. 1905. The origin of species through isolation. Science 22: 545–562.

JORDAN, K. 1896. On mechanical selection and other problems. Novit. Zool. 3: 426–525.

——. 1905. Der Gegensatz zwischen geographischer und nichtgeographischer Variation. Z. wiss. Zool. 83: 151–210.

LOCK, R. H. 1906. Variation, heredity, and evolution. London, J. Murray.

LORKOVIĆ, Z. 1958. Some peculiarities of spatially and sexually restricted gene exchange in the Erebia tyndarus group. Cold Spring Harbor Symposia on Quantitative Biology 23.

MAYR, ERNST. 1942. Systematics and the origin of species. New York, Columbia University.

——. 1947. Ecological factors in speciation. Evolution 1: 263–288.

——. 1954. Evolution as a process, 157–180. London, Allen and Unwin.

——. 1955. Karl Jordan's contribution to current concepts in systematics and evolution. Trans. Royal Ent. Soc. London 107: 45–66.

——. 1957a. Species concepts and definitions. The species problem. Amer. Assn. Adv. Sci. Publ. 50: 1–22.

——. 1957b. Die denkmöglichen Formen der Artentstehung. Revue Suisse de Zoologie 64: 219–235.

MOORE, JOHN A. 1957. An embryologist's view of the species concept. The species problem. Amer. Assn. Adv. Sci. Pub. 50: 325–338.

POULTON, E. B. 1903. What is a species? Proc. Ent. Soc. London, lxxvii–cxvi.

——. 1908. Essays on evolution, 1889–1907. Oxford, Clarendon Press. (A more readily available reprint of Poulton, 1903.)

RENSCH, B. 1933. Zool. Systematik und Artbildungsproblem. Verh. Dtsch. Zool. Ges. 1933: 19–83.

SEEBOHM, H. 1887. The geographical distribution of the family Charadriidae. London.

WAGNER, MORITZ. 1841. Reisen in der Regentschaft Algier in den Jahren 1836, 1837, und 1838. 1–3. Leipzig, Leopold Voss.

——. 1868.* Die Darwin'sche Theorie und das Migrationsgesetz der Organismen. Leipzig, Duncker und Humblot.

——. 1889.* Die Entstehung der Arten durch räumliche Sonderung. Gesammelte Aufsätze. Basel, Benno Schwabe.

WALLACE, A. R. 1889. Darwinism. London, Macmillan.

WEISMANN, AUGUST. 1872.* Ueber den Einfluss der Isolirung auf die Artbildung. Leipzig, Wilhelm Engelmann.

——. 1902. Vortraege ueber Deszendenztheorie, 2: 315–336. Jena, J. Fischer.

* Citations from Wagner and Weismann were translated by the author.

24

Reprinted from *Science* 152:167–172 (1966)

Speciation in Flowering Plants

Rapid chromosome reorganization in marginal populations is a frequent mode of speciation in plants.

Harlan Lewis

Everyone knows there are species, although no one has yet proposed a definition acceptable to all biologists, nor is anyone likely to. Nevertheless, there seems to be no disagreement as to what the process of speciation involves. Since species differences, no matter how species are defined, can be maintained only by barriers of some sort to gene exchange, speciation obviously involves the establishment of such barriers. Speciation can be discussed, therefore, without a precise definition of the end product. Most biologists, however, are likely to ask what there is to discuss, for not only has the process been described repeatedly in recent years, but nearly all treatments of the subject have been in essential agreement since Goldschmidt's arguments for speciation by "hopeful monsters" (*1*) were refuted a quarter of a century ago.

Evolution leading to speciation, except speciation by polyploidy, is generally considered to be a gradual process that includes a succession of stages, from the formation of barely detectable ecological or geographical races to ecogeographic differentiation readily recognizable at the taxonomic level of subspecies. Subsequent development of reproductive barriers carries differentiation to the level of species. Speciation in this manner undoubtedly occurs in flowering plants, for in some genera all stages of the sequence can be found. On the other hand, the normal mode of speciation in many genera appears to have no direct relation to the formation of ecogeographic races or subspecies. It was also Goldschmidt's thesis (*1*) that speciation is a process distinct from subspeciation. He postulated that speciation results from the establishment of systemic mutations that in-

The author is professor of botany and dean of the Division of Life Sciences, University of California, Los Angeles.

volve chromosome reorganization and change the reaction norm of the entire genotype, but he was unable to substantiate this mechanism convincingly. I agree with him, however, that evolution involving chromosome reorganization is very different from that resulting from gradual accumulation of genic differences. This is not to say that chromosome rearrangements never become established in the course of ecogeographic differentiation, but rather that chromosome reorganization frequently is not a gradual one-by-one process. In the case of rapid chromosome reorganization, speciation is not an extension of ecogeographic race formation.

Although I wish primarily to discuss very rapid, saltational speciation, which in recent years has generally received little attention, it is useful, for comparison, to consider first some of the general characteristics of species and speciation in groups of flowering plants when little or no chromosome reorganization is involved. My purpose is to emphasize that there are two distinct modes of speciation, that the products are not equivalent in their relationship to one another, and that they set the stage for different patterns of subsequent evolution. I realize that some of my statements are oversimplifications and that other examples would show that the alternatives are not always as sharply defined as they are presented here.

Gradual Speciation

Evolutionary divergence in groups of flowering plants in which chromosome arrangement remains essentially constant follows the generally accepted rules of geographical speciation, except that barriers between the resulting species are usually incomplete and remain

incomplete for indefinite periods of time, even when the species are sympatric (that is, grow within normal pollinating range of one another). Complete barriers, when they occur, are more often accidental by-products of evolution that the result of selection for reproductive isolation. Closely related species that may have gradually diverged often occur in different geographical areas; if they are sympatric they usually occupy distinct habitats. Except for selection by the habitat and some degree of spatial separation that goes with ecological differentiation, barriers to gene exchange between species that are in contact are mostly of the sort that decrease the rate of hybridization but do not restrict gene recombination within hybrids that are produced; they depend on pollinator preference, structural differences in the flower that impede pollen transfer, or a seasonal difference in flowering time, all of which require constant selection to remain effective unless, of course, they completely eliminate hybridization.

Gene exchange is seldom eliminated by natural selection because barriers between natural species, other than ecological differentiation, are evolutionarily superfluous and incidental to the continued adaptedness of the population concerned. Two examples will serve to illustrate these points: One concerns the barriers between two species of columbine that hybridize extensively where they come into contact; the other, two species of sage that are in contact over a wide area with very little evident hybridization.

Aquilegia formosa and *A. pubescens* are conspicuously different; the former has pendulous bright-red flowers with relatively short spurs, whereas the flowers of the latter are larger, erect, cream or pale in color, and have relatively long spurs. Both occur in the Sierra Nevada of California where *A. formosa* characteristically grows along shady streams and *A. pubescens* on open rocky slopes at generally higher elevations. The careful observations of Grant (*2*) have shown that the red-flowered species is normally pollinated by hummingbirds and the other species by hawk moths. Although the morphological and ecological modes are extremely different, the distribution of columbines is continuous in many places and, where talus spills onto a meadow or a stream flows down a rocky slope, in the area of overlap a wonderful array of morphological recombinants invariably is found. Hybridization is undoubtedly frequent, and the hybrids produce progenies which in turn produce an abundance of seeds. The only barriers to gene exchange appear to be selection by the habitat, propinquity of similarly adapted individuals, and pollinator preference.

Although no one has ever questioned their specific status, the relationship between these columbines is directly comparable to that between the ecological races that have been designated as subspecies in the well-known studies on *Potentilla glandulosa* (3) (for example, *P. glandulosa hanseni*, the meadow race, and *P. glandulosa reflexa*, on the adjacent drier slopes) except that the floral differences in *Potentilla*, which are just as numerous but less conspicuous, have not been shown to be associated with pollinator preference. But even subtle differences in floral morphology are not essential to the maintenance of adaptation to different adjacent habitats, as is indicated by Turesson's classical studies (4) of ecotypic differentiation. Turesson has shown in several species, for example, that populations growing on the sea cliffs, and differing conspicuously in leaf shape, habit, and other vegetative traits from populations on adjacent dunes, maintain their distinctive characteristics although the differences are genetically determined and there are no barriers to interpopulational hybridization, other than a negligible spatial separation.

The evidence leads to the conclusion, therefore, that the conspicuous morphological difference between the columbines, which is maintained by pollinator preference, is essential only to the maintenance of species-distinguishing characters and is incidental to ecological adaptation, neither enhancing nor preserving it. One might ask then: How did the difference arise in the first place? How is it maintained despite extensive hybridization? And why has hybridization not been further reduced by the evolution of additional barriers?

The first question, of course, can never be answered precisely, but it is not difficult to visualize that populations of columbines in different areas, whether widely separated or adjacent, would become adapted to different pollinators if the pollinator which they initially had in common became rare in one of the areas. Since continued adaptation of any population depends on production of adapted progeny, selection for floral traits that will attract the same pollinator to similarly adapted in-

dividuals follows automatically. Consequently, differences in floral morphology between ecologically differentiated populations, once established, will be maintained indefinitely by selection, regardless of rate of hybridization.

Additional barriers to hybridization have not evolved by natural selection because, in some areas, hybrids are apparently as well or better adapted physiologically than either species. Furthermore these areas are at the points of contact where hybridization is most prevalent. As long as hybridization results in the production of adapted progeny, hybridization will not be eliminated by selection. If the area to which hybrid derivatives are adapted is small, the populations within that area may remain highly variable in morphology because newly formed hybrid combinations continually become established. On the other hand, should the intermediate habitat expand in area, or if an extensive intermediate habitat becomes available, a third species may arise which is morphologically as uniform as either of the parents (for example, *Delphinium gypsophilum*) (5) and which may be adapted (for example *Penstemon spectabilis*) to a third and very distinct pollinator (6).

Barriers between sympatric species are generally more effective in reducing hybridization than one finds in the case of the columbines, and maintenance of specific status may appear, erroneously, to be less dependent on ecological adaptation. This is the case in *Salvia*. *Salvia mellifera* and *S. apiana* are morphologically so distinct in both vegetative and floral traits that they are placed in different subsections of the genus (7). Both species are conspicuous components of the soft shrubby coastal sage association, which covers much of southern California at lower elevations. Throughout this large area the two species are frequently in close contact or grow together but show very little evidence of hybridization in undisturbed habitats. The barriers to hybridization are several (8): The species are preferentially visited by different bees; the small-flowered *S. mellifera* by various small solitary bees in addition to the introduced honey bee; and the larger-flowered *S. apiana* by large carpenter bees or bumblebees. When individuals of both species are visited by the same bee, pollination usually does not occur because of the great difference in flower structure. The two species also have modally different flow-

ering seasons. Together these barriers undoubtedly reduce hybridization to a low frequency. In addition, hybrids that do become established set relatively few seeds. Despite the interaction of all these barriers, however, hybrid swarms consisting of a spectacular array of morphological recombinants are found in habitats that have been extensively disturbed by man (9). This can only mean that the essential barrier between these extremely divergent species is that hybrids and hybrid derivatives are not adapted to the undisturbed habitat (10); the other barriers are incidental.

The *Salvia* example differs from *Aquilegia* in only one important respect, namely, there is at present no natural habitat consistently available to the hybrids. Since production of hybrid seeds that cannot become established would reduce the reproductive potential of the plant that produced them, barriers that greatly reduce the rate of hybridization would be expected to develop. The question remains, however, why complete barriers to hybridization have not evolved. This has not happened, I believe, because the barriers that have developed reduce hybridization to a point where the loss in reproductive potential from the formation of hybrids is no greater than loss due to vagaries of the environment on which selection cannot act.

Discussions of speciation generally focus on the stage of divergence at which populations become genetically independent or "reproductively isolated," largely, I suspect, because this stage offers an objective basis for delimiting species. With this emphasis, it has become customary to equate all barriers to gene exchange, whether they merely reduce the frequency of hybridization and hence the rate of recombination or whether they prevent certain combinations from occurring, under the rubric "isolating mechanisms." With respect to flowering plants, this orientation has led many to the rationalization that morphologically well-defined species such as those in *Aquilegia* and *Salvia* must be reproductively isolated, although obviously they are not. On the contrary, the success of these and many other genera, measured in terms of morphological and ecological diversity, is due in large measure to the absence of reproductive isolation; the evolutionary potential of such groups is not limited by the genetic resources of each species alone.

Speciation by Saltation

Evidence that speciation occurs as a result of saltational reorganization of the chromosomes, which I shall call saltation, comes from the observation that adjacent populations, which are very similar in morphology and in ecological adaptation, may differ greatly in chromosome arrangement and sometimes in basic chromosome number. Because of multiple chromosomal differences, hybrids between such populations have very low fertility and would ordinarily be called sterile. Populations intermediate in chromosome arrangement do not occur. The first indication of saltation I had, for example, came from unexpected results following experimental hybridization between two diploid populations of *Clarkia* that were so similar that anyone would have considered them conspecific (*11*). Since they came from ecologically comparable sites less than a mile apart, I was surprised to find that the hybrids were essentially sterile because of multiple differences in their chromosomes. At the same time, one of these populations produced fertile hybrids with other populations which differed in a number of vegetative and floral traits, including some populations that had been placed in another species.

A similar lack of correspondence between morphological divergence and hybrid fertility has since been found in other sections of *Clarkia* (*12, 13*) and is also known to occur in genera belonging to other families (for example, *Haplopappus*, and *Holocarpha* in the Compositae) (*14*). The most obvious characteristic these diverse genera have in common is that they are mostly annuals. One reason, although not the only one, is that the initial products of saltation are morphologically and ecologically so similar to parental populations that hybridization is necessary to detect the barriers between them, and annuals are notably useful for studies involving systematic hybridization between populations. I am convinced, however, that saltation also occurs in woody plants, although the evidence, as discussed in a later section, is more indirect.

Morphologically indistinguishable or very similar sympatric species are generally called sibling species, with the obvious implication that they are derived from a common parent (*15*). Following saltation, however, the relation between species is clearly that of parent

and offspring, although two or more species independently derived from one parental species may appropriately be thought of as sibs. In *Clarkia*, for example, Mosquin (*16*) has evidence that two species have been independently derived from *C. mildrediae*, and Vasek (*17*) has found four diploid species derived from *C. unguiculata*; in *Chaenactis* (Compositae), Kyhos (*18*) has demonstrated that two desert species, *C. stevioides* and *C. fremontii*, have been derived from a more coastal species, *C. glabriuscula*. The detailed analysis of chromosomal relationships in *Chaenactis* also illustrates the precision with which the direction of evolution can be demonstrated cytologically.

Another characteristic of saltation is that the derivative and parental species are unable to grow together in mixed populations, even though they are ecologically very similar, unless a barrier subsequently evolves that prevents or greatly limits hybridization. *Clarkia biloba* and its derivative *C. lingulata* illustrate this clearly. These species, which differ in external morphology only in the shape of the petal, hybridize freely when they are in contact, but the hybrids have very low fertility. In experimentally mixed populations, one or the other species was rapidly eliminated, depending on their relative abundance (*19*).

The species in lower frequency produced a larger proportion of hybrids, which in turn decreased its own relative frequency. As its numbers decreased, elimination was accelerated by the ever-increasing proportion of hybrids in its progenies. The net effect of such elimination ·is mutual exclusion. Once either species becomes established in a particular site, any migrant from the other is eliminated by hybridization regardless of which species is better adapted to that site. At the one place where *C. biloba* and *C. lingulata* come into contact in nature, the overlap is a narrow band about 3 meters broad which represents the limit to which one can penetrate the territory of the other before it is eliminated by hybridization. Mutual exclusion also accounts for the patterns of distribution between other morphologically very similar species of *Clarkia* and undoubtedly those in many other genera. In *Lasthenia* (Compositae), for example, two morphologically very similar species, *L. fremontii* and *L. conjugens*, occur in what appear to be comparable ecological sites close to one an-

other but are not found growing together. Significantly, these species hybridize readily in cultivation, and the hybrids have low fertility due to chromosomal differences (*20*).

When the fertility of hybrids is very low, one would expect a strong positive selection for any factor that prevents hybridization in areas where hybridization is frequent. This has not occurred in the case of *Clarkia biloba* and *C. lingulata* described above, but the contact between these species is apparently very recent. In most instances, however, secondary barriers have developed in response to selection. For example, two very closely related species, *Clarkia williamsonii* and *C. speciosa*, which until recently were considered conspecific, readily form hybrids if the plants that are crossed come from populations far removed from the area where the two species grow together; if they come from within or close to the area where the species are sympatric, they cannot be crossed (*21*).

Mechanism of Saltation

The problem is to account for multiple structural differences in adjacent populations when plants heterozygous for one of these rearrangements have low fertility. For any one rearrangement to replace the original throughout a population, the new arrangement must increase in frequency, despite its effect on fertility, and produce homozygotes that are better adapted than the heterozygotes and the original homozygotes, unless replacement occurs by chance in a very small population. Reardless of how replacement occurs, its frequency must be very low, otherwise populations would frequently be found to differ in chromosome arrangement. If the probability of the replacement of one arrangement by another is low, the probability that it will recur independently in any given population four, six, or more times is effectively nil. Yet *Clarkia franciscana*, which consists of a single population that we initially included in *C. rubicunda* (*22*), differs chromosomally from that species by at least three translocations and four inversions, whereas *C. rubicunda*, which is morphologically and ecologically diverse, is chromosomally uniform throughout its entire geographic range (*13*). Were this the only example, we could dismiss it, for even the most improbable events can happen once.

There are, however, similar examples not only in *Clarkia* but apparently in other genera such as *Holocarpha, Lasthenia,* and *Allophyllum* (*14, 20*). The conclusion seems warranted, therefore, that multiple chromosomal differences, under some circumstances, arise and become established simultaneously. Simultaneous establishment is also a highly improbable event, but much less so than gradual accumulation within a given population because it need occur only once in any one of a vast number of populations during an indefinitely large number of generations.

Saltation is initiated by one or more individuals heterozygous for structural rearrangements that greatly reduce fertility. Such individuals, were they in any normal population, would have very little chance of contributing to the next generation, let alone of affecting the chromosome organization of the entire population. If, however, an individual which is nearly sterile is removed from competition with normal members of the parental population, its degree of fertility is of no consequence if it is able to produce any progeny at all. The probability of a progeny may be very small but, if the population does not become extinct, heterozygosity that reduces fertility will rapidly be eliminated. The resulting population may or may not have the original chromosome arrangement. If not, and if hybrids with the parental species have low fertility, the derivative population will be able to maintain itself against encroachment by the parental species, even though it comprises less vigorous, less fecund individuals.

A population consisting of only one individual is not essential to saltation and presumably could not have been the case in *Chaenactis* described above, because the parental species and both derivatives are self-incompatible (*18*). I wish to emphasize, however, that spatial isolation of one or very few individuals from the parental population is required and must be maintained until the derivative population is able to eliminate migrants through hybridization or to grow with them without hybridizing. The distance required for isolation may be very short, however, because the area over which seeds and pollen are normally dispersed is often very limited.

Spatial isolation of one or a few individuals can occur either by dispersal into a site not occupied by the species or by survival after all other members

of the population have been eliminated. Both undoubtedly occur, but the latter, when due to catastrophic selection that suddenly eliminates nearly all of a population at the ecological limits of the species, is most likely to lead to saltational speciation. Individuals that survive an exceptional environmental extreme, such as unusual drought, find themselves in an open habitat that is ready to be repopulated and to which their progenies may be adapted with respect not only to the normal environment but also to an environmental extreme which may recur. Evidence that catastrophic selection rather than dispersal is associated with saltation in *Clarkia,* which occurs in semi-arid regions with highly seasonal rainfall, comes from the observations that all derivative species are adapted to a shorter growing season than their respective parents and that unusually short growing seasons, limited by water, have catastrophic effects on populations (*23*).

Regardless of how spatial isolation occurs, a more difficult problem is to account for multiple breakage of the chromosomes in the particular individuals that are isolated. It would be ridiculous to suggest that individuals that become isolated from the parental population are by chance heterozygous for several chromosomal differences. Excluding chance, however, leaves only two alternatives: either the factor responsible for isolation induces breakage, or isolation itself is conducive to breakage. Although the possibility cannot be excluded that an extreme condition producing catastrophic selection may also induce breakage, there are no data to indicate that it does. On the other hand, there is evidence for the second alternative.

Isolated individuals, or small groups of individuals, must inbreed if the population is to continue. As is well known, forced inbreeding of normally outcrossed individuals often results in progenies showing decreased vigor, abnormal development, or reduction in fertility. Of particular relevance to speciation by saltation is that inbreeding may lead to extensive chromosome breakage (*24*).

The significance of a sudden shift to intense inbreeding on the genetics of a population has been discussed in detail by Mayr (*15*) with respect to the role of small "founder" populations in speciation, and his arguments for "genetic revolution" are equally applica-

ble to small "survivor" populations at the ecological limits of a species. Regardless of how a very small population may arise, adaptive gene complexes that emerge from the bottleneck of inbreeding must be preserved from disruptive recombination if they are to form the basis of a successful new species. Chromosome reorganization, of course, has this effect.

The frequency with which successful chromosome reorganization occurs after forced inbreeding undoubtedly varies tremendously from one group of organisms to another, but it need not be frequent to be highly significant. In *Clarkia,* for example, where at least 14 out of 28 diploid species have almost certainly had a saltational origin, only one successful reorganization throughout the countless marginal populations of the entire genus would be required every thousand generations or so, even if we assume that all 14 are more recent than the last glacial maximum.

In conclusion, the chromosomal barrier to gene exchange that results from saltation may be considered an accidental by-product of forced inbreeding, which has the effect of immediately establishing an irreversible genetic independence between parental and derivative populations with regard to a large portion of their respective genotypes. If hybridization between the resulting populations is frequent, secondary barriers that greatly reduce or eliminate hybridization would be expected to develop by natural selection. Immediate irreversible independence, which permits a genetically depauperate population to explore new sorts of genetic combinations in the course of reconstructing an adaptive genetic system, may lead to relatively rapid divergence from the parental populations. In contrast, slowly differentiating groups that retain the potentiality of interspecific gene exchange have far greater capacities to adapt in response to changes in the environment but, since they evolve more or less as a unit, are less likely to give rise to developmentally new adaptive modes.

Saltation in Woody Plants

Saltational reorganization of chromosomes is demanded as an explanation only when morphologically similar, adjacent populations differ chromosomally in such a way that piecemeal accumulation of the rearrangements is not a reasonable explanation. This is frequently the case among annual plants, as I have indicated, but appears to be rare and has not been demonstrated in woody plants. Nevertheless, there is evidence that leads me to believe that saltational speciation has played a significant role in the evolution of woody as well as herbaceous groups, particularly with respect to the initiation of divergence leading to categories higher than species.

This conclusion is based on comparative data, primarily basic chromosome numbers. The significance of basic numbers is twofold: (i) they are very conservative, particularly among woody plants where one frequently finds the same chromosome number throughout a family, subfamily, or other large taxonomic group. Even among herbaceous groups, basic chromosome number is generally constant throughout a genus or major sections of it, although the number is frequently different from one genus to another in the same family. In general, a difference in basic number is not characteristic of closely related species, although examples are known in which populations that have been considered taxonomically conspecific differ in basic number (*14*). It seems clear that change in basic chromosome number is not a normal consequence of gradual differentiation, but a rare event resulting from unusual circumstances. (ii) In nearly all instances in which a difference in basic chromosome number in plants has been studied in detail, gross differences in chromosome arrangement have been found in addition to those required to effect the change. This suggests that saltation has been involved.

The differences in chromosome number within some groups of woody plants in Australia, compared to those within groups of related woody plants in other parts of the world, are particularly instructive. Smith-White (*25*) has shown that the chromosome numbers of taxa endemic or nearly endemic in Australia, such as the Chamaelaucoideae (Myrtaceae) and Boronieae (Rutaceae), are much more diverse than those within comparable taxa in the same family outside Australia. The differences in number are characteristic of genera, not species, and the distribution of species in the same genus indicates that chromosome numbers have long been stable. He concludes, therefore, that the earliest flowering plants to migrate into

Australia met with conditions conducive to chromosome change and that these conditions have not persisted. He also points out that availability of diverse new habitats unoccupied by angiosperm competitors provided an evolutionary opportunity for the more flexible lineages to expand into diverse habitats and has suggested that this was conducive to genetic experimentation, including change in chromosome number. Although I doubt that opportunity to expand is alone a sufficient condition for change in chromosome number, if one adds isolation of one or a few individuals by chance dispersal or catastrophic selection, it does become understandable. The latter means of isolation seems very likely because surely not all the tropical species of flowering plants that crossed the first bridgehead to Australia migrated steadily across the face of the continent without periodic setbacks from over extension of their range. After saturation of available habitats by angiosperms, however, a sudden reduction of a population of woody plants to a few individuals would not, ordinarily, have left a habitat open for a genetically depauperate derivative population to increase in numbers.

Conditions in Australia that resulted in chromosome changes, which now distinguish genera, were doubtless comparable to those that accompanied the much earlier expansion of flowering plants throughout the rest of the world. The changes that occurred at that time, however, may be reflected in the chromosomal differences we now perceive between families or other major taxonomic groups.

Summary

At the risk of gross oversimplification, I have contrasted two modes of speciation and compared the products, with the intent of emphasizing that speciation is not always an extension of gradual ecogeographic differentiation. The genetic relationship between species resulting from adaptation to persistent environmental differences is not comparable to that between species resulting from saltational reorganization of the chromosomes following a unique event that isolates one or a few individuals in an open habitat free from conspecific competition. Species resulting from gradual differentiation are characterized by incomplete barriers to gene exchange, which are maintained by

selection and remain incomplete for indefinite periods of time even though the species are in contact. The potentiality of acquiring genetic variability from one another provides such groups of species with a high degree of adaptability.

Chromosomal reorganization, which is most likely to occur following a sudden change to intensive inbreeding in extremely small marginal populations, is an improbable event, and the resulting genetically impoverished population has an inauspicious future. Once established, however, such a population is able to exclude parental migrants while its genetic system is being reconstructed. The immediate genetic independence of the population should, however, permit novel gene combinations to become established which might provide the derivative population with an evolutionary potential very different from that of the parental species; the stage may occasionally be set for major divergence.

Saltational speciation in flowering plants is required as an explanation only for the relationships between particular populations of annuals that have been studied intensively. By reasonable extrapolation, however, it appears to be the prevalent mode of speciation in many herbaceous genera and to have had a significant role in the evolution of woody plants.

References and Notes

1. R. B. Goldschmidt, *The Material Basis of Evolution* (Yale Univ. Press, New Haven, 1940).
2. V. Grant, *Aliso* 2, 82 (1952); *Origin of Adaptations* (Columbia Univ. Press, New York, 1963), p. 356.
3. J. Clausen, D. D. Keck, W. M. Hiesey, *Carnegie Inst. Wash. Publ. 615* (1958).
4. G. Turesson, *Hereditas* 3, 211 (1922).
5. H. Lewis and C. Epling, *Evolution* 13, 511 (1959).
6. R. M. Straw, *ibid.* 9, 441 (1955).
7. C. Epling, *Ann. Missouri Botan. Garden* 25, 95 (1938).
8. K. A. Grant and V. Grant, *Evolution* 18, 196 (1964).
9. C. Epling, *Amer. Naturalist* 81, 104 (1947); *Evolution* 1, 69 (1947).
10. E. Anderson and B. Anderson, *Ann. Missouri Botan. Garden* 41, 329 (1954).
11. M. R. Roberts and H. Lewis, *Evolution* 9, 445 (1955); *ibid.* 10, 126 (1956).
12. H. Lewis, *J. Arizona Acad. Sci.* 1, 3 (1959).
13. P. H. Raven and H. Lewis, *Evolution* 12, 319 (1958); P. H. Raven, unpublished. A total of 29 populations of *Clarkia rubicunda* from throughout the ecological and geographical limits of the species have been intercrossed.
14. J. Clausen, *The Evolution of Plant Species* (Cornell Univ. Press, Ithaca, N.Y., 1951), p. 94; R. C. Jackson, *Am. J. Botany* 49, 119 (1962). Species with more than one basic chromosome number may also belong in this category; for example, species of *Allophyllum*, A. Grant and V. Grant, *Aliso* 3, 93 (1955).
15. E. Mayr, *Animal Species and Evolution* (Belknap Press of Harvard Univ. Press, Cambridge, Mass., 1963).

16. T. Mosquin, Ph.D. thesis (Univ. of California, Los Angeles, 1961).
17. F. C. Vasek, *Evolution* **18**, 26 (1964); oral communication.
18. D. W. Kyhos, *Evolution* **19**, 26 (1965).
19. H. Lewis, *American Naturalist* **95**, 155 (1961).

20. R. Ornduff, *Univ. Calif. (Berkeley, Los Angeles) Publ. Botany*, in press.
21. H. Lewis, unpublished data.
22. ――― and M. E. Lewis, *Univ. Calif. (Berkeley, Los Angeles) Publ. Botany* **20**, 241 (1955).
23. H. Lewis, *Evolution* **16**, 257 (1962).

24. K. R. Lewis and B. John, *Chromosoma* **10**, 589 (1959); A. Müntzing and S. Akdik, *Hereditas* **34**, 485 (1948).
25. S. Smith-White, *Cold Spring Harbor Symp. Quant. Biol.* **24**, 273 (1959).
26. Research on which this article is based has been supported by NSF.

25

Models of Speciation

New concepts suggest that the classical sympatric
and allopatric models are not the only alternatives.

M. J. D. White

The modern or synthetic view of organic evolution regards speciation as a special and perhaps usually brief stage in evolutionary divergence, during which genetic isolating mechanisms develop to a level which makes the phyletic separation of the incipient species irreversible (except for the special case of alloploidy, almost entirely restricted to plants). As formulated and extended by Mayr (*1*), this process is conceived of as occurring when the diverging populations are geographically separated and occupy different territories. It is this *allopatric* model of speciation which has frequently been presented in terms of the well-known "dumbbell" diagram (*2*, figure 5-1). Allopatric speciation has been put forward as an alternative to the now largely discredited hypothesis of *sympatric* speciation, that is, the idea that "biological" or "ecological" races of a species can coexist geographically in an area and gradually diverge genetically until they constitute distinct species.

General acceptance of the allopatric model as the *only* mechanism of speciation in animals (or virtually the only one—exceptions are sometimes admitted in the case of endoparasites and a few other instances in which ecological separation is practically equivalent to geographic separation) has been mainly due to detailed study and reinterpretation of the examples which were earlier alleged to establish the existence of sympatric speciation. When examined more closely, most of these proved to be examples of forms that had already diverged to the level of full species and might well have done so allopatrically, with subsequent range extension leading to geographical coexistence. Apart

The author is professor of genetics in the University of Melbourne, Australia.

from the collapse of the case that had been used to support it, sympatric speciation also seems incompatible with ordinary principles of population genetics, since it would require genetic isolating mechanisms to be built up within a single population, by natural selection, and this implies the spread of mutations which would prevent matings occurring or render them fruitless.

For these reasons, and because there are innumerable instances that seem to support it, allopatric speciation has now been accepted by almost all vertebrate zoologists. Cases where no paleontological or cytogenetic data exist are automatically interpreted in terms of the allopatric model, even if the particular interpretation seems somewhat forced (*3*).

Lingering doubts as to the universality of the allopatric model have persisted, however, among entomologists and botanists. Some students of the "species flocks" in ancient freshwater lakes also feel that the allopatric model does not fit these cases, although others believe that even in such instances an allopatric interpretation is plausible. For some time past there seems to have been renewed pressure to find out in much greater detail what the genetic basis for isolating mechanisms really is and how it develops. And recently, almost suddenly, a number of papers have appeared that seem to open the question (which should probably have been asked earlier): are the sympatric and allopatric models really the only conceivable alternatives? Even if we admit that all speciation has a geographic basis, in the broad sense, does it necessarily follow that allopatric speciation (in the sense of the dumbbell diagram) is the only form of geographic speciation?

These questions are intimately bound up with the relative roles of "point mutations" and chromosomal rearrangements of a relatively gross kind in speciation. (The existence of intermediate categories of chromosomal changes still further clouds the issue, but will not be discussed here.) It is a matter of empirical observation that, as far as the higher animals are concerned, even the most closely related species are usually found to differ in karyotype when the chromosomes are examined under the microscope. The only sure exceptions to this generalization seem to be certain species complexes in the genus *Drosophila*; *D. mulleri, D. aldrichi,* and *D. wheeleri* have been said not to differ at all in the banding pattern of their polytene chromosomes (*4*), and the same is apparently true of several Hawaiian species complexes, which have been described in consequence as *homosequential* (*5*). In other groups of organisms apparent or reported cases of distinct species with indistinguishable karyotypes have been based on comparisons of metaphase chromosomes alone, banded polytene chromosomes not being available. In the sciarid, chironomid, and simuliid midges, where polytene chromosomes do occur and have been analyzed by numerous workers, homosequential species complexes have not been found and even the most closely related species seem to differ in karyotype (*6*). In the case of *Chironomus thummi* and *piger,* however (regarded by me as species, but by Keyl as subspecies), the difference in banding pattern consists in the reduplication of a number of individual bands rather than in any large-scale rearrangements (*7*). In those groups of grasshoppers and beetles that have been subjected to critical cytogenetical analysis (but only on the basis of metaphase chromosomes, since polytene elements do not exist in these groups), each species seems, in general, to be karyotypically unique (*8*).

The above facts are obviously compatible with the view that certain types of chromosomal rearrangements such as inversions and translocations of various kinds (including chromosomal fusions and dissociations, producing changes in chromosome number) may play a primary determining role in the speciation process in many groups of animals. But the existence of the homosequential species complexes referred to above proves conclusively that karyotypic changes are not a universal *sine* qua non for speciation. And further-more, even in those groups where the most closely related species differ karyo-typically, the prima facie evidence can-not conclusively prove that chromo-somal rearrangements cause speciation —such changes could be mere epiphe-nomena of the speciation process. We need above all to know what part these rearrangements play in interracial and interspecific hybrids, that is, in the off-spring of crosses between forms that have reached various stages of evolu-tionary divergence. Only then can we discuss them as possible genetic isolat-ing mechanisms. The matter is ex-tremely complex, because we cannot necessarily assume that a chromosomal rearrangement at the present time has exactly the same genetic properties or behaves at meiosis in the same manner as when it first arose; selection may have altered it in the course of cen-turies and millenia.

By and large it seems safe to accept the generalization that most point mu-tations have a finite and generally quite high (on the evolutionary time scale) rate of recurrence, whereas gross struc-tural changes in the chromosomes are, in practice, unique events, since they depend on the coincidence of two or more very rare events (that is, two or more chromosome breaks at particular loci) in the same cell, followed by re-union in a new sequence. This proposi-tion seems undeniable when we are con-sidering chromosomal rearrangements in Diptera such as Drosophila, where the breakage points can be defined very precisely in terms of the banding pattern in the polytene chromosomes. In other groups of organisms, how-ever, it is less easy to be absolutely certain—two rearrangements may look identical under the microscope, but may have slightly different end points. It is unlikely, however, that this is a seri-ous source of error in cytogenetic anal-ysis of evolutionary processes. Thus we may accept the general concept of a monophyletic origin for chromosomal rearrangements versus a polyphyletic one for point mutations; and this view-point is basic to the discussion presented here.

Mayr (1) has argued forcefully against all theories of species arising from single mutant individuals and has emphasized that speciation is a "population phenomenon." While the general proposition is undeniable, it is clear that all mutations arise in the first place in single individuals. If we are considering the spread of a particu-lar point mutation throughout a popula-tion we may consider such a mutation as arising independently in a number of individuals, distributed in space and in time over many generations, each of these individuals acting as a focus from which dispersal of the altered gene occurs. In the case of a structural chromosomal change, however, we should think in terms of a single in-dividual as the sole point of origin of the new type of chromosome. It is thus easier to conceive of an entire population changing in respect of a point mutation (complete replacement of one allele by another) because this process can be initiated spontaneously at a number of focal points of origin. In the case of a structural rearrange-ment, having a single point of origin, the spreading process must be on a different scale of magnitude, either in space or time, or both.

Contiguous Subspecies

Criticism of the view that all specia-tion is essentially allopatric seems to have developed among both zoological and botanical evolutionists recently, largely as a result of detailed studies of animals and plant distributions in space. A number of workers appear to have discovered, almost simultaneously, that in many instances closely related taxa (geographic subspecies, semispe-cies, or incipient species) do not over-lap broadly in geographic distribution (the sympatric situation), neither do they live in entirely separate areas. On the contrary, they occupy contiguous areas, with an extremely narrow zone of overlap, within which hybridization is theoretically possible and may actual-ly occur. Such situations, which have been studied in grasses (9), pocket-gophers (10), and wingless grasshop-pers (11), have been designated para-patric by some authors. Geographic distribution patterns of this type are hardly likely to exist in highly mobile organisms, but may be expected to be common in ones which are sessile or exhibit a low degree of vagility. Some parapatric distribution patterns seem to depend on a sharp ecological discon-tinuity (for example, in soil type); but others exist in spite of an apparent uni-formity of the environment.

In plants, Lewis (12) has distin-guished two modes of speciation which he calls "gradual" and "saltational." Gradual speciation is described as due to multiple genetic changes without ma-jor chromosomal rearrangements; spe-ciation by saltation involves multiple structural changes of the karyotype (Clarkia franciscana differs from its presumed ancestor C. rubicunda by at least three translocations and four in-versions). Whereas closely related spe-cies may appropriately be designated siblings, the relationship in the case of speciation by saltation is more akin to that of parent and offspring, since one can distinguish clearly between the ancestral and the derivative species. It is characteristic of such cases that the hybrids show a high degree of sterility, as a result of the multiple karyotypic differences.

Higher plants are, of course, ses-sile. Their "vagility" depends on the precise pollination mechanism on which they depend. The vagility of many wingless insects and other inverte-brates is probably of the same order of magnitude. On a priori grounds we might expect to find some resem-blances between methods of speciation in these groups and the higher plants; by contrast, the birds, larger mammals, pelagic organisms, and animals liable to accidental dispersal over great dis-tances might be expected to show a different pattern.

The races and species (some per-haps semispecies in the sense of Mayr) of wingless grasshoppers belonging to the viatica group (Eumastacidae, Mora-binae; there is no valid generic name for these insects at present) show typi-cally contiguous or "parapatric" ranges in southeastern Australia (Fig. 1). They differ in respect of certain easily identi-fiable chromosomal rearrangements such as fusions, pericentric inversions, and a translocation (11). The eastern, 19-chromosome race of viatica ($2n\,\delta$ $= 19$, $2n\,\female\, = 20$) has a karyotype that probably differs little from that of the common ancestor of the whole group. The western, 17-chromosome race of the same species and an un-named species "P24" differ from viatica in having a fusion between a long "B" chromosome and a small chromosome "6" (the B + 6 fusion). There are three cytological races of P24: one with an acrocentric X chromosome and no Y, one with a neo-XY in the male (the result of a centric fusion between the X and autosome "1"), and a third race (also XY) homozygous for a trans-location between the "A" chromosome and the B + 6 element. Species "P25" has two races, one with XO males, the other with a neo-XY mechanism (the result of a centric fusion between the X and chromosome B). Species "P45b" also has XO and XY races, but in this case the X-autosome fusion is a tandem one (that is, not a centric one) between the original X and chromosome 6. Species "P45c" has a karyotype much like the "primitive" one of *viatica*, but the short limbs of most of the acrocentric chromosomes are significantly longer than in other members of the group. Chromosome 6, which has been involved in two of the fusions, is late-labeling after tritiated thymidine autoradiography (*13*).

Wherever the ranges of two forms of this group come in contact, there is a hybrid zone, at most a few hundred meters in width. Similar distribution patterns exist in numerous other genera and species groups of morabine grasshoppers in Australia; one might say that many species groups show a mosaic distribution pattern, with little or no sympatry (approximately 220 species of morabine grasshoppers, the great majority still undescribed, are known to exist in Australia). As far as the *viatica* group is concerned, ethological isolation between parapatric forms seems to be generally absent or so weak that the production of hybrids is not prevented in the zone of overlap. Overlap zones have not been found between all the taxa we have recognized but this is undoubtedly owing in the main to destruction of the original vegetation since the introduction of agriculture, which has greatly reduced the areas suitable for supporting populations of these insects. However, four zones of hybridization have now been studied in the Australian morabine grasshoppers (three of them in the *viatica* group), and we have presumptive evidence of several more. In the case of the hybrids between the 15- and 17-chromosome races of *Keyacris scurra* (*14*) and in that of the two races of *viatica* (*15*) there is clear evidence of a significant reduction in the fecundity of male hybrids collected in nature, as a result of meiotic asynapsis or malorientation of multivalents at the first metaphase. Studies of laboratory-reared hybrids, in numerous other instances where natural hybrids have not yet been found, suggest that this is always so in the case of parapatric taxa of morabine grasshoppers (*11, 16*). The proportion of aneuploid sperms formed in this way ranges from per-

haps 4 percent in hybrids between the 15- and 17-chromosome races of *K. scurra* (*14*) to over 40 percent in some of the hybrid combinations in the *viatica* group. In addition, certain male F_1 hybrids in the *viatica* group are stunted in development and their testes never develop to the stage where meiosis occurs [for example, hybrids between P45c ♂ and P25 (XY race) ♀], while in certain hybrids between the XO and XY races of P45b meiosis occurs but there is a massive degeneration of secondary spermatocytes and spermatids, so that no sperms are formed. Obviously these gross disturbances of development and spermatogenesis represent genetic isolating mechanisms that have developed subsequently to the primary (and weaker) isolating mechanisms inherent in the chromosomal rearrangements. No really adequate studies have been carried out on the meiosis of female hybrids in the *viatica* group, but there is no reason to suppose that the course of meiosis is significantly different in the two sexes (although the

bivalents are more sharply stretched on the spindle of the egg), so that female hybrids probably produce aneuploid eggs in about the same proportion as the males produce aneuploid sperms.

It would hardly be profitable to discuss in a semantic manner just what taxonomic rank we should assign to the members of the *viatica* group. Obviously they represent various stages in evolutionary divergence. In a case such as this, raciation and speciation are parts of a continuous process and cannot be sharply distinguished.

Two conclusions seem to follow from these facts. The first is that some types of chromosomal rearrangements function as fairly strong, primary genetic isolating mechanisms between incipient species of morabine grasshoppers. The narrowness of the zones of overlap is evidence of strong selection against fused chromosomes in "unfused territory" and vice versa (in those cases where a fusion is involved; some pericentric inversions may have functioned in a similar manner). Naturally, the

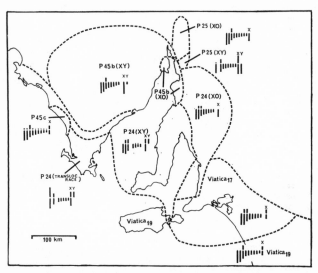

Fig. 1. Map of a portion of South Australia, showing the present distribution limits of the members of the "coastal" group of forms of the *viatica* group of grasshoppers. [Based on figure 1 of White, Blackith, Blackith, and Cheney (*11*), revised slightly.] The two "inland" species P50 (which occurs to the north of *viatica₁₉*) and P 26/142 (which is sympatric with the XO race of P25 but extends further north and east) have been omitted. During the Pleistocene glaciation the gulfs between the Eyre, Yorke, and Fleurieu peninsulas were dry land, and Kangaroo Island was also a part of the mainland. The ideograms show the haploid karyotypes of the various forms, with both the X and the Y included in the case of the XY races. In *viatica₁₉* the chromosomes from left to right are designated A, B, CD, 1, 2, 3, 4, 5, 6, X. The karyotype of the XO race of P45b is not shown; it is not significantly different from that of the XO race of P25.

narrowness of the hybrid zone depends also on the extremely sedentary nature of these wingless insects; if their vagility was greater the hybrid zones would be much wider.

The second conclusion which we must draw from the cytogenetic and field observations is that, in spite of the strong selection against them, these chromosomal rearrangements have in fact proved highly successful in an evolutionary sense, having spread over large areas of territory. Several theoretical possibilities exist with regard to this process. We may imagine the rearrangements as establishing themselves in the first instance in a marginal colony (perhaps a small and isolated one) and then spreading out in the homozygous state into territory previously unoccupied by the species (Fig. 2A). Alternatively, the rearrangements might originate well within the existing range of the species and spread out from there (Fig. 2B). A third possibility, combining some features of the first two, would be for a rearrangement to establish itself first of all in a peripheral isolate and then spread through the existing range of the species (Fig. 2C). The first of these models is essentially an allopatric one, although different from the "dumbbell" model. The second and third are variants of what we have called the *stasipatric* model, since it involves the spread of a chromosomal rearrangement which forms the basis of a cytogenetic isolating mechanism throughout a substantial part of the range of an already existing species (*11*).

Stasipatric Speciation

As far as the *viatica* group of morabine grasshoppers is concerned, reasons have been given for rejecting the classic allopatric model (*11*). It virtually necessitates three unlikely assumptions: (i) that in addition to a B + 6 fusion, there was a subsequent B − 6 dissociation, (ii) that the B + 6 fusion occurred right at the beginning of the phylogeny of this group of species in spite of the fact that it does not seem to constitute a very effective isolating mechanism between *viatica*$_{19}$ and *viatica*$_{17}$, and (iii) that an invasion of territory by the *viatica* group took place in a northwesterly direction (presumably during the Pleistocene), whereas if any migration did take place it was probably in the opposite direction (that is, southeasterly).

An interpretation of the cytogenetic evolution of the "coastal" forms of the *viatica* group is shown in Fig. 3. It is assumed that a widespread species which we may call *proto-viatica* became fragmented into the existing races and species as a result of: (i) a conversion of the original metacentric X chromosome into an acrocentric, pre-

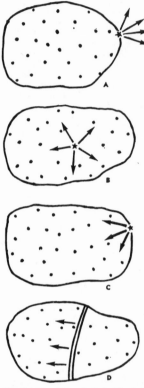

Fig. 2. Allopatric and stasipatric models of geographical speciation.   (A) The chromosomal rearrangement manages to establish itself in a geographically isolated peripheral deme and spreads into territory previously unoccupied by the species (one form of allopatric model). (B) The chromosomal rearrangement establishes itself in a nonperipheral local colony and spreads through the range of the species on an advancing front (the stasipatric model).   (C) The chromosomal rearrangement establishes itself in a peripheral colony and then spreads through the existing species population (modified form of stasipatric model). (D) The result of B or C: a narrow hybrid zone showing a slow secular movement across the territory occupied by the species until it is arrested in some way.

sumably by pericentric inversion (stage 1A in Fig. 3), (ii) the B + 6 fusion (stage 1B), (iii) three different X-autosome fusions and a translocation (stage 3). It is not necessarily implied that stage 1A occurred before stage 1B; when both of these are superimposed we have the situation shown in stage 2, when we have the present-day species already in existence. The relation between the XO races of P25 and P45b is not clear; these taxa do not seem to differ karyotypically, but can be distinguished by a character of the external male genitalia.

It is assumed in Fig. 3 that each of the chromosomal rearrangements arose in the first instance somewhere within the territory occupied by *proto-viatica*, that is, in the manner shown in Fig. 2B (rather than as in Fig. 2C). However, neither of the two variants of the stasipatric model seem at first sight easy to accept, in view of the apparently strong selection against the new types of chromosomes as a result of the lowered fecundity of the heterozygotes. There does not seem to be the slightest possibility that the chromosomal fusions and dissociations that have established themselves in the morabine grasshoppers (and at least 36 of the former and 21 of the latter are known in the subfamily as a whole) were ever part of adaptive polymorphisms dependent on heterozygote superiority. Thus the cytotaxonomic differences between morabine species, unlike the paracentric inversion differences between dipteran species, are definitely *not* the remnants of former heterotic polymorphisms.

What, then, is the solution of this paradox? Genetic "drift" in numerous small isolated or semi-isolated demes may have played a part in the "stasipatric" process, particularly if homozygotes for the new chromosome have a considerably higher fitness than either the heterozygotes or the homozygotes for the original condition. It is difficult, however, to accept genetic drift as the sole or even the main cause for the spread of these chromosomal rearrangements, particularly since the result seems to be a relatively straight or curved "frontier" between two structurally homozygous populations, rather than a complex mosaic of demes, some homozygous for one cytological condition and some for the other.

The most plausible explanation for the "stasipatric" process shown diagrammatically in Fig. 2, B, C, and D, would seem to be that the rearrangements which have succeeded in spreading geographically, when they "should" have become extinct as a result of natural selection, are ones which have enjoyed the benefit of a segregational advantage (meiotic drive) in the egg. A cytological study of several hundred eggs from heterozygous females, in order to determine whether the "new" type of chromosome passes into the egg nucleus more frequently than into the polar body, would have to be carried out in order to test this hypothesis. It may be that the very few chromosomal rearrangements which play a critical role in speciation through their ability to generate powerful isolating mechanisms are precisely those which happen to possess a segregational advantage in the female meiosis. Meiotic drive has earlier been considered as a force which could have evolutionary consequences, but not quite in the sense considered here (*17*).

By comparison with the "saltational" model put forward for the plant genera *Clarkia, Holocarpha, Lasthenia,* and *Allophyllum* (*12*), the karyotypic differences between contiguous or parapatric species (or semispecies) of morabine grasshoppers seem to be due to single rather than multiple rearrangements. Obviously, the "saltational" model of Lewis and my "stasipatric" model are not quite equivalent, any more than the modes of life or population structures of higher plants and grasshoppers are identical. But a similarity certainly exists.

Although the stasipatric and allopatric models seem essentially different, they are not entirely antithetical, and it is therefore possible to imagine various ways in which they might be combined. Thus in the case of a chromosomal rearrangement which first establishes itself near the edge of a species distribution, one can imagine it spreading both inwards through the range of the species (stasipatrically) and outwards into previously unoccupied territory (allopatrically); in other words, a combination of models A and C of Fig. 2 is conceivable.

Although the stasipatric model was developed in the first instance to explain the pattern of evolutionary differentiation in the *viatica* group, it clearly fits the facts in some other groups of morabine grasshoppers as well, although the details have not yet been worked out fully. It would be premature to speculate just how far it applies in other groups where the cytogenetic analysis has not been pushed

to the extent of determining what happens in the critical zones of contact or overlap. The case of the ladybird beetles *Chilocórus tricyclus* and *hexacyclus* in Canada seems to fall into the same category as the morabine grasshopper cases in that there is a very narrow zone of overlap, within which interspecific hybrids, whose fertility is severely reduced by cytogenetic processes, occur (*18*). The possibility that the stasipatric rather than the allopatric mechanism of geographic speciation has played a role in some groups of small mammals such as insectivores (*19*) and rodents (*20*) should certainly be considered.

The question as to which of the two variants of the stasipatric mechanism (Fig. 2B or 2C) has occurred in the *viatica* group (and, by implication, in the other groups of morabine grasshoppers) can be answered only on the basis of statistical probability. At first sight it might appear easier for a new chromosomal rearrangement to establish itself in a small isolated peripheral population (Fig. 2C). But

a rearrangement which is capable of spreading through a continuous (or semicontinuous) population of a species should also be capable of initially establishing itself in the interior of a population. In other words the evolutionary success of these rearrangements *is* puzzling, but their initial establishment seems to be no more difficult to explain than their subsequent spread, if we accept the notion that populations of these insects are in any case broken up into numerous small colonies on single shrubs or groups of shrubs. There is thus no compelling reason to believe in a peripheral initial establishment. On the contrary, statistical arguments seem to strongly favor an "internal" origin for the rearrangements (Fig. 2B). The vast majority of the individuals of a sedentary species are "internal" rather than peripheral at any time. And—what is probably more important in this case—because of ecological discontinuities of the environment, the great majority of small isolated demes will be "internal." The distinction between the two models

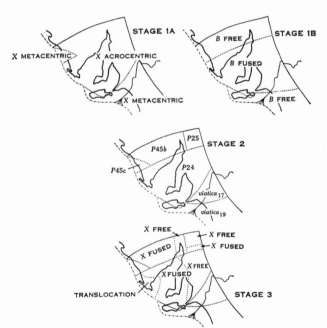

Fig. 3. Diagram illustrating the suggested mode of origin of the "coastal" species and races of the *viatica* group of grasshoppers in the state of South Australia. The dot-dash line indicates the approximate location of the Pleistocene coastline, when the sea level was about 100 meters lower than at present. [From White, Blackith, Blackith, and Cheney (*11*)]

symbolized in Fig. 2, B and C, is, however, a relatively minor one, and Fig. 2C should definitely not be considered as an allopatric model in the classical sense of the dumbbell diagram.

The concepts presented here are put forward in the hope that they may stimulate renewed interest in the cytogenetic processes involved in animal speciation. It is beginning to appear that there are more different kinds of mechanisms involved than was suspected a few years ago. Differences in modes of speciation are clearly related to differences in population dynamics and population structure; but they may also depend on differences in the genetic system.

References and Notes

1. E. Mayr, *Systematics and the Origin of Species* (Columbia Univ. Press, New York, 1942); "Change of genetic environment and evolution," in *Evolution as a Process*, J. Huxley *et al.*, Eds. (Allen and Unwin, London, 1954); "Species concepts and definitions," in *The Species Problem* (AAAS, Washington, D.C., 1957), pp. 371–388; *Animal Species and Evolution* (Harvard Univ. Press, Cambridge, Mass., 1963).
2. G. L. Stebbins, *Processes of Organic Evolution* (Prentice-Hall, Englewood Cliffs, N.J., 1966).
3. A. K. Lee, *Australian J. Zool.* **15**, 430 (1967).
4. M. Wasserman, *Proc. Nat. Acad. Sci. U.S.* **46**, 842 (1960); *Univ. Texas Publ. 6205, Studies in Genetics* **2**, 85–117 (1962).
5. H. L. Carson, F. E. Clayton, H. D. Stalker, *Proc. Nat. Acad. Sci. U.S.* **57**, 1280 (1967).
6. M. D. McCarthy, *Amer. Naturalist* **79**, 104 (1945); H.-G. Keyl, *Chromosoma* **13**, 464–514 (1962); R. W. Dunbar, *Can. J. Zool.* **27**, 497–525 (1959); *Nature* **209**, 597 (1966); P. O. Ottonen, *Can. J. Zool.* **44**, 677 (1966); K. Rothfels and M. Freeman, *ibid.*, p. 937.
7. H.-G. Keyl, *Chromosoma* **17**, 139–180 (1965).
8. S. G. Smith, *Can. Entomologist* **94**, 941 (1962); *Can. J. Genet. Cytol.* **7**, 363 (1965).
9. J. L. Aston and A. D. Bradshaw, *Heredity* **21**, 649 (1966).
10. T. A. Vaughan, *Evolution* **21**, 148 (1967).
11. M. J. D. White, R. E. Blackith, R. M. Blackith, J. Cheney, *Australian J. Zool.* **15**, 263 (1967).
12. H. Lewis, *Science* **152**, 167 (1966).
13. G. C. Webb, unpublished work.
14. M. J. D. White, *Australian J. Zool.* **5**, 285 (1957); —— and L. J. Chinnick, *ibid.*, p. 338.
15. M. J. D. White, H. L. Carson, J. Cheney, *Evolution*, **18**, 417 (1964).
16. M. J. D. White, unpublished work.
17. L. Sandler and E. Novitski, *Amer. Naturalist* **91**, 105 (1967).
18. S. G. Smith, *Chromosoma* **18**, 380 (1966).
19. A. Meylan, *Rev. Suisse Zool.* **72**, 636 (1965); **73**, 548 (1966).
20. R. Matthey, *ibid.* **73**, 585 (1966).
21. Some of the cytogenetic studies discussed in this article have been supported by Public Health Service grant No. GM-07212 from the Division of General Medical Sciences, U.S. National Institutes of Health, and by a grant from the Reserve Bank of Australia.

Reprinted from *Science* **168**:1414–1418 (1970)

Chromosome Tracers
of the Origin of Species

Some Hawaiian *Drosophila* species have arisen from
single founder individuals in less than a million years.

Hampton L. Carson

The most spectacular aspect of organic evolution is the origin of adaptations (*1*). These arise primarily as the result of genetic changes which are incorporated into populations through the action of natural selection on a variable and freely recombining pool of genes. The population genetics of such evolutionary change has been well understood since the theoretical work of the 1930's (*2*). The origin of certain adaptations on the microevolutionary level (for example, protectively colored moths in industrially blackened areas) has been closely analyzed (*3*).

Adaptive evolution is basically a phyletic process—that is, it occurs during succeeding generations within naturally interbreeding populations of a single biological species. To put it another way, this kind of evolutionary change can occur without any multiplication of reproductively isolated population units, or species. Both phyletic change and speciation are evolutionary processes—that is, both involve descent with change. Whereas phyletic evolution has yielded to elegant mathematical and experimental analysis, the speciation process has been generally refractory to studies of comparable precision. In this sense, the origin of species is a major unsolved problem of evolutionary biology. The present article provides a new approach which may help in its solution.

Speciation is almost exclusively a geographical process (*4*). Populations of existing species are entities distributed in space and time; somehow, such a species population becomes split into subpopulations (subspecies). In time, one or more of these latter may emerge as species.

The author is professor of biology at Washington University, St. Louis, Missouri.

The difficulties of studying the dynamics of geographic speciation are manifold. In the first place, it is a slow process by human standards. The formation of a species in the usual continental situation probably takes thousands or hundreds of thousands of years or more, even in organisms which have a relatively rapid generation time. Furthermore, the geographical relationships of most organisms are extraordinarily complex. Species populations which are in the crucial initial stages of evolutionary divergence may be very difficult to recognize. Many species have worldwide or at least continental distributions; this makes it difficult to decide which portion of the species, if any, deserves study from the point of view of the speciation process. Then again, continental or widespread species often have enormous populations, through which gene flow may be active. Such flow may inhibit the very speciation processes the evolutionist wishes to concentrate on. If endemic continental species with small, semi-isolated populations are selected for study, it is often difficult or impossible to tell whether this represents an incipient species or whether it is an ancient isolation with secondary intergradation. Continents and their biotas are thus frequently too complex geographically, historically, and ecologically to permit accurate inferences concerning the process of the origin of species. Islands, especially oceanic islands, have simpler conditions.

An oceanic island is one that is thrown up in the vastness of one of the earth's great oceans. The volcanic action which is frequently responsible produces at first a fiery, sterile mass. When cooling occurs, life starts to move in. Mostly it comes by chance, through long-distance dispersal, especially if the islands concerned—like the Hawaiian Islands, for example—are thousands of miles from any other land mass. Those lucky few propagules that may reach a new volcanic island and establish colonies set in motion forces which provide a new evolutionary beginning for the group concerned. Even though the propagule that arrives may already have millions of years of evolution behind it, the isolation from its ancestral relatives and contemporaries, coupled with the new, raw, and often difficult ecological conditions it faces, provides a renewed evolutionary opportunity. The results often strike the continental biologist as bizarre, "explosive," or otherwise extraordinary when measured against experience with life on the continents.

Contemplating the fauna of the oceanic Galápagos Islands, Darwin wrote, with characteristic understatement, "the inhabitants of these islands are eminently curious." As everyone knows, his observations of the simplified conditions existing there led him to a train of thought which catapulted evolutionary thinking into the center of biological attention, a position which it still holds today.

The Hawaiian Islands are in many ways uniquely suited for the study of the process of speciation. They are by far the most isolated oceanic islands in the world. The archipelago is 2000 miles (3200 kilometers) from any continent and lies in the warm tropical region of the Pacific Ocean. The vast volcanoes, of which the islands are the emergent tops, rise to great heights; the summit of Mauna Kea is more than 4200 meters above sea level and acquires a snow mantle each winter. The slopes of the islands erode rapidly under the heavy tropical rains. The older volcanic domes are dissected into deep valleys, separated by sharp ridges. Most of the rain falls on the windward slopes, leaving the lee sides desert-like. These features combine to produce extraordinarily diverse habitats: there are windswept alpine meadows, rain forests, and blisteringly hot southwestern lowland slopes.

Terrestrial life came to Hawaii by chance from all directions; descendants of these few ancestors have populated the islands with a unique biota. Chance, it appears, not only affected what organisms reached the older islands 5 million or more years ago but also played a role in the spread of life within the archipelago from the older islands to the younger. Although this evolution has produced some remarkable biological innovations and adaptations, the paramount feature is the enormous number of species of flowering plants, ferns, terrestrial invertebrates, and, especially, insects (5).

The genus *Drosophila* as it exists on the continents includes hundreds of species of small flies most of which are adapted to humid environments where they breed on decaying or fermenting vegetation. They are easy to handle in the laboratory, and certain species have become prime objects for the study of evolutionary and population genetics (6). From the Hawaiian Islands, considerably smaller in area than the state of Massachusetts, more than 250 species of the genus *Drosophila* have been described (7). All but about 12 have evolved in Hawaii and are found nowhere else. This number is approximately one-fourth of the species of the genus known in the entire world. It is probable, furthermore, that many *Drosophila* species in Hawaii are yet to be described. The islands also have a large number of species of Drosophilidae belonging to genera closely related to *Drosophila* (for example, *Scaptomyza*). Clearly, Hawaii has one of the greatest concentrations of this family of flies in the world.

The Hawaiian Islands appear to be geologically very recent (8). Thus, potassium-argon measurements (9) indicate that the oldest lava flows, on the northernmost island, Kauai (Fig. 1), are approximately 5.6 million years old, an age that places them in the late Pliocene. On the other hand, the island of Hawaii appears to have been formed very recently indeed. Thus, lava flows on the Kohala volcano yield both potassium-argon and paleomagnetic data which indicate that the mountain is no older than 700,000 years (late Pleistocene). The four southernmost volcanoes, two of which are currently active, are even younger than this. The adjacent island of Maui, separated from Hawaii by a 30-mile-wide channel (Fig. 1), is also of Pleistocene age; its lava flows give ages from 1.3 to 1.5 million years. Thus, Maui is considerably older than Hawaii. The channel between the two islands (Alenuihaha Channel) is 1950 meters deep, and it appears that Maui was never connected to Hawaii by a land bridge. On the other hand, there is strong evidence that Pleistocene land bridges once

linked the present islands of Maui, Molokai, and Lanai (Fig. 1).

In short, it is clear that the island of Hawaii is the youngest in the archipelago. In this article I focus attention on the origin of certain of the *Drosophila* species endemic to this island. Chromosomal data make it possible to trace the precise ancestry of a number of these species from certain Maui populations.

Chromosomes of Hawaiian Drosophila

Extensive accounts of the evolutionary biology of Hawaiian *Drosophila* have been recently published (10–12). Among these are descriptions of nearly a hundred species of large flies forming a clear subgroup belonging to the genus *Drosophila*. Because they are characterized by patterns of dark spots on the wings, these species have been informally referred to as the "picture-winged" flies (see cover). All so far examined have a metaphase chromosome group of $2n = 12$ (13). The five major polytene chromosomes of 69 of these species have been mapped in terms of a set of arbitrary Standard band sequences—namely, those found in the species *D. grimshawi* from Auwahi, Maui. Banding comparisons of unknowns with the Standard have been facilitated by the use of a binocular drawing tube (14). This device permits comparison of the sequence of a chromosome of unknown banding order under the microscope

directly at table level with a photographic cutout of a known Standard sequence (Fig. 2).

Except for one case of an apparent deletion, all microscopically observable polytene chromosome mutations in these species are due to changes in gene order (paracentric inversions). One hundred and fifteen inversions have been fixed among the 69 species of picture-winged flies (10). Each inversion has been designated by a separate lower-case letter after the chromosome number; the alphabet has been used several times with numerical superscripts—for example, a^2, b^2, and so on. By means of the method of Wasserman (15), a chromosomal phylogeny based on inversion-sharing has been prepared. Such phylogenies contain no intrinsic information about the direction of evolution. That is, it is possible to start at any point and derive all the other sequences in a stepwise fashion. The designation of a starting point, which converts such a relationship diagram into a phylogeny showing direction of evolution, must come from information outside the data on chromosomal sequences.

Relevant outside geographical and geological information exists in this case. First, it seems clear that the *Drosophila* fauna of the Hawaiian Islands is derived from the mainland, rather than vice versa. In this connection, one of the picture-winged subgroups (the *D. primaeva* subgroup, known so far only from Kauai) shows a sequence in the relatively conservative

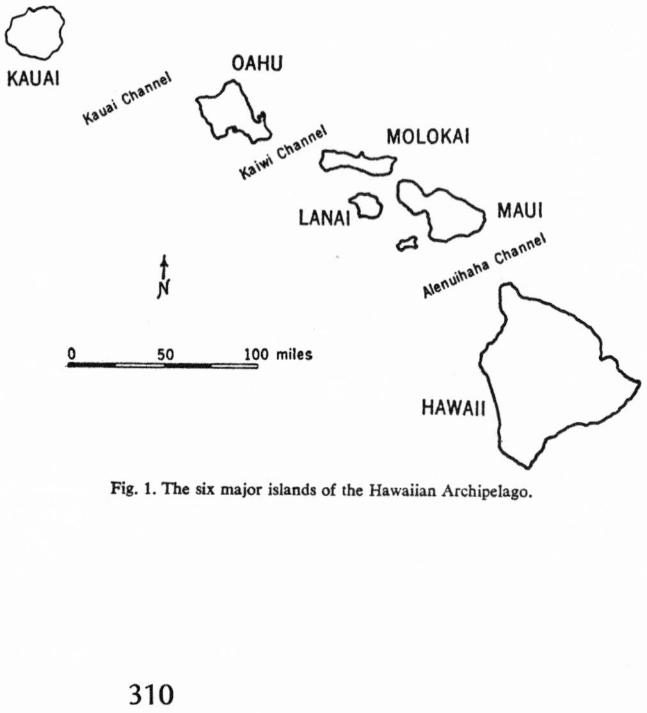

Fig. 1. The six major islands of the Hawaiian Archipelago.

Table 1. Comparison of chromosomal formulas between certain *Drosophila* species from the island of Hawaii and their Maui counterparts. Lowercase letters refer to specific fixed inversions.

Island	Species	Chromosomal formula				
		Set No. 1				
Hawaii	D. silvestris	Xijkopqrst	2	3d	4b	5
	D. heteroneura	Xijkopqrst	2	3d	4b	5
Maui	D. planitibia	Xijkopqrst	2	3d	4b	5
		Set No. 2				
Hawaii	D. ciliaticrus	Xg	2	3o	4	5
	D. engyochracea	Xg	2	3	4l	5
	D. murphyi	Xg	2	3/3o	4	5
Maui	D. orphnopeza	X	2	3/3o	4	5
	D. balioptera	Xg	2	3	4	5
	D. orthofascia	Xg	2	3n	4	5
		Set No. 3				
Hawaii	D. setosimentum	Xikouvwxym^2	2cdl	3fjkl	4bopqb^{2}c^{2}d^{2}e^{2}f^{2}n^{2}o^2	5f
	D. ochrobasis	Xikouvwxym^2	2cdk	3fjk	4bopqb^2	5f
Maui	D. adiastola	Xikouvwxy	2cd	3fjk	4bopq	5f

chromosome 5, which is the closest arrangement among any of the island flies to the homologous chromosome in certain Palearctic-Nearctic mainland species of the subgenus *Drosophila* (*16*). This fact places the *D. primaeva* subgroup at the base of the Hawaiian chromosome phylogeny. Further evidence on the direction of evolution comes from facts pertaining to the increasing geological youth of the Hawaiian islands as one proceeds southeastward from the northernmost major island, Kauai. These facts all serve to focus on, and to underscore, the newness—indeed, the present terminal nature in space and time—of the fauna of the island of Hawaii itself.

Origin of Species on
the Island of Hawaii

Of approximately 21 species of picture-winged flies in collections from the island of Hawaii (Fig. 1), 17 have been analyzed for polytene chromosome sequences. All 17 are highly distinctive species. They are endemic to this island, being found nowhere else in the world, not even on the island of Maui, only 30 miles away. Although much smaller in size than Hawaii, the Maui complex is richer in species of this group. Of approximately 41 species known in collections, 30 have been analyzed chromosomally.

So far, all of the species from the island of Hawaii tested by hybridization techniques appear to be reproductively isolated from all other species. Thus, in studies with laboratory strains, no fertile hybrids have been obtained between any of the Hawaii species or

between these species and their Maui relatives. The data, however, are not extensive (*17*).

Seven of the 17 species from Hawaii are of particular interest. The chromosomal formulas for these species relative to the Standard (X 2 3 4 5) are given in Table 1. The method of notation may be illustrated by the formula for *Drosophila ciliaticrus*, which differs from the Standard by one inversion in the X chromosome (Xg) and one in chromosome 3 (3o). Illustrations showing the breakpoints of these inversions

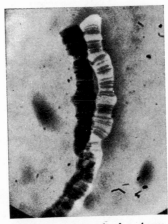

Fig. 2. Photomicrograph of a chromosome end (left, darker object) viewed simultaneously with a cutout of a photograph (right, lighter object) of a portion of the homologous chromosome of the Standard, *Drosophila grimshawi*. The image of the chromosome end is juxtaposed with the cutout at table level by a binocular drawing tube. This facilitates matching of the banding orders.

have been published (*10*). Chromosomes 2, 4, and 5 of this species have the Standard gene order.

The seven Hawaii species listed in Table 1 fall into three sets; each set is related to one or more species known from Maui. The first set of two species, *Drosophila silvestris* and *D. heteroneura*, are homosequential—that is, they have identical arrays of fixed inversion sequences relative to the Standard. In addition, the two species are homosequential with respect to a third species, *D. planitibia* from Maui (Table 1).

Homosequential species are a striking feature of Hawaiian *Drosophila*. Their homosequentiality not only underscores their very great basic similarity but also makes clear the fact that much evolutionary chromosome change occurs at the submicroscopic or molecular level (*18*). In addition to *D. planitibia* and its two Hawaii relatives, 11 more such homosequential sets have so far been recognized from all the islands, involving 36 species in all (*12*). Members of a homosequential set often vary so much that studies of morphology, genitalia, and behavior sometimes fail to suggest that they should be grouped together.

In the present case, however, the significant fact is that, of the 13 species which fall into the *Drosophila planitibia* subgroup of the picture-winged flies (*10*), only *D. planitibia*, *D. silvestris*, and *D. heteroneura* have the key inversion Xr. This is one of the nine inversions by which the X chromosome of these species differs from Standard. Thus, of all the possible candidates for an ancestor of the two Hawaii members, only *D. planitibia* of Maui fulfills the requirements chromosomally.

Accordingly, it is concluded not only that the ancestor of the Hawaii species was derived from Maui but also that it may be specifically traced chromosomally to a population ancestral to the present-day *Drosophila planitibia*. A founder which crossed the Alenuihaha Channel following the raising of the island of Hawaii above sea level is inferred (Fig. 3). The chromosomal formula for this putative ancestor is given across the arrow in Fig. 3.

A founder for the *Drosophila murphyi* complex of three species (Table 1, set No. 2) can also be inferred; it has some special properties of interest. All three species from Hawaii show the inversion Xg. *Drosophila ciliaticrus* has, in addition, the fixed condition 3o, but *D. murphyi* populations are polymorphic, carrying both the Standard 3 and 3o. All expected karyotypes (the homozygotes 3/3 and 3o/3o as well as the heterozygote 3/3o) have been found within present-day populations of this latter species. *Drosophila engyochracea* does not have 3o but has a new fixed inversion (4 1) which it does not share with any other known species.

No single Maui species is known which combines both the fixed Xg and the polymorphic 3/3o karyotypes. On the other hand, two species collectively fulfill these conditions. Thus, *Drosophila balioptera* has Xg only, whereas *D. orphnopeza* populations, like those of *D. murphyi*, are polymorphic for 3/3o. This species, however, has the Standard X chromosome. Accordingly, it is inferred that an ancestral population once existed on Maui which was polymorphic for both X/Xg and 3/3o. A migrant from this population, carrying Xg in the fixed state and the heterozygous condition 3/3o, reached the island of Hawaii as the founder which subsequently gave rise to the *D. murphyi* cluster of species. Present-day *D. murphyi* appears to have the chromosomal formula closest to that of this putative ancestor (Table 1 and Fig. 4). In the process of descent, it appears that *D. ciliaticrus* has fixed 3o, whereas *D. engyochracea* has refixed Standard 3. As in the case of the *D. planitibia* subgroup, the key inversions which serve as tracers are unknown in species other than those listed and, most significantly, are not found among any of the many species known from Oahu or Kauai. They appear to be specific "Maui-Hawaii" markers, having apparently arisen by mutation in a past population on the Maui complex.

The third case involves the two species *Drosophila setosimentum* and *D. ochrobasis* of Hawaii, which relate to *D. adiastola* of the Maui complex (Table 1). Each of the Hawaii species has a basic group of 18 inversions in common with *D. adiastola*. On the other hand, the two Hawaii species have certain new inversions (Xm², 3l, and 4b²). In addition, each has certain inversions of its own which are not found in the other. A striking feature is the accumulation of a large series of 4th chromosome inversions in *D. setosimentum*. This process appears to be continuing, as *D. setosimentum* shows extensive intraspecific 4th chromosome polymorphism in addition to the fixed inversions shown in Table 1 (*10*).

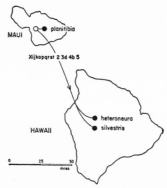

Fig. 3. A postulated interisland species founder going from Maui to Hawaii during the late Pleistocene. The open circle represents a population ancestral to the three present-day species *Drosophila planitibia*, *D. heteroneura*, and *D. silvestris* (solid circles). The inferred chromosomal formula of the interisland founder is superimposed on the arrow.

As in the other two cases of Table 1, it is concluded that the two modern Hawaii species of this complex are descended from a founder stemming from a population directly ancestral to present-day *Drosophila adiastola* and homosequential with it (Fig. 4).

Of the five members of the *Drosophila adiastola* subgroup of flies of the Maui complex, two others are homosequential with *D. adiastola* and appear to mark equally well the ancestral lineage of the two Hawaii species. One of these, *D. cilifera*, is endemic to Molokai, and the other, *D. peniculipedis* of Maui, has a peculiar constriction in

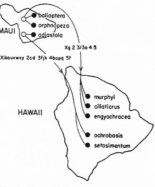

Fig. 4. Two additional interisland species founders going from Maui to Hawaii (see legend to Fig. 3, and text).

chromosome 4 which is not found in the Hawaii species. In any event, the founder is likely to have been derived from a population ancestral to these three homosequential species, rather than from any one modern species.

The three cited founder events are not isolated cases; there are at least three other known instances of one or more Hawaii species that has its closest chromosomal relative on Maui (*10*). They are less diagrammatic than the cases discussed above, however, because, in these other instances, similar homosequential species occur on Oahu or Kauai, thus founders could have come to the island of Hawaii directly from one of those islands, bypassing Maui.

The Founder Event and Speciation

The island of Hawaii, which is the youngest in the archipelago, has apparently received much of its picture-winged *Drosophila* fauna from the adjacent island of Maui. In three especially clear instances the founders may be traced chromosomally to Maui only, and their precise inversion formulas may be inferred. The species of the island of Hawaii are endemic to that island, and, since the island appears to be no more than 700,000 years old, the evolutionary events which produced the species must have consumed less time than that. Thus, these species must have evolved less than three-quarters of a million years ago on the island of Hawaii. Such precise statements can rarely be made about evolutionary events.

There is no evidence of repeated simple colonizations of the island of Hawaii. No subspecies of species from Maui or any other island have as yet been found there, at least in the group under discussion. This suggests that the founder event is an exceedingly rare one, and that the break between the donor population and the new colony on the invaded island is a deep one biologically.

One of the most striking features of this situation is the fact that speciation invariably has followed the founder event. This suggests further that the founder event may be accomplished by a single propagule, probably a single fertilized female.

In Figs. 3 and 4, three founder events have been postulated as being responsible for the origin of seven species. In each case the law of parsimony has been invoked and it has been assumed that, for instance, only a single founder was ancestral to the clusters of two (or, in one case, three) species which occur on the island of Hawaii. On the other hand, the "one founder, one new species" view might be defended. It appears, however, that if such double colonizations from a chromosomally identical stock did occur, the likely result would be subspecies of some Maui species, not new unique species, such as are observed.

As was proposed above, evolution seems very often to display two major processes: an adaptation (fitness for a specific function in a specific environment) appears to be made by intraspecific phyletic change, whereas species result from a multiplicative process whereby populations become divided and isolated. The situation on oceanic islands, as revealed in the data given here, suggests a clarifying separation, in time and in process, of these two aspects of evolution. Thus, the hypothesis may be made that a speciation phase precedes an adaptive phase. The speciation episode appears to be characterized by the successful colonization of a relatively open ecological habitat by a single founder female. This event would be expected to have several important genetic consequences. First, a maximization of the phenomenon of random genetic drift would be accomplished as the new colony is formed. Second, early success of the new colony in a locally permissive habitat might result in a population flush. Certain new genetic recombinants might be multiplied and preserved by chance in the demes which survive the inevitable population crash.

The resulting interdeme selection and related processes, it is argued, might well lead to the appearance of a genetic gap between the new colony and its progenitor. This gap might be recognized as the equivalent of speciation (19). In my view, this might be accomplished in a relatively small number of generations. If this is the case, then the synthesis of species under controlled conditions might indeed be accomplished in the laboratory or field plot more easily than has been previously

thought. Indeed, a striking report of a suggestive case has appeared recently (20).

When the gene pool of a population is being rigorously shaken up by chance events of the kind discussed above, speciation is not likely to be accompanied by adaptive evolution. It is suggested that, where species founders play a role, as in these terrestrial populations of oceanic islands, the adaptive evolutionary phase is likely to occur only after the chance events leading to speciation are essentially complete. Thus, the gene pool of the new species undergoes new phyletic evolution in isolation from its ancestors and contemporaries. Since genetic drift and the founder effect undoubtedly provide a genetic revolution (21), the species is faced with the alternatives of extinction or the welding of a somewhat discordant gene pool into something ecologically workable. The result is seen in the somewhat bizarre yet generally well-adapted products of insular speciation.

The separation of phyletic evolution from speciation, as called for in the foregoing hypothesis, would not, of course, be expected to apply to all patterns of speciation. For example, where a widespread continental species becomes broken up into subspecies, the result is frequently a gradual population change involving both adaptation and speciation. Thus, in these cases, it is probable that speciation and adaptation are synchronic population processes. Only where the founder effect is prominent may the features of the two processes be clearly seen as essentially separate evolutionary phases, one with and one without a large element of chance.

Summary

Organic evolution produces species and adaptations. Data from terrestrial populations existing on oceanic islands suggest that the processes whereby species and adaptations arise are different and are sometimes separated in time. Thus, in *Drosophila* from the island of Hawaii, speciation appears to follow the establishment of a new island population from a single founder individual from a nearby island. In these cases, it is hypothesized, speciation is characterized by isolation, random genetic drift, and the abrupt, nonadaptive changes in the gene pool which would be expected to immediately follow the founder event. The process is aided by interdeme selection. Adaptations, which follow in time, are forged genetically by the well-known intrademic processes of mutation, recombination, and selection.

References and Notes

1. V. Grant, *The Origin of Adaptations* (Columbia Univ. Press, New York, 1963); B. Wallace and A. M. Srb, *Adaptation* (Prentice-Hall, Englewood Cliffs, N.J., 1964).
2. R. A. Fisher, *The Genetical Theory of Natural Selection* (Clarendon, Oxford, 1930); J. B. S. Haldane, *The Causes of Evolution* (Longmans, Green, London, 1932); S. Wright, *Genetics* 16, 97 (1931).
3. H. B. D. Kettlewell, *Annu. Rev. Entomol.* 6, 245 (1961).
4. E. Mayr, *Animal Species and Evolution* (Harvard Univ. Press, Cambridge, Mass., 1966).
5. E. C. Zimmerman, *Insects of Hawaii* (Univ. of Hawaii Press, Honolulu, 1948), vol. 1.
6. J. T. Patterson and W. S. Stone, *Evolution in the Genus Drosophila* (Macmillan, New York, 1952).
7. D. E. Hardy, *Insects of Hawaii* (Univ. of Hawaii Press, Honolulu, 1965), vol. 12.
8. H. T. Stearns, *Geology of the State of Hawaii* (Pacific Books, Palo Alto, Calif., 1966).
9. I. McDougall, *Bull. Geol. Soc. Amer.* 75, 107 (1964); *ibid.* 80, 2597 (1969).
10. H. L. Carson and H. D. Stalker, *Univ. Tex. Publ. No. 6818* (1968), p. 355.
11. W. B. Heed, *ibid.*, p. 387; H. T. Spieth, *Evol. Biol.* 2, 157 (1968).
12. H. L. Carson, D. E. Hardy, H. T. Spieth, W. S. Stone, in *The Evolutionary Biology of the Hawaiian Drosophilidae, Essays in Evolution and Genetics in Honor of Theodosius Dobzhansky*, M. K. Hecht and W. C. Steere, Eds. (Appleton-Century-Crofts, New York, 1970), p. 437.
13. F. E. Clayton, *Univ. Tex. Publ. No. 6818* (1968), p. 263; *Univ. Tex. Publ. No. 6918* (1969), p. 96.
14. The binocular drawing tube was obtained from Wild Heerbrugg Instruments Company.
15. M. Wasserman, *Amer. Natur.* 97, 333 (1963).
16. H. D. Stalker, *Proc. Int. Congr. Genet. 12th* (1968), vol. 1, p. 194; H. L. Carson and H. D. Stalker, *Univ. Tex. Publ. No. 6918* (1969), p. 85.
17. H. Yang and M. R. Wheeler, *Univ. Tex. Publ. No. 6918* (1969), p. 133.
18. H. L. Carson, F. E. Clayton, H. D. Stalker, *Proc. Nat. Acad. Sci. U.S.* 57, 1280 (1967).
19. H. L. Carson, in *Population Biology and Evolution*, R. C. Lewontin, Ed. (Syracuse Univ. Press, Syracuse, N.Y., 1968), p. 123.
20. Th. Dobzhansky and O. Pavlovsky, *Proc. Nat. Acad. Sci. U.S.* 55, 727 (1966).
21. E. Mayr, in *Evolution as a Process*, J. Huxley, Ed. (Allen and Unwin, London, 1954), p. 157.
22. Support for this work came from NIH grant GM10640 to the University of Hawaii and from NSF grants GB3147 and 7754 to Washington University and GB711 to the University of Texas. I thank Geraldine Oda and Marion L. Stalker for preparing the figures. A list of the many contributors to this work has been published [see Carson *et al.* (12)].

27

Reprinted from *Science* 177:664-669 (1972)

Species of Drosophila

New excitement in an old field.

Theodosius Dobzhansky

The species problem is the oldest in biology. Adam was allegedly called upon to distinguish and name species in the Garden of Eden. Preliterate people faced this task wherever they lived. Some of them were perspicacious naturalists who recognized mostly the same species as zoologists and botanists do, while others were less successful (*1, 2*). To Linnaeus and his followers, species were the basic constituents of the living world, the primordial created entities. Variations within a species were merely imperfections in the manifestation of the immutable archetype (Platonic eidos), of which every species was the embodiment. Evolutionists showed that species are not separated by unscalable walls. Intraspecific variations are important as raw materials from which race and species differentials are compounded in the process of evolution. Lamarck and Darwin stressed that species were not all uniformly discrete. Darwin concluded that "species are only strongly marked and permanent varieties, and that each species first existed as a variety" (*3*).

To classical taxonomists, species and races (varieties) were categories of classification. To students of evolution they are also biological phenomena. Much confusion would be avoided if this duality of the species concept were understood clearly. A biological species concept is therefore necessary. Its beginning goes back to John Ray, who stated in 1686 that "one species never springs from the seed of another" [quoted in (*1*)]. Attempts were made later to define species as forms that are unable to cross, or that produce inviable or sterile offspring when crossed. These definitions are valid as far as they go, but they do not go far

enough. In the light of the biological (synthetic) theory of evolution it became clear that, in sexual and outbreeding organisms, species are reproductive communities. They are separated by any one, or by a combination of several, reproductive isolating mechanisms, (*1, 4–7*). Hybrid inviability and sterility are among such mechanisms, but there are others (for example, ethological and ecological isolations) which may be just as effective in nature. The recognition that species are reproductive communities was a step forward, but it raised more problems than it solved.

Multiformity of Species

Sexuality is a widespread method but not the only method of reproduction. There are organisms that are exclusively asexual, parthenogenetic, or self-fertilizing. The species concept based on reproductive isolation is inapplicable in such organisms. Arrays of structurally and ecologically diverse forms may nevertheless be present; systematists describe some of the arrays as races, others as species, genera, and so on. This is legitimate for cataloging purposes, but which arrays are to be designated species becomes arbitrary. "Species" in asexual or parthenogenetic forms are really pseudospecies, biological phenomena unlike species in sexual outbreeders. The contrast may, however, turn out to be less radical than it seems, owing to the discoveries of parasexuality, transformation, and transduction in organisms which were believed to be strictly asexual (*8*).

The genetic nature of species is a function of the reproductive biology of the organism concerned. Allopolyploidy, chromosome doubling in species hybrids, may lead to sudden emergence of reproductively fully discrete and sympatric neospecies. More often a

species is transformed into a new one in time, or gives rise to two or more derived contemporaneous species, by gradual accumulation of genetic differences. The divergence of the incipient species occurs, as a rule, allopatrically, in geographically separate populations (*1*). Because the process of speciation is gradual, one expects to find instances of populations between which the gene flow is incompletely repressed. Such instances have indeed been found, and they have led to a misapprehension that all species are arbitrary groupings. This is not so. Borderline situations between race and species are, on the whole, rare; they may be annoyances to classifiers but are precious to experimental evolutionists.

Somewhere between 1.5 and 2 million species have been described and named. Species are not only numerous but of many kinds. Neither the classical typological nor the more modern biological (populational) species concept accommodates easily the great, and until recently scarcely appreciated, diversity of the evolutionary patterns in the animal, plant, and prokaryote kingdoms. Evolutionary biologists are challenged to reexamine the old and to look for new approaches. A new consensus is yet to emerge. Excitement and clash of opinion have returned to to the field, which at times during its long history threatened to freeze in an orthodoxy. Some feel that species must have the same meaning in sexual and asexual, prokaryote and eukaryote, contemporaneous and allochronic organisms. This procrustean operation sacrifices reality for generality. Others underestimate the role of reproductive isolation in evolution, and claim that: "For sexual organisms it is the local interbreeding population and not the species that is clearly the evolutionary unit of importance" [(*9*); see also (*10*)]. Still others, and I believe their approach is heuristically the most productive, stress that species are not all of the same kind, and different sorts of species should be understood in relation to different strategies of evolutionary adaptation.

Only a fraction of the evolutionary patterns that exist in the living world are encountered among drosophilid flies. Yet they are diverse enough and, owing to many drosophilids being favorable for experimental work, they can be studied in depth. The highlights of these studies may, I believe, be of general interest.

The author is Adjunct Professor of Genetics at the University of California, Davis 95616. This article is adapted from a talk given on 30 December 1971 at the AAAS annual meeting, Philadelphia, Pennsylvania.

"Good" Species

There are probably no fewer than 2000 species of drosophilid flies (*11, 12*). Species that live in the same territory (sympatric species) are generally more numerous in the tropics than in temperate and cold zones. More than 100 species of *Drosophila* have been recorded for the republic of Salvador, 39 in one locality in Texas, only 9 in Alaska, and a single species introduced by man in Tierra del Fuego. The archipelago of Hawaii, with total area smaller than the state of Massachusetts, has over 500 species of drosophilids, all but 17 of which are endemics (*12*).

It can easily be shown that species of *Drosophila* are biologically real, not arbitrary, entities. With rare exceptions, sympatric species are reproductively fully isolated in their natural habitats. The isolation usually persists in laboratory environments as well. Taking almost any pair of sympatric species, one finds as a rule not one but several isolating mechanisms in operation, and often different ones between different species. Because species have distinct food and microhabitat preferences, conspecific individuals meet more often than individuals of different species. More widespread and more potent than this ecological isolation is ethological (behavioral, sexual) isolation. Comparative studies of courtship and mating habits in drosophilid flies have been pioneered by Spieth (*12, 13*). Males of many species are promiscuous, in the sense that they approach any moving object of about their size. "Tapping" with foretarsi leads, however, to recognition of the species and sex tapped. Females have rejection signals whereby they may repulse males of their own and foreign species. Species-specific courtship and mating patterns are amply diversified. The diversity is especially prominent in Hawaii, where sympatric species are most numerous. This is as it should be if premating isolating mechanisms are mostly not accidental by-products of genetic divergence but adaptive contrivances that guard against breakdown of functionally coherent adaptive systems.

Ethological isolation may be incomplete under laboratory conditions between the same pair of species that are completely isolated in their natural habitats. Hybrids of *Drosophila pseudoobscura* and *D. persimilis* are easily obtainable in the laboratory, but they are absent in localities where both species occur side by side (*14*). Mechanical isolation, noncorrespondence of the genitalia, is found also more often in the laboratory than in nature. *Drosophila melanogaster* males that attempt to copulate with *D. pseudoobscura* females may become locked together, and die unable to separate. I found such a couple in nature. Hybrid inviability and sterility are, for obvious reasons, hard to ascertain in nature. Hybrids of *D. melanogaster* and *D. simulans* are inviable either as females or as males (depending on the direction of the cross), and the surviving sex is sterile. Yet these species occasionally cross in the laboratory as well as outdoors (*15*). *Drosophila pseudoobscura* and *D. persimilis* are often sympatric; only four females inseminated by foreign species, and one hybrid, have been taken in nature among thousands studied. Conclusive evidence that these species do not effectively hybridize in nature comes from studies on their chromosomal polymorphisms. Both species are highly polymorphic for chromosomal inversions, but only a single, presumably ancestral, gene arrangement is common to both species. Other inversions are species specific. No individual of *D. pseudoobscura* has ever been found carrying an inversion characteristic of *D. persimilis*, or vice versa. Either these species do not cross in nature at all, or if they do the foreign genetic material is promptly cast out by natural selection (*16*). Similar, although less extensive, evidence of lack of gene exchange is available for sibling species of the *D. willistoni* group [compare (*17*) and (*18*)].

Sibling Species

Pairs or groups of species that are morphologically indistinguishable, or distinguishable with difficulty, are called sibling species (*6*). Although known in many groups of organisms, sibling species are notably common among drosophilids. It can reasonably be inferred that sibling species are genetically more similar on the average than morphologically distinguishable species in the same group of organisms. Yet it should not be assumed that sibling species always represent examples of uncompleted speciation. As pointed out above, *D. pseudoobscura* and *D. persimilis* are in nature completely isolated reproductively. Their males can be distinguished by a minute difference in the genitalia (*19*), and females solely by means of genetic, cytological, and biochemical tests (*16, 20*).

Some museum taxonomists as well as modern computer classifiers refuse to recognize sibling species because they cannot distinguish them. Yet sibling species are important to evolutionists; they permit dissection of the process of speciation into studiable components. Sibling species and ordinary morphologically distinct species are biologically similar phenomena. Visible morphological distinctions between "good" species range from very striking to none. Reproductive isolation evidently can arise with little or no morphological differentiation. Whether or not it can arise also with little physiological and adaptive differentiation is another problem that I shall discuss below. It is remarkable that despite explosive proliferation of drosophilid species in Hawaii, most of them are morphologically distinct, and sibling species are rare (*12, 21*). In contrast, the *willistoni* group consists of at least six sibling species, four of which are widespread, common, and sympatric over much of tropical America (*22*).

Superspecies and Semispecies

While sympatric species, including siblings, are as a rule unambiguously distinct, the same cannot be said of allopatric, geographically separate, populations. A variety of situations are encountered. *Drosophila willistoni* and *D. paulistorum* are contrasting examples. They are reproductively isolated sibling species. But while the former is a simple, nearly monolithic species, the latter is a complex superspecies on the verge of breaking up into at least five derived species. The distribution of *D. willistoni* extends from Mexico and southern Florida to Argentina (La Plata). With a single exception, strains from anywhere in this tremendous territory interbreed freely and give fertile hybrids (*23*). The exception is a strain from Lima, Peru. The Lima strain crosses easily with all other strains with which it has been tested. Crosses in which Lima is the male parent give fertile hybrids of both sexes. The reciprocal crosses also give fertile hybrid females. Male hybrids are also fertile when Lima females are outcrossed to strains from Mexico, Central America, and Ecuador, but sterile in outcrosses to Brazilian, Trinidadian, and Colombian strains (*24*). It would be gratuitous to regard Lima anything other than a member of the species *D. willistoni*.

Drosophila paulistorum is distributed less widely than *D. willistoni* (from Guatemala to southern Brazil). It is a superspecies composed of five semispecies. The semispecies are nearly identical morphologically (*25*), and yet they have evolved reproductive isolation sufficient to enable them to coexist sympatrically in some places, apparently with little or no hybridization (*22, 26*). Laboratory tests show a strong, though incomplete, ethological isolation; females usually rebuff males of all but their own semispecies. Each semispecies has a courtship ritual somewhat different from the others (*27*). When cross-insemination nevertheless takes place, vigorous hybrids are produced which are fertile as females but completely sterile as males. Every semispecies has a geographic distribution different from the others, and yet while in many places only a single semispecies is found, from the Amazon Valley to Panama two or even three semispecies live together.

Sympatric coexistence of populations without gene exchange is prima facie evidence of a speciation process having been completed. A cogent argument can be made that *D. paulistorum* is really a set of five species. On the other hand, the incompleteness of the ethological isolation and the unimpaired fertility of female hybrids suggest that some gene exchange between the semispecies may be taking place. As pointed out above, examination of the chromosomes in populations of *D. pseudoobscura* and *D. persimilis* has given strong evidence that these sibling species do not interbreed. Similar studies on *D. paulistorum* do not rule out the possibility of some gene exchange, at present or in a recent past, between the semispecies (*18*). *Drosophila paulistorum* is a superspecies which still conserves a common, although deeply fissured, gene pool.

No other superspecies quite like *D. paulistorum* have yet been discovered in *Drosophila*. This is not surprising in view of the tendency of the speciation process in these flies to occur with little or no visible differentiation in externally visible characteristics. The remarkable cluster of forms that constitute the *D. mesophragmatica* complex (*28*) come perhaps closest to the status of a superspecies composed of semispecies. Superspecies and semispecies are known in birds, mammals, butterflies, mollusks, and planarians (*1*), but few of them are suitable for experimental study. They are known also in the plant kingdom (*29*).

Magnitude of Genetic Differences between Species

Classical theories of population structure grossly underestimated the amount of genetic variability. The usual assumption was that the bulk of individuals of a sexual, diploid, and outbreeding species (such as man or *Drosophila*) are homozygous for the same wild-type gene alleles at a great majority of gene loci. Consonant with this, related species were surmised to differ in only few genes; several "lucky" mutations, possibly a single one, could give rise to a new species. Doubt was cast on these beliefs by the discovery of vast amounts of variability concealed in "normal" individuals and populations. This variability consists chiefly of recessive gene alleles and gene complexes, and in *Drosophila* and some other forms, of inversions of blocks of genes in some chromosomes (*4*). Gradually it became clear that no two individuals in a sexual outbreeding species are at all likely to be genetically identical. However, it was only through analyses of enzyme and other protein polymorphisms and monomorphisms by electrophoretic techniques that it became possible to obtain even rough estimates of the proportions of genes that are represented by similar or distinct alleles in individuals of the same or different species (*30*).

About ten species of *Drosophila* have been studied more or less extensively for protein polymorphisms. Between 25 and 70 percent of the gene loci proved to be polymorphic in natural populations, that is, represented by two or more alleles with appreciable frequencies. An individual fly in these populations is estimated to be heterozygous for between 8 and 28 percent of its genes (*30, 31*). Estimates within the above ranges have been obtained also for animals other than *Drosophila*, man included. To what extent the differences between the estimates recorded for different species are real, and the genes coding for the proteins studied are unbiased samples of all genes, are open questions. However, let us take the lowest of the above estimates, and accept the figure 100,000 as the number of gene loci in *Drosophila*. Some 25,000 genes are then polymorphic in a *Drosophila* population, and an average fly is heterozygous for some 8,000 genes. Genetic variability of this magnitude would have seemed unbelievable to most geneticists even a decade ago!

A study of the proportions of proteins that are electrophoretically similar and different in species of *Drosophila* has been pioneered by Hubby and Throckmorton (*32*). These workers examined nine triplets of species, each triplet including two sibling species and one closely related but easily distinguishable species. The different triplets belonged to different species groups, or to different subgenera of *Drosophila*. Thus, they had three levels of structural, and presumably also genetic, differentiation. The sibling species had on the average only 50 percent of their proteins in common, the percentages ranging from 23 to 86 for different pairs. The two siblings and the related nonsibling shared only 11.6 percent of the proteins on the average, and members of different triplets were even less similar. By contrast, some related but morphologically distinguishable Hawaiian species of *Drosophila* proved to be remarkably similar in their electrophoretically diagnosed proteins (*33*).

A more detailed study has been made of the sibling species of the *willistoni* group (*34*). Wherever possible, samples from different parts of the geographic area of each species were examined. Hubby and Throckmorton's findings (*32*) were confirmed—individuals of different sibling species differ on the average in somewhat more than one half of their gene loci. Perhaps even more impressive are the percentages of the loci that are diagnostic for the species, that is, that permit identification of the species in single individuals by their protein variants (*20*). The percentages of the diagnostic loci are shown in Table 1. Even *D. paulistorum* and *D. pavlovskiana*, siblings so close that they were originally regarded as semispecies of a superspecies, can be diagnosed by an estimated 14 percent of their genes.

Very promising beginnings have been made in estimation of the magnitudes of species differences by means of their DNA (*35*) or their DNA-RNA "hybridizations." The complementary strands of the DNA chain molecules can be separated by heating, and the separate strands can then reanneal when the temperature is lowered. The DNA's of different species undergo the reannealing more slowly or not at all, depending upon the degree of the resemblance of their nucleotide sequences. Similar in principle is the hybridization, or annealing, of separated DNA strands with RNA transcribed from them. Both techniques have been used to compare the closely related species *D. melanogaster* and *D. simulans*, and also *D. funebris* which belongs to a subgenus different from the first two. The DNA's of *D. melanogaster* and *D. simulans* are estimated to contain about 80 percent of the nucleotide sequences in common, while the DNA of *D. funebris* has only about 25 percent of sequences similar to the other two species. The hybridization of the DNA of *D. melanogaster* with RNA of *D. simulans*, or vice versa, is only 40 to 50 percent as effective as that of DNA and RNA of the same species; with *D. funebris* the effectiveness drops as low as 10 percent (*36*). It would be premature to use these figures as estimates of the proportions of similar and dissimilar genes in these species. The figures reveal mainly the so-called repeated sequences, that is, the genes that are represented numerous times within a single gene complement. Nonetheless the great extent of the interspecific differences is most interesting.

Chromosomal Differences

From the above data it cannot be validly inferred that species in general, or that species of *Drosophila* in particular, always differ in numerous genes. Speciation can occur in more than one way. Biologists who are too fond of simplicity and homogeneity may be chagrined by the "inventiveness" of the evolutionary process.

The availability in *Drosophila* of giant polytene chromosomes facilitates the analysis of the variations in the gene arrangements within and between species. It has been known for several decades that natural populations of many species are polymorphic for variant chromosome structures, owing mainly to the occurrence of inversions of blocks of genes. Yet some species are chromosomally monomorphic [see (*4*)]. Species, sibling as well as morpho-

Table 1. Percentages of gene loci coding for electrophoretically distinguishable protein variants that are diagnostic for any two sibling species of the *Drosophila willistoni* group with a probability greater than .99 for each locus (*20*).

Species	tropicalis	equinoxialis	paulistorum	pavlovskiana	insularis
D. willistoni	17.9	21.4	25.0	25.0	32.1
D. tropicalis		21.4	35.7	28.6	28.6
D. equinoxialis			14.3	25.0	28.6
D. paulistorum				14.3	32.1
D. pavlovskiana					32.1

logically distinct species, may have the genetic materials in their chromosomes more or less radically rearranged. Individuals of the sibling species *D. pseudoobscura* and *D. persimilis* differ in at least two, usually more, inversions. The six siblings of the *willistoni* group can be simply and conclusively identified by inspection of their chromosomes in the larval salivary gland cells. The number and kinds of the chromosomal reconstructions have not been precisely identified. *Drosophila pseudoobscura* and *D. willistoni* with their siblings belong to different sections of the same subgenus (*Sophophora*). The gene arrangements in their chromosomes have diverged so greatly that not only can the species be discriminated at a glance, but the corresponding (homologous) chromosomes can no longer be recognized (further examples in *4*, *37*, *38*).

The discovery of homosequential species came as a considerable surprise (*12*, *39*). These are species that have identical gene arrangements in their chromosomes, as inferred from the banding patterns in the polytene chromosomes, in cells of the larval salivary glands. Carson (*21*) lists ten groups of Hawaiian endemics, with two to five homosequential species per group. He emphasizes that these are not siblings but morphologically easily distinguishable forms, some of them even strikingly different in outward appearance. The conclusion is inevitable that genetic divergence and speciation may occur without rearrangement of the genetic materials in the chromosomes, although more often the two processes go hand in hand. It may be noted that homosequential species are not confined to Hawaii, since at least one example of continental homosequential species has been recorded (*40*).

Founder Principle and Neospecies

The usual, by now orthodox, view among evolutionists has been that species formation occurs by slow genetic

divergence, and subsequent reproductive isolation, of geographically separated and differentially adapted races or subspecies (Darwin's "varieties"). Sudden emergence of new species by allopolyploidy is an exception, irrelevant to *Drosophila* and most bisexual animals. In several brilliantly argued contributions (*12*, *21*, *41*, for example), Carson advances a novel and unorthodox view—speciation may occur rapidly, and a neospecies of *Drosophila* may, without prior adaptive divergence, emerge within relatively few generations. The idea stems from Mayr's founder principle (*1*, *7*, *42*), which is in turn a special case of Wright's random genetic drift (*4*).

The founder principle is "establishment of a new population by a few original founders (in an extreme case, by a single fertilized female) that carry only a small fraction of the total genetic variation of the parental population" (*1*). Founder events are inevitably followed by inbreeding for one or several generations. The populations descended from the founders are then restructured by natural selection, which operates on a changed gene pool and usually in an altered environment. This theoretical scheme was verified in experiments with chromosomally polymorphic populations of *D. pseudoobscura* (*43*). Natural selection in experimental populations derived from small numbers of founders resulted in a greater variety of outcomes than in comparable populations descended from numerous founders. It should be noted that, although the genetic variability among the descendants of a single pair of founders is reduced compared to the population from which the founders came, it is by no means absent. Experiments on several species of *Drosophila* have shown that recombination of genes in a single pair of chromosomes drawn at random from a natural population can give rise to considerable genetic variability (*44*).

Carson postulates that founder events

Table 2. Observed matings between selected and unselected strains of *Drosophila paulistorum*. (LU, Llanos unselected; LS, Llanos selected; OU, Orinocan unselected; OS, Orinocan selected.)

Strains		Matings				Isolation coefficient
A	B	A♀ × A♂	A♀ × B♂	B♀ × A♂	B♀ × B♂	
LU	OU	61	44	51	65	0.14 ± 0.07
LS	OS	52	4	4	41	0.67 ± 0.07
LS	OS	45	7	3	54	0.82 ± 0.05
LS	OS	46	6	8	49	0.74 ± 0.06
LS	LU	44	64	29	66	0.08 ± 0.07
OS	OU	24	26	25	38	0.10 ± 0.09

must have played a key role in the spectacular proliferation of species of drosophilid flies on the Hawaiian archipelago. These volcanic islands were never connected with any continent, and most of them not with each other. The oldest island inhabited by drosophilids (Kauai) is some 5.6 million years old, the youngest (Hawaii) is only 0.7 million years old, while others (Oahu, Maui) are intermediate in age. Their drosophilid fauna, about 500 species, is descended from probably two, or even a single species, introduced by accidental long-distance transport across the ocean. A great majority of the species are endemic not only to the archipelago but to single islands (or adjacent islands which were connected in geologically recent past). With the aid of cytogenetic, morphological, and distributional studies, it is possible to establish with a high degree of probability which species on one island, particularly a geologically younger one, have descended from ancestors similar or identical with species on the older islands. The youngest and largest island, Hawaii, has a particularly interesting array of 11 groups of 23 species, the nearest relatives of which are found mostly on the next youngest island, Maui, and only one each on Oahu and Kauai.

Carson infers that each species is descended from a single gravid female that arrived from the donor island. What is remarkable is that these single founders gave rise to new species, rather than simply to new colonies of the old donor species. Carson argues that the genetic upheavals that result from the initial inbreeding, followed by rapid expansions of the newly founded populations, are propitious for the origin of reproductively isolated neospecies. Reproductive isolation arises, according to his view, as a chance concomitant of the genetic upheaval that follows the founding event. In his words: "The key genetic shifts leading to the crucial species differences may be non-adaptive. I suggest that they may precede, in time, an adaptive phase wherein a large genetically variable population is exposed to the usual and well known forces of natural selection" (*21*).

This is a radical departure from the orthodox view. What is the biological function of speciation? The most reasonable interpretation seemed to be that speciation makes the adaptive divergence of evolving populations irreversible. Or to put it differently—reproductive isolation safeguards the adaptive gene systems that have evolved in differentially adapted species from disruption owing to gene exchange. According to Carson's scheme, reproductive isolation and speciation precede differential adaptedness. If so, speciation would seem to be devoid of biological function, until a differential adaptedness arises following the speciation. This is not merely a new form of the old dispute, whether reproductive isolation is simply a by-product of adaptive divergence, or an ad hoc contrivance built by natural selection (*1, 4*). The issue is whether reproductively isolated species remain, at least for a time, adaptively equivalent in similar environments. Be it noted that Carson does not claim universality for his speciation scheme: ". . . where a widespread continental species becomes broken up into subspecies, the result is frequently a gradual population change involving both adaptation and speciation" (*41*). It may well be that two fairly contrastive methods of speciation occur among drosophilid flies, as well as among other organisms. If so, only future research can give a measure of the incidence and importance of these methods. One would like to know, for example, whether the proportions of genes involved in differences among neospecies are comparable to those found between "good" species.

Origin of an Incipient Neospecies in the Laboratory

The origin of neospecies through the process postulated by Carson may conceivably be observed in the laboratory. Such an event may have taken place in my laboratory sometime between 1958 and 1963 in a strain of *D. paulistorum*. This strain is descended from a single inseminated female captured in the Llanos of Colombia in March 1958. As described above, the superspecies *D. paulistorum* consists of five semispecies. The semispecies show a strong, although incomplete, sexual isolation, complete sterility of hybrid males, and sometimes geographic isolation. When tested in 1958, the Llanos strain gave fertile hybrids with strains of the Orinocan semispecies, and was accordingly considered to belong to that semispecies. Yet from 1963 onward, it has produced sterile male hybrids when crossed to Orinocan. The emergence of the hybrid sterility was not, however, accompanied by ethological isolation. The changed Llanos strain mates freely with Orinocan, as though it still belongs to that semispecies (*45*).

In experiments started in 1966, I and Pavlovsky have endeavored to superimpose an ethological isolation on the existing hybrid sterility by artificial selection (*46*). Two recessive mutants, rough eye in the Llanos and orange eye in an Orinocan strain, are being used as markers. In every generation rough-eyed Llanos and orange-eyed Orinocan females are exposed to mixtures of males of both kinds. Matings of likes (that is, rough crossed with rough and orange crossed with orange) produce progenies showing the respective mutant traits. Matings of unlikes produce hybrid flies with nonmutant (wild type) characteristics. The hybrids are destroyed, and the selection is carried forward by again exposing rough or orange females to both kinds of males. Thus far the selection has been carried for exactly 100 generations. The Llanos and Orinocan strains no longer mate at random (Table 2).

It can be seen that the unselected (U) Llanos (L) and Orinocan (O) strains mate among themselves almost as frequently as they do with each other (line 1 in Table 2). After 50, 58, and 90 generations of selection (lines 2 to 4 in Table 2) matings within the selected (S) strains are decidedly more frequent than between them. A convenient measure of the departure from randomness in mating is the isolation coefficient devised by Professor Howard Levene (of Columbia University); this coefficient is zero if matings are at random, and unity if the ethological isolation is complete. The coefficients achieved by selection (0.67 to 0.82) are of about the same magnitude as those observed between the more closely related natural semispecies. The selected Llanos and Orinocan strains continue however to mate at random with the respective unselected controls without the mutant gene markers (lines 5 and 6, Table 2).

That the selected Llanos strain should be considered at least an incipient neospecies is warranted. The nature of the event responsible for the initiation of the hybrid sterility between Llanos and Orinocan some 20 years ago remains a problem, however. One possibility is that a change took place in the population of intracellular symbionts, which seem to be present in all strains of the superspecies *D. paulistorum* (47, 48). A second possibility has to do with the geographic derivation of the Llanos strain. This strain comes from a marginal locality where the distribution area of the Orinocan semispecies abuts the mountain range of the Andes. According to Carson, geographically marginal populations may be subject to changes of the same sort as island populations derived from single founders. A third possibility is that the Llanos strain was a form intermediate, and possibly even hybrid, between the Orinocan and Interior semispecies. Interior (which was discovered after the changes in the Llanos strain) is a near relative of Orinocan, and the changed Llanos gives fertile male hybrids with Interior strains. There is obviously no way to tell whether Llanos would have given fertile hybrids with Interior as well as with Orinocan in 1958. Anyway, what happened was not simply a conversion of Interior to Orinocan; there is a pronounced ethological isolation between these semispecies, and not between the unselected Llanos and the Orinocan.

Conclusion

Anything that can be said about a new, or recently renewed, field risks being superseded or negated by further discoveries. As the situation appears to be now, there is one consideration which seems unlikely to be changed: there is not a single kind but there are several kinds of species and of processes of speciation in *Drosophila* and, of course, even more in the living world at large. As a category of classification, species was and is being applied to all organisms, and this has led to futile search for universal biological properties of all species. What is actually found is a remarkable variety of different kinds of species. Even confining our attention to sexually reproducing and outbreeding forms, we find more or less monolithic "good" species, superspecies, and semispecies. Finally, it begins to look as if reproductive isolation may sometimes follow and at other times precede the adaptive divergence of gene pools of populations.

References and Notes

1. F. Mayr, *Animal Species and Evolution* (Harvard Univ. Press, Cambridge, Mass., 1963).
2. J. D. Diamond, *Science* 151, 1102 (1966); T. A. W. Davis and P. W. Richards, *J. Ecol.* 22, 106 (1934); J. Murça Pires, Th. Dobzhansky, G. A. Black, *Bot. Gaz.* 114, 467 (1953); P. H. Raven, B. Berlin, D. E. Breedlove, *Science* 174, 1210 (1971).
3. C. Darwin, *On the Origin of Species* (Harvard Univ. Press, Cambridge, Mass., facsimile ed., 1964).
4. Th. Dobzhansky, *Genetics of the Evolutionary Process* (Columbia Univ. Press, New York, 1970).
5. Th. Dobzhansky, *Genetics and the Origin of Species* (Columbia Univ. Press, New York, 1937); G. L. Stebbins, *Variations and Evolution in Plants* (Columbia Univ. Press, New York, 1950).
6. E. Mayr, *Systematics and the Origin of Species* (Columbia Univ. Press, New York, 1942).
7. E. Mayr, *Populations, Species, and Evolution* (Harvard Univ. Press, Cambridge, Mass., 1970).
8. W. Bodmer, *Symp. Soc. Gen. Microbiol.* 20, 279 (1970).
9. P. R. Ehrlich and P. H. Raven, *Science* 165, 1228 (1969).
10. R. R. Sokal and T. J. Crovello, *Amer. Natur.* 104, 127 (1970); A. C. Kinsey, "The Gallwasp Genus *Cynips*," *Indiana Univ. Stud. No. 16* (1930).
11. D. E. Hardy, *Insects of Hawaii: Diptera* (Univ. of Hawaii Press, Honolulu, 1965).
12. H. L. Carson, D. E. Hardy, H. T. Spieth, W. S. Stone, in *Essays in Evolution and Genetics*, M. K. Hecht and W. C. Steere, Eds. (Appleton-Century-Crofts, New York, 1970).
13. H. T. Spieth, *Bull. Amer. Mus. Natur. Hist. No. 99* (1952); *Evol. Biol.* 2, 157 (1968); in *Essays in Evolution and Genetics*, M. K. Hecht and W. C. Steere, Eds. (Appleton-Century-Crofts, New York, 1970).
14. Th. Dobzhansky, *Proc. Nat. Acad. Sci. U.S.A.* 37, 792 (1951).
15. J. S. F. Barker, *Amer. Natur.* 101, 277 (1967); A. M. Mourad and G. S. Mallah, *Evolution* 14, 166 (1960).
16. Th. Dobzhansky, *Carnegie Inst. Wash. Publ.* 554, 47 (1944).
17. A. B. da Cunha, H. Burla, Th. Dobzhansky, *Evolution* 4, 212 (1950).
18. C. D. Kastritsis, *Chromosoma* 23, 180 (1967).
19. B. Spassky, *Univ. Tex. Publ. No. 5712* (1957), p. 48.
20. F. J. Ayala and J. R. Powell, *Proc. Nat. Acad. Sci. U.S.A.* 69, 1094 (1972).
21. H. L. Carson, *Stadler Symp.* 3, 51 (1971).
22. B. Spassky, R. C. Richmond, S. Perez-Salas, O. Pavlovsky, C. A. Mourão, A. S. Hunter, H. Hoenigsberg, Th. Dobzhansky, F. J. Ayala, *Evolution* 25, 129 (1971).
23. W. W. Anderson and L. Ehrman, *Amer. Midland Natur.* 81, 47 (1969).
24. Th. Dobzhansky, in *The Genetics of Colonizing Species*, H. G. Baker and G. L. Stebbins, Eds. (Academic Press, New York, 1965).
25. G. Pasteur, *Evolution* 24, 156 (1970).
26. Th. Dobzhansky, "The Hooker Lecture," *Proc. Linnean Soc. London* 174, 1 (1963).
27. S. Koref-Santibañez, *Evolution* 26, 108 (1972).
28. D. Brncic, *Proc. Int. Congr. Genet. 10th* 1, 420 (1959); in *Essays in Evolution and Genetics*, M. K. Hecht and W. C. Steere, Eds. (Appleton-Century-Crofts, New York, 1970).
29. V. Grant, *Plant Speciation* (Columbia Univ. Press, New York, 1971).
30. R. C. Lewontin and J. L. Hubby, *Genetics* 54, 595 (1966).
31. R. C. Richmond, *ibid.* 70, 87 (1972); F. J. Ayala, J. R. Powell, M. L. Tracey, C. A. Mourão, S. Perez-Salas, *ibid.*, p. 113; S. Prakash, *Proc. Nat. Acad. Sci. U.S.A.* 62, 778 (1969).
32. J. L. Hubby and L. H. Throckmorton, *Amer. Natur.* 102, 193 (1968).
33. H. L. Carson, private communication.
34. F. J. Ayala, C. A. Mourão, S. Perez-Salas, R. Richmond, Th. Dobzhansky, *Proc. Nat. Acad. Sci. U.S.A.* 67, 225 (1970); F. J. Ayala and J. R. Powell, *Biochem. Genet.*, in press.
35. C. D. Laird and B. J. McCarthy, *Genetics* 60, 303 (1968).
36. F. W. Robertson, M. Chipchase, N. T. Man, *ibid.* 63, 369 (1969).
37. H. D. Stalker, *ibid.* 70, 457 (1972).
38. W. S. Stone, W. C. Guest, F. D. Wilson, *Proc. Nat. Acad. Sci. U.S.A.* 46, 350 (1960); M. Wasserman, *Amer. Natur.* 97, 333 (1963).
39. H. L. Carson, F. E. Clayton, H. D. Stalker, *Proc. Nat. Acad. Sci. U.S.A.* 57, 1280 (1967).
40. B. L. Ward, W. B. Heed, J. S. Russell, *Genetics* 60, 235 (1968).
41. H. L. Carson, *Science* 168, 1414 (1970).
42. E. Mayr, in *Evolution as a Process*, J. S. Huxley, Ed. (Allen & Unwin, London, 1954).
43. Th. Dobzhansky and O. Pavlovsky, *Evolution* 7, 198 (1957).
44. Th. Dobzhansky, H. Levene, B. Spassky, *Genetics* 44, 75 (1959).
45. Th. Dobzhansky and O. Pavlovsky, *ibid.* 55, 141 (1967).
46. ———, *Nature* 230, 289 (1971).
47. D. L. Williamson and L. Ehrman, *Genetics* 55, 131 (1967).
48. R. P. Kernaghan and L. Ehrman, *Chromosoma* 29, 291 (1970).

Editor's Comments
on Future Studies

Interesting and informative results often occur when attempts are made to predict the results of a yet to be performed experiment. Surely one is foolhardy to attempt to suggest results in an entire field of study. Since our purpose is to stimulate thought and suggest lines of investigation, we will ignore the pitfalls and risk the hazards.

Some trends are clear and it is not greatly intuitive to predice continuation of these trends. New techniques from the physical sciences will be applied to speciation problems and will provide various insight. DNA sequencing will allow exact comparison of homologous structures in different species. Cell fusions will be used to determine chromosome homologies and genetic incompatibilities between species that do not hybridize. Methods to determine the amino acid sequences of trace amounts of proteins will allow us to study very closely related forms. The fossil record can make even greater contributions to the study of speciation as physical and chemical techniques provide for better dating and more complete knowledge of the molecular structure of the fossil. We should be able to determine in what ways structural and regulatory genes are involved in speciation.

The integration of theory and applications will continue to improve field observations, laboratory experiments, and analytical techniques. While there is still a great gap between the laboratory-oriented and the field-oriented biologist the new naturalists have reduced and will continue to reduce that difference. This will lead to a better understanding of the amount and kinds of integration in the genetic system of the individual and the population.

Some specific questions appear nearer to resolution. For example, the role of random and deterministic events in anagenesis is continually clarified and progress in determining the frequency of sympatric speciation and of saltational events can be projected. The role of behavioral isolation in organisms large enough to be observed should improve our understanding of behavioral isolation and of otherwise difficult to assess phenomena such as gene dispersal.

The increasing understanding of the structure of the ecosystem and of community ecology will provide a better basis to ask questions about ecological, demographic and social factors in speciation. The evolution of communities requires the evolution of the species involved. Thus when a plant-animal pollinator system undergoes cladogenesis the changes in the system depend on the species and the interaction between the species. Similarly, questions can be asked about the changes in evolving socially structured populations such as social insects.

And what are the specific questions to be asked next? Ah! That's the stuff that produces benchmarks!

REFERENCES

Anderson, E. (1949) *Introgressive Hybridization.* New York: John Wiley & Sons, Inc.

Ayala, F. A. (1975) Genetic differentiation during the speciation process. *Evolutionary Biology* 8:1-78.

Barker, J. S. F., and Cummins, L. J. (1969) Disruptive selection for sternopleural bristle number in *Drosophila melanogaster. Genetics* 61:697-719.

Bartholomew, B.; Eaton, L. C.; and Raven, P. H. (1973) *Clarkia rubicunda*: A model of plant evolution in semiarid regions. *Evolution* 27:505-517.

Bateson, W. (1894) *Materials for the Study of Variation, Treated with Especial Regard to Discontinuity in the Origin of Species.* London: Macmillan and Co.

Bazykin, A. D. (1969) Hypothetical mechanism of speciation. *Evolution* 23:685-687.

Blair, W. F. (1953) Size difference as a possible isolation mechanism in *Microhyla. Am. Naturalist* 89:297-302.

Brown, W. L. and Wilson, E. O. (1956) Character displacement. *Systematic Zoology* 5:49-64.

Bush, G. (1975) Modes of animal speciation. *Annual Review of Ecology and Systematics* 6:339-364.

Chabora, A. J. (1968) Disruptive selection for sternopleural chaeta number in various strains of *Drosophila melanogaster.* Am. Nat. 102:525-532.

Crenshaw, J. (1966) Disruptive selection and speciation. Proc. Fifth Ann. Nat. Poultry Breeders Roundtable, p. 40-45.

Darwin, C. and Wallace, A. (1859) On the tendency of species to form varieties; and on the perpetuation of varieties and species by natural means of selection. J. Proc. Linnean Soc. 3:45-62.

Dobzhansky, T. (1937) *Genetics and the Origin of Species.* 1st ed. New York: Columbia University Press.

—— (1940). Speciation as a stage in evolutionary divergence. *Am. Naturalist* 74:312-321.

—— (1941) *Genetics and the Origin of Species.* 2nd ed. New York: Columbia University Press.

—— (1951) *Genetics and the Origin of Species.* 3rd ed. New York: Columbia University Press.

References

—— (1970) *Genetics of the Evolutionary Process.* New York: Columbia University Press.

Dobzhansky, T., and Sturtevant, A. H. (1936) Inversions in the third chromosome of wild races of *Drosophila pseudoobscura,* and their use in the study of the history of the species. *Proc. Nat. Acad. Sci.* 22:448–450.

Ehrman, L. (1965) Direct observation of sexual isolation between allopatric and between sympatric strains of different *Drosophila paulistorum* races. *Evolution* 19:459–64.

Fisher, R. A. (1922) On the dominance ratio. *Proc. Royal Soc. Edin.* 42:321–341.

—— (1930) *The Genetical Theory of Natural Selection.* 1958 revised edition. New York: Dover Publ.

Galton, F. (1894) Discontinuity in evolution. *Mind,* n.s. 3:362–72.

Goldschmidt, R. (1940) *The Material Basis of Evolution.* New Haven: Yale University Press.

Gottlieb, L. B. (1973) Enzyme differentiation and phylogeny in *Clarkia franciscana, C. rubicunda* and *C. amoena. Evolution* 27:205–214.

Grant, V. (1963) *The Origin of Adaptations.* New York and London: Columbia University Press.

—— (1971) *Plant Speciation.* New York: Columbia University Press.

Gulick, J. T. (1873) On diversity of evolution under one set of external conditions. *J. Proc. Linnean Soc.* 11:496–505.

—— (1904) Divergence under the same environment as seen in Hawaiian snails. *Am. Naturalist* 38:494–496.

Haldane, J. B. S. (1927) A mathematical theory of natural and artificial selection. Part V, Selection and Mutation. *Proc. Cambridge Phil. Soc.* 23:838–844.

—— (1930a) A mathematical theory of natural and artificial selection. Part VI, Isolation. *Proc. Cambridge Phil. Soc.* 26:220–230.

—— (1930b) A mathematical theory of natural and artificial selection. Part VII. *Proc. Cambridge Phil. Soc.* 27:131–136.

—— (1931) A mathematical theory of natural and artificial selection. Part VIII. *Proc. Cambridge Phil. Soc.* 27:137–142.

—— (1932) *The Causes of Evolution.* Longmans, Green & Co., Limited. Cornell Paperbacks, 1966.

Hiesey, W. M. (1964) The genetic-physiologic structure of species complexes in relation to environment. Genetics Today. *Proc. Eleventh Intern. Congr. of Genetics.* pp. 437–445.

Hubby, J. L., and Throckmorton, L. H. (1965) Protein differences in *Drosophila* II. Comparative species genetics and evolutionary problems. *Genetics* 52:203–215.

Huxley, J. S. (1942) *Evolution, the Modern Synthesis.* London: Allen and Unwin.

Huxley, T. H. (1887) On the reception of the Origin of Species. In: Darwin, F. *The life and Letters of Charles Darwin.* New York: Appleton & Co. pp. 533–588.

Irwin, M. R. (1953) Evolutionary patterns of antigenic substances of the blood corpuscles in Columbidae. *Evolution* 7:31–50.

—— and L. J. Cole (1936) Imunogenetic studies of species and of species hybrids, and the separation of species-specific characters in backcross generations. *J. Exp. Zool.* 73:285–305.

Jackson, R. C. (1971) The karyotype in systematics. *Ann. Rev. Ecology and Systematics.* 2:327–368.

Jordan, D. S. (1905) The origin of species through isolation. *Science* 22:545–562.

324

Kessler, S. (1966) Selection for and against ethological isolation between *Drosophila pseudoobscura* and *Drosophila persimilis*. *Evolution* 20:634–645.

Kimura, M. (1968) Evolutionary rate at the molecular level. *Nature* 217:624–26.

Levin, D. A. (1970) Reinforcement of reproductive isolation: plants vs. animals. *Am. Naturalist* 104:571–582.

Lewis, H., and Raven, P. H. (1958) Rapid evolution in *Clarkia*. *Evolution* 12:319 336.

Lewontin, R. C. (1974) *The Genetic Basis of Evolutionary Change*. New York: Columbia University Press.

Li, H. (1977) *Stochastic Models in Population Genetics*. Benchmark Papers in Genetics, Volume 7 Stroudsburg, Pa.: Dowden, Hutchinson & Ross.

Mayr, E. (1942) *Systematics and the Origin of Species*. New York: Columbia University Press.

—— (1947) Ecological factors in speciation. *Evolution* 1:263–288.

—— (1949) Speciation and selection. *Proc. Amer. Phil. Soc.* 93:514–519.

—— (1959) Change of genetic environment and evolution. In: Huxley, J. S.; Hardy A. C.; and Ford, E. B. (eds.), *Evolution as a Process*. London: George Allen & Unwin, Ltd.

—— (1963) *Animal Species and Evolution*. Cambridge, Mass.: Belknap Press.

—— (1974) The definition of the term disruptive selection. *Heredity* 32:404–406.

Mecham, J. S. (1961) Isolating mechanisms in anuran amphibians. In: Blair, W. F. (ed.), *Vertebrate Speciation*. Austin: University of Texas Press. pp. 24–61.

Miller, R. A. (1964) Ecology and distribution of pocket gophers (Geomyidae) in Colorado. *Ecology* 45:256–272.

Muller, H. J. (1940) Isolating mechanisms, evolution and temperature. *Biol. Symposium* 6:71–125.

Olby, R. C. (1966) *Origins of Mendelism*. New York: Schocken Books.

Provine, William B. (1971) *The Origins of Theoretical Population Genetics*. Chicago and London: University of Chicago Press.

Roberts, H. F. (1929) *Plant Hybridization before Mendel*. Princeton, N.J.: Princeton University Press.

Scharloo, W. (1964) The effect of disruptive and stabilizing selection on the expression of a cubitus interruptus mutant in *Drosophila*. *Genetics* 50:553–562.

Schmidt, J. (1917) Statistical investigations with *Zoarces viviparus*. *J. Genetics* 7:105–118.

—— (1919) Racial studies in fishes. III. Diallel crossings with trout (*Salmo trutta* L.). *J. Genetics* 9:61–68.

—— (1920) Racial studies in fishes. IV. Experimental investigations with *Zoarces viviparus* L. *J. Genetics* 10:179–192.

Simpson, G. G. (1944) *Tempo and Mode in Evolution*. New York: Columbia University Press.

—— (1953) *Major Features of Evolution*. New York: Columbia University Press.

Stebbins, G. L., Jr. (1940) The significance of polyploidy in plant evolution. *Am. Naturalist* 74:54–66.

—— (1950) *Variation and Evolution in Plants*. New York: Columbia University Press.

—— (1959) The role of hybridization in evolution. *Proc. Amer. Phil. Soc.* 103:231–251.

—— (1971) *Chromosomal Evolution in Higher Plants*. London: E. Arnold

—— (1976) Chromosome, DNA and Plant Evolution. *Evolutionary Biology* 9:1–34.

References

Stone, W. S. (1955) Genetic and chromosomal variability in *Drosophila. Cold Spring Harb. Symp. Quant. Biol.* 20:256-269.

——; Guest, W. C.; and Wilson, F. D. (1960) The evolutionary implications of the cytological polymorphism and phylogeny of the *virilis* group of *Drosophila. Proc. National Acad. Sci.* 46:350-361.

Sturtevant, A. H., and Novitski, E. (1941) The homologies of the chromosome elements in the genus *Drosophila. Genetics* 26:517-541.

Sumner, F. B. (1917) Modern conceptions of heredity and genetic studies at the Scripps Institution. *Bulletin Scripps Institution for Biological Research* 3:1-24.

—— (1923) Some facts relevant to a discussion of the origin and inheritance of specific characters. *Am. Naturalist* 57:238-254.

—— (1929a) The analysis of a concrete case of integradation between two subspecies. *Proc. National Acad. Sci.* 15:110-120.

—— (1929b) The analysis of a concrete case of integradation between two subspecies, II. *Proc. National Acad. Sci.* 15:481-493.

—— (1934) Taxonomic distinctions viewed in the light of genetics. *Am. Naturalist* 68:137-149.

Tan, C. C. (1946) Genetics of sexual isolation between *Drosophila pseudoobscura* and *D. persimilis. Genetics* 31:558-573.

Thoday, J. M. (1972) Disruptive selection. *Proc. Roy. Soc. London* 182:109-143.

—— and Gibson, J. B. (1970) The probability of isolation by disruptive selection. *Am. Naturalist* 104:219-230.

de Vries, H. (1889) *Intracellulare Pangenesis.* Jena. Trans. By C. S. Gager. Chicago: Open Court Publ. Co., 1910.

—— (1906) *Species and Varieties, Their Origin by Mutation* (Lectures delivered at the University of California) 2nd ed. Chicago: Open Court Publ. Co.

Wagner, M. (1868) *Die Darwinische Theorie und das Migrationsgesetz der Organismen.* Leipzig: Duncker und Humbolt.

Wallace, A. R. (1889) *Darwinism: An Exposition of the Theory of Natural Selection.* London: Macmillan.

White, M. J. D. (1970) Cytogenetics of Speciation. *J. Australian Entomological Soc.* 9:1-6.

—— (1973) *Animal Cytology and Evolution.* London: Cambridge University Press.

Wright, S. (1931) Evolution in mendelian populations. *Genetics* 16:97-159.

—— (1932) The roles of mutation, inbreeding, crossbreeding and selection in evolution. *Proc. Sixth Intern. Congr. of Genetics* 1:356-366.

—— (1965) Factor interaction and linkage in evolution. *Proc. Royal Soc.,* B 162:80-104.

Wright, S. (in press) *Evolution and the Genetics of Populations.* Vols. 3 & 4. Chicago: University of Chicago Press.

Zirkle, C. (1935) *The Beginnings of Plant Hybridisation.* Morris Arboretum Monograph No. 1. Philadelphia: University of Philadelphia Press.

—— (1946) The early history of the idea of the inheritance of acquired characters and of pangenesis. *Trans. Amer. Phil. Soc.,* New Series 35:91-151.

—— (1959) Species before Darwin. *Proc. Amer. Phil. Soc.* 103:636-644.

AUTHOR CITATION INDEX

SUBJECT INDEX

333

Subject Index

Spermatogenesis, 137, 153
Stable polymorphism, 198, 209
Stasipatric speciation, 9, 306, 307
Sterile males, 153, 316
Sterility, 118, 121, 262, 293, 294
Stimulus-reaction pattern, 162
Stochastic processes, 3
Subspecies, 105
Superspecies, 315, 316, 319
Sympatric speciation, 7, 174, 197, 272, 290, 292, 298, 303, 315, 321

Tephrosia, 122
Tetrazolium oxidase, 103
Thalarctos, 95
Theropithecus, 95
Three phase shifting balance theory, 5, 15
Triose phosphate isomerase, 103

Tripsacum, 251, 252, 278

Ursus, 95

Vaccinium, 279
Variability of the F_1 hybrids, 136
Variety, 287, 288
Viability, 141

Wallace effect, 250, 252, 253, 260, 266
  hypothesis, 249, 265
Wing lengths, 148

Xanthine dehydrogenase, 103
Xenopus, 97

Zalophus, 95
Zauschneria, 280
Zea, 251, 252, 277

About the Editor

DAVID L. JAMESON is Professor of Biology at the University of Houston, Houston, Texas. He was previously Director of the University of Houston Coastal Center, Director of the Clear Lake Graduate Center, and Dean of the Graduate School. He has also taught at Pacific University, the University of Oregon, and San Diego State University. He received the B.S. from Southern Methodist University and the M.A. and Ph.D. from the University of Texas. He has done postdoctoral study at Oak Ridge, Brown University, American Museum of Natural History, University of Barcelona, and the University of Wisconsin. He has published papers on the population biology of mammals and amphibians and several books including a general biology text. He has served as Editor of *Copeia*, Secretary of the Society for the Study of Evolution, and as a member of the Council of the American Association for the Advancement of Science and of the Board of Governors of the American Institute of Biological Sciences. He was awarded a Fulbright Fellowship and in 1977 year he served as a National Academy of Science Exchange Scholar at the Institute of Zoology, Bulgarian Academy of Science, Sofia, Bulgaria.